P9-ARN-473

DICTIONARY OF
ASTRONOMICAL TERMS

American Museum Science Books are published for The American Museum of Natural History by the Natural History Press. Directed by a joint editorial board made up of members of the staff of the Museum and Doubleday, this series is an extension of the Museum's scientific and educational activities, making available to the student and general reader inexpensive, up-to-date, and reliable books in the life and earth sciences, including anthropology and astronomy. The Natural History Press is a division of Doubleday & Company, Inc. and has its editorial offices at The American Museum of Natural History, Central Park West at 79th Street, New York 24, New York, and its business offices at 501 Franklin Avenue, Garden City, New York.

DICTIONARY OF ASTRONOMICAL TERMS

ÅKE WALLENQUIST

Edited and translated from the Swedish by
SUNE ENGELBREKTSON

WITHDRAWN

021551

Ref
QB
14
.W313
1966

AMERICAN MUSEUM SCIENCE BOOKS
Published for
The American Museum of Natural History

The Natural History Press
GARDEN CITY, N.Y.

H068

DICTIONARY OF ASTRONOMICAL TERMS was originally published in Sweden, under the title ASTRONOMISKT LEXIKON, by Bokförlaget Prisma in 1962. Copyright © 1962, Åke Wallenquist.

Library of Congress Catalog Card Number 66–12201
Translation and Editing Copyright © 1966 by
Sune Engelbrektson
All Rights Reserved
Printed in the United States of America

FOREWORD TO THE ENGLISH EDITION

This book is a translation of ASTRONOMISKT LEXI-KON by Åke Wallenquist, Professor of Astronomy at the Kvistaberg Observatory of Uppsala University near Stockholm, Sweden. An astronomer with many contributions to that science, Wallenquist has carried out photometric investigations of the Milky Way, star clusters, and double stars. In addition, he has found time to write books pertaining to popular astronomy. In the present work, he has compiled a dictionary which will be useful as a reference for readers with a beginning interest in astronomy as well as college students who may require a supplement to a college text in astronomy.

Although care has been exercised in making the dictionary complete, omissions are unavoidable and do exist. However, these are minor terms representing English words not used in the Swedish language and therefore omitted from the original work, Swedish terms without English equivalents, and Swedish proper names.

Several topics, namely those pertaining to space science, have been updated to include the latest achievements in space exploration. The most recent flights of the Mercury and Vostok manned space vehicles fall within this category. Whenever possible, the translator followed the style of the author when providing additional and new material.

Astronomers of The American Museum-Hayden Planetarium are due special acknowledgment. Grateful appreciation is expressed to Dr. Kenneth L. Franklin for reading the completed manuscript as well as for his valuable assistance in its preparation. The translator also wishes to express his thanks to Dr. Franklyn M. Branley for providing encouragement and inspiration and to Dr. Thomas D. Nicholson for technical advice and many suggestions contributed.

vi

Acknowledgment is made to Mr. George E. Cook who typed the manuscript.

Sune Engelbrektson

The American Museum of Natural History
August 1964

FOREWORD TO THE SWEDISH EDITION

The collection of material for an astronomical dictionary of restricted limitations that is concise as well as comprehensible is not an easy task. Therefore, the author has been obliged to limit this book to essentials and was frequently faced with the problem of proper selection of topics. New words, definitions, and concepts constantly appear in professional astronomical journals, especially in the rapidly evolving subdisciplines such as radio astronomy and theoretical astrophysics. Generally, the book contains only the technical terms already in use or expected to be applied in popular science. The selection of words relating to space technology and astronautics was especially difficult. Strictly interpreted, these fields are not part of astronomy although they are considered to be by the majority of readers. Except in a few instances, only purely astronomical terms could be included. Generally, more extensive biographical information about contemporary astronomers outside Scandinavia was omitted because of space limitations. To facilitate the use of the dictionary and to avoid too many references, even at the risk of being repetitious, a term or title-word is treated in two or more places, sometimes as an isolated word and at other times as part of a broader relationship.

ÅKE WALLENQUIST

DICTIONARY OF
ASTRONOMICAL TERMS

KEY

Boldface = Main entry. Also, a word in boldface in parentheses is a term meaning exactly what the main entry does.
EXAMPLE: **Cassegrainian telescope (Cassegrainian system)**

Italics and *Starred* (*) *Italics* = Terms which are defined elsewhere in the dictionary. References.
EXAMPLE: "See: *star*" or "They are named **Fraunhofer lines* . . ."

A

aberration **1.** ABERRATION OF STARLIGHT. An apparent displacement of a star's position due to the finite velocity of light combined with the velocity of the earth. If a telescope is pointed toward a star, S, the direction should coincide with the optical axis and reach the observer at J, if the earth were stationary with respect to the star. As a result of the earth's motion in the direction of the arrow, light from the star reaches the observer at point J' causing the star to be displaced in the direction of the earth's motion as shown in Fig. A1. Differentiation is made between *diurnal aberration*

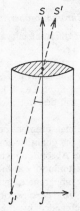

A1. Aberration of starlight.

caused by the earth's rotation which amounts to a maximum of $0\overset{''}{.}3$; *annual aberration* caused by the earth's revolution around the sun reaching a value of $20\overset{''}{.}47$; and *secular aberration* caused by the motion of the solar system through space. Aberration was discovered in 1725 by the English astronomer Bradley. **2.** ABERRATION OF LENSES. (a) *Spherical aberration.* The difference in the position of the focal points for light passing through different parts of a lens or reflected from different parts of a spherical mirror. A sharp image cannot be

formed because the light entering the edge of the lens is refracted more than the central rays. (Fig. A2a.) (b) *Chromatic*

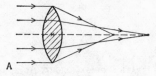

A2a. Spherical aberration.

aberration. The difference in the position of the focal points
for light of different colors. Violet light is refracted more than
red light. (Fig. A2b.) Chromatic aberration can be reduced

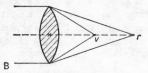

A2b. Chromatic aberration.

by combining lenses of different curvature and composition.
See: *achromatic objective.*

aberrational ellipse Aberration causes a star to describe a small
ellipse on the celestial sphere with a semi-major axis equal
to the *constant of aberration,* i.e., 20".47. A star located at
the pole of the ecliptic will describe a circle and a star on the
ecliptic, a straight line.

absolute luminosity The measurement or indication of the true
intensity of starlight or the quantity of surface radiation from
the star per unit of time. Absolute magnitude is also expressed
in the terms of the sun's luminosity as the unit of measurement.

absolute magnitude The apparent magnitude of a star if located at a distance of 10 **parsecs,* or 32.6 light-years. The
*parallax, the angle subtended by the radius of the earth's
orbit as seen from the star, will be 0".1. If the star's distance
in parsecs, r, and its **apparent magnitude* or observed brightness, m, is known, the absolute magnitude, M, of the star can
be calculated by the formula $M = m + 5 - 5 \log r$. One of the
most important tasks of stellar astronomy is to determine the
absolute magnitude of stars. This can be done in many ways,
one of which is by studying the intensity of the lines and
bands in the spectra of the stars. The resulting quantity is
called the star's spectroscopic absolute magnitude. See: *luminosity criteria* and *cepheids.*

absolute temperature Temperature measured from absolute zero, −459°4 F. or −273°16 C. Absolute temperature is measured in the Kelvin system, named after Lord Kelvin. For example, 0° C. = 273°16 K.

absolute zero The temperature at which all molecular motion theoretically ceases (−459°4 F. or −273°16 C.). *Absolute temperature* is measured from this point.

absorption The decrease in intensity of light in passing through a substance or medium. **1.** ABSORPTION IN THE EARTH'S ATMOSPHERE (*extinction*). The light from a celestial body is dimmed in passing through the atmosphere, the absorption increasing from the zenith to the horizon and amounting to several magnitudes. Absorption is selective, affecting short-wave radiation more than the long-wave. At the horizon, celestial bodies will appear redder than they are in reality. **2.** INTERSTELLAR ABSORPTION. Material between the stars, **interstellar matter,* produces a selective absorption of light from the stars. Interstellar absorption must be considered in calculating the distances to remote stars' galaxies. Although this causes a reddening of starlight and of the light from galaxies, this effect should not be confused with the "red shift" (q.v.). **3.** ABSORPTION OF LIGHT IN SPACE. Generally, intergalactic space is considered to be relatively free from absorption. Within the Milky Way, absorption is greatest in the vicinity of the galactic plane where clouds of dust and gases dim the light from remote stars and distant galaxies. Absorption amounts to approximately an average of 0.2 magnitudes per 1000 light-years. Since absorption is greater for blue and violet light than for yellow and red, starlight is reddened in passing through the absorption layers. See: *color excess.* **4.** ABSORPTION OF STARLIGHT. The scattering of starlight in passing through interstellar material causing reddening and dimming of the light. Since interstellar dust and gas permeate the disc of the Milky Way, allowances must be made for the effects of absorption when measuring distances by photometric methods. As a result of absorption, the intensity of starlight decreases at a greater rate than the square of the distance.

absorption lines Dark lines in a star's spectrum which are caused by the absorption of light of particular wave lengths by the gases in the outer layers of the star's atmosphere. The dark absorption lines in the sun's spectrum are named **Fraunhofer lines,* after their earliest investigator. They were discovered by Wollaston, who did not, however, realize their significance. The study of absorption lines has been of great

significance in the investigation of the chemical composition
of stellar atmospheres and the motions of stars. See: *spectral
analysis.*

absorption spectrum   A continuous spectrum interlaced by dark
lines and bands. These patterns are produced when light passes
through a gaseous layer of lower temperature than the light
source.

acceleration   Change in velocity. (*De*celeration is negative "acceleration." The term acceleration is used for both, the distinction being taken care of in the algebraic sign of the quantity.) **1.** SECULAR ACCELERATION OF THE MOON. An increase
in mean orbital velocity resulting in the advance of the moon's
apparent position, amounting to 8" per century. The phenomenon is a result of a decrease in the eccentricity of the earth's
orbit due to secular perturbations and the lengthening of the
earth's period of rotation. **2.** ACCELERATION OF THE PLANETS.
The increase in orbital velocity of planets from aphelion (the
most distant point in the orbit from the sun) toward perihelion
(the nearest point to the sun). **3.** ACCELERATION OF GRAVITY.
The increase in velocity of a falling body on the earth is
32 ft/sec^2.

Achernar   (Alpha Eridani) The brightest star in the constellation of Eridanus, the River. Achernar is a spectral type B5
star of 0.6 visual magnitude.

Achilles   A member of the *Trojans,* a group of asteroids revolving around the sun in the same orbit as Jupiter. Discovered
in 1904.

achromatic objective   An objective constructed with a double
convex lens made of crown glass and a plano-concave lens of
flint glass to correct **chromatic aberration* as much as possible. Refraction is about the same for both kinds of glass but
the dispersive power is twice as great for flint glass as it is for
crown glass. To further diminish chromatic aberration, three
or more lenses may be used. (Fig. A3.)

CROWN GLASS

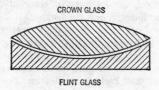

FLINT GLASS

*A3. Achromatic objective lens
(crown glass and flint glass).*

acronical Occurring when night begins. A star opposite the sun in the sky has acronical rising at sunset and acronical setting at sunrise.

actinometer An instrument to measure intensity of radiation such as solar radiation. One type is called a *pyrheliometer.*

active sun The condition of the sun characterized by spots, flares, prominences, and very pronounced variations in radio frequency radiation.

activity regions Regions of the sun with increased activity, such as *sunspots, *prominences,* and *solar *flares.*

Adams, John Couch (1819–1892) English astronomer and professor at Cambridge University. Adams, in England, and Leverrier, in France, independently determined the orbit of the then unknown planet Neptune from observed perturbations of the orbital motion of the planet Uranus.

Adams, Walter Sydney (1876–1956) American astronomer. Adams and Kohlschutter developed a method for determining spectroscopic stellar parallax by studying the intensities of absorption lines. During the years 1923–46, Adams was director of the Mt. Wilson Observatory in California.

Adonis An asteroid discovered in 1936 which can pass very close to the earth and whose perihelion is located near the orbit of Mercury.

aerolite A stony meteorite consisting of less iron and nickel and more silicon and magnesium than the usual iron meteorites (siderites) and the intermediate type (siderolites).

age 1. THE AGE OF THE EARTH AND METEORITES is determined by radioactive methods. The oldest method is based on the fission of the uranium atom which, after a series of intermediate stages, produces helium and lead. The half-life of uranium is 5×10^9 years. The age of rock (or meteorites) is found by measuring the content of uranium, helium, and lead. The amount of disintegration of uranium will make the estimation of age possible. Recently, age has been determined by the disintegration of rubidium to an isotope of strontium with a half-life of 61×10^9 years. Other methods include potassium-argon (potassium isotope K^{40} and argon A^{40}) for rocks over 10^7 years and potassium-calcium for ages of about 10^9 (calcium isotope Ca^{40}). The maximum age of meteorites is estimated by radioactive methods at 7×10^9 years. The oldest rocks have an age of about 4×10^9 years; the earth is believed to be 5×10^9 years. 2. AGES OF STARS are found through the theoretical investigations of the nuclear processes that are responsible for energy production within the stars. The age of the youngest stars is on the order of 10^6 years, while the oldest members of Population II reach 10^{10} years. **3. THE AGES OF STAR CLUSTERS** are found from the distribution of the stars on the H-R diagram. See: *Hertzsprung-Russell diagram*. The main body of stars in an older cluster is found to be farther down the diagram than the stars in a younger cluster. Age can also be estimated from the observed motions of the stars in the cluster, and in galactic clusters is found to lie between 10^6 and 5×10^9 years. The age of globular clusters is between 5×10^9 and 10^{10} years, and perhaps more. **4. THE AGE OF THE UNIVERSE** is determined from the amount of *red shift which is a measure of the velocity of expansion of the universe. The rate of expansion dates the age of the universe to be between 10^{10} and 2×10^{10} years. This value is very uncertain. If the universe is pulsating, alternately expanding and contracting, its age cannot be determined. **5. THE AGE OF THE MOON**, expressed in days, is the amount of time passed since the new moon phase.

age determination See: *age*.

Air Pump Constellation in the southern hemisphere. See: *Antlia*.

Al-Battani (Lat. *Albategnius*) d. 929 A.D. Greatest Arabian astronomer, who made extensive observations. He determined the obliquity of the ecliptic, measured precession and the eccentricity of the earth's orbit.

albedo (Lat. *albus,* white) A measurement of an object's reflecting power. In astronomy, albedo is defined as the ratio between the intensity of the light reflected and the light received from the sun. The planets have the following albedoes: Mercury, 0.07; Venus, 0.59; earth, 0.29; Mars, 0.15; Jupiter, 0.44; Saturn, 0.42; Uranus, 0.45; Neptune, 0.52; Pluto, 0.03; and the moon, 0.07.

Albireo The star Beta (β) Cygni, a double star; the components' apparent visual magnitudes are 3.2 and 5.4 and a separation of $35''$.

Alcor (Lat. for rider) The star 80 Ursae Majoris makes a visual double with Mizar (Zeta [ζ] Ursae Majoris). The pair form the middle stars in the handle of the *Big Dipper*.

Alcyone Eta (η) Tauri, the brightest star in the *Pleiades* (Seven Sisters), located in the constellation of *Taurus,* the Bull. Alcyone's apparent visual magnitude is 3.0 with spectral type B5.

Aldebaran Alpha (α) Tauri (Bull), a red giant star with an apparent visual magnitude 1.1 and spectral type K5.

Alfvén's cosmogony In 1954, H. Alfvén (1908–), professor in Stockholm, Sweden, proposed a theory for the origin of the solar system based upon the effects of electromagnetic forces. Alfvén assumes that neutral gases collapsed into the sun and became ionized through collisions between gas molecules under the influence of electromagnetic forces. Stopped by the magnetic field of the sun, large amounts of gas were concentrated in the plane of the sun's rotation. The ionized gases condensed and congealed into larger bodies, forming the planets. The electromagnetic forces transferred the energy of the sun's rotation to the planets, explaining the slow rotation of the sun compared with the periods of revolution of the planets.

Alfvén waves The name of the hydrodynamic waves discovered by H. Alfvén. See: *magnetohydrodynamics*.

Algenib The star Gamma (γ) Pegasi, with an apparent visual magnitude 2.9 and spectral type B2.

Algol The star Beta (β) Persei, the first eclipsing binary star discovered (Goodricke, 1783). Its period is 68.8 hours, with a variation in magnitude between 2.2 and 3.5. The larger and fainter component revolves about the smaller but brighter star at a distance of about 10 million miles. The brighter component is of spectral type B8 and is about three times the diameter of the sun. A third star revolves around the other two in a period of 1.87 years. (Fig. A4.)

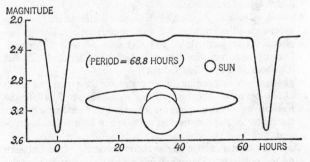

A4. Algol's light curve.

algol type variables The same as eclipsing variables, or eclipsing binary stars. See: *binary stars*. The prototype of these stars is *Algol*, or Beta (β) Persei.

alidade A movable arm equipped with an index, which is fastened to a refracting or reflecting instrument. The index arm moves along a graduated arc. The setting of the instrument can be read off the graduated arc. (Fig. A5.)

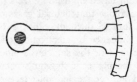

A5. Alidade.

Alioth The star Epsilon (ε) Ursae Majoris (Great Bear), with an apparent visual magnitude 1.7 and spectral type A0p.

Almagest (Arab. *Al-Magisti,* the greatest, from the Greek name *Megale Syntaxis*) A large compendium that summarized astronomy of antiquity and gave a detailed description of the geocentric world system. This work was developed by *Claudius Ptolemaeus* (**Ptolemy*) of Alexandria about A.D. 140.

almanac A yearly calendar containing a collation of astronomical events, church holidays, etc. See: *ephemeris.*

almucantar Every circle on the celestial sphere parallel to the horizon, also called *parallel of altitude.*

Alpha (α) First letter in the Greek alphabet, usually used to identify the brightest star in a constellation. For example, α Aurigae, or Capella, is the brightest star in Auriga, the Charioteer. See: *Auriga.*

Alphard The star Alpha (α) Hydrae (Water Snake), of apparent visual magnitude 2.2 and spectral type K2.

Alphecca The star Alpha (α) Coronae Borealis (Northern Crown), apparent visual magnitude 2.3 and spectral type A0. Alphecca is also called Gemma.

Alphonsus A ring mountain, or crater, on the moon just south of the center of the lunar disc. On November 3, 1958, the Russian astronomer Kozyrev observed a phenomenon near the center of Alphonsus that appeared to be a volcanic eruption.

Alps A mountain range on the moon bordering Mare Imbrium on the northwest. The range is pierced by a very striking depression called the Valley of the Alps.

Al-Sufi (903–986) Arabian astronomer. He compiled a star catalogue which included stellar magnitudes.

Altair The star Alpha (α) Aquilae (Eagle), a white star of apparent visual magnitude 0.9 and spectral type A5.

Altar Constellation in the southern hemisphere. See: *Ara*.

altazimuth instrument An instrument used to determine the position of a celestial body in the horizon system of co-ordinates (altitude and azimuth). A telescope is turned vertically around a horizontal axis which in turn can be rotated horizontally about a vertical axis. Altitude is measured from a vertical circle with fine graduations, while azimuth readings are possible from a horizontal circle.

altitude A co-ordinate in the *horizon system* that measures a star's angular distance from the horizon on its vertical circle from 0° to 90°.

altitude, parallel of A circle on the celestial sphere parallel to the horizon; an *almucantar*.

altitude of the pole The angle between the celestial pole and the horizon, measured along the meridian. The altitude of the pole is equal to the geographic latitude of the point of observation.

aluminizing A method of coating a mirror with aluminum. The aluminum is vaporized in a vacuum, causing a film of metal to be deposited on the glass mirror. This method, rather than silvering, is used with astronomical mirrors because aluminum is more durable and more reflective, especially in the ultraviolet region.

American Ephemeris and Nautical Almanac, The The tabulation of the positions of celestial bodies for regular intervals of time, issued by the Nautical Almanac Office, United States Naval Observatory. In 1960, the *American Ephemeris* was combined with *The Astronomical Ephemeris* issued by H. M. Nautical Almanac Office, Royal Greenwich Observatory.

ammonia clock A precision clock based on the behavior of the ammonia molecule, which contains one nitrogen and three hydrogen atoms in the form of a double pyramid. The hydrogen atoms are placed in the corners of the equilateral triangle that forms the pyramid's base and the nitrogen atom vibrates through the base between the apices of the pyramids. The frequency of vibration is used to measure time.

Amor An asteroid that can approach a distance of 10 million miles from the earth. Amor was discovered in 1932.

amplitude A measurement of the light variation of variable stars, expressed as the difference between maximum and minimum brightness.

Andromeda Constellation in the northern hemisphere at 1h
right ascension (α = 1h), 40° north declination (δ = +40°),
between Perseus and Pegasus. Andromeda contains the triple
star Gamma (γ) Andromedae (Almach) and the famous
spiral galaxy, the Andromeda galaxy (*Great Nebula in Andromeda*).

Andromeda Galaxy (Andromeda Nebula, M31) The nearest
spiral star system or spiral galaxy beyond the Milky Way. It
is visible to the unaided eye as a lenticular patch of light. Its
distance is 2.2 million light-years; diameter, 200,000 light-
years; and mass, $3 \times (10^{11})$ solar masses. The outer arms
of the Andromeda galaxy can be resolved into individual
stars. A great number of Cepheid variable stars, as well as
over 100 novae, have been observed in this galaxy. In addition, this stellar system contains dark and bright nebulae,
open and globular clusters. The Andromeda galaxy is accompanied by two elliptical galaxies, M32 and N.G.C.205.

Andromedids (Bielids) A meteor swarm or shower which appears about November 25, with its *radiant* located in the
constellation of Andromeda. The Andromedids are the debris
of Biela's comet, a short-period comet discovered in 1826
which divided into two parts in the middle of the 19th century
and later vanished. The remains of the comet were scattered
along its orbit. When the earth passes the comet's orbit at the
end of November, the meteor shower called the Andromedids
is visible.

Ångstrom unit (Å) Unit of length used to describe wave
lengths = 10^{-7}mm (10^{-10}m).

angular diameter See: *apparent diameter*.

angular distance See: *apparent distance*.

annual aberration The *aberration* of starlight caused by the
motion of the earth in its orbit and consequently having a
period of one year.

annual equation An irregularity in the moon's orbit which can
amount to 11′ in a period of one year. It is the result of the
sun's disturbing effect on the motion of the moon, due to
varying distance between them. The earth's orbit is elliptical
and the moon is closer to the sun when the earth is at perihelion than when it is at aphelion.

annual motion The apparent motion of the sun among the
stars. The year is defined by this motion.

annual parallax The heliocentric parallax of a star. The displacement of a star's position as a result of the earth's motion

around the sun. Annual parallax is generally exceedingly
small because of the great distance to the stars. The nearest
naked-eye star, Alpha (α) Centauri, has an annual parallax
of 0".751. One of the most difficult problems in astronomy
is to determine the annual parallax of a star. See: *trigonometric parallax.*

annual variation The annual precession in right ascension and
declination for a given epoch, which may be found in star
catalogues.

annular eclipse (ring eclipse) An eclipse of the sun which
occurs when the earth is near perihelion and the moon is near
apogee. The shadow of the moon is not long enough to reach
the earth and, therefore, the moon does not entirely cover the
disc of the sun but leaves a ring of the sun round the dark
moon. See: *eclipse.*

anomalistic month The period of revolution of the moon in
relation to its perigee point, or 27.5546 days. As a result of
the advance of the line of apsides in the direction of the
moon's orbital motion, the anomalistic month is about six
hours longer than the *sidereal month.*

anomalistic year The period of revolution of the earth around
the sun in relation to its perihelion point, or 365.2596 days.
As a result of the advance of the line of apsides in the direction of the earth's orbital motion, the anomalistic year is
0.0174 days longer than the *tropical year.*

anomaly An angular value that is used in describing orbital
motion. The three distinct kinds are: **1.** TRUE ANOMALY. The
angle between the perihelion, the sun, and the planet, mea-

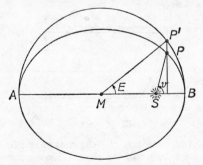

*A6. Anomaly. S = sun, P = planet, B = perihelion, M =
center of ellipse, v = true anomaly, E = eccentric anomaly.*

sured in the direction of the planet's motion. **2.** MEAN ANOM-
ALY. According to Kepler's second law, a planet's speed is
greater at perihelion than at aphelion. Mean anomaly is defined as the angle between the perihelion, the sun, and a fictitious planet with the same period as the real planet moving
with a constant velocity. **3.** ECCENTRIC ANOMALY. The angle
P'MB in Fig. A6. From center M, draw a circle with a diameter equal to the major axis of the ellipse. Construct a perpendicular from the planet P to the line of apsides, and extend
to the circle at point P'.

Ansae The portion of Saturn's rings that is visible on each
side of the planet.

antalgol stars Earlier name for short-period cepheid stars:
cluster type variables, or *RR Lyrae variables.* See: *Lyra.*

antapex The point on the celestial sphere opposite the direction of the sun's motion. It is situated in the constellation
Columba.

Antarctic The south pole area south of latitude 66° 33′ 8″ S.

Antares Alpha (α) Scorpii (Scorpion), red giant star of apparent visual magnitude 1.2 and spectral type M0. Antares
is a *supergiant* with a diameter 330 times that of the sun.

antenna (aerial) An apparatus used to change radio waves
into electrical currents. Different kinds of antennas are used
in radio astronomy. The most widely used is the so-called

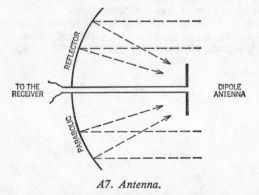

A7. Antenna.

dipole antenna, consisting of metal rods of lengths depending
upon the wave length of the signals. These antennas are divided in the middle, forming two poles. In order to gather
faint radio waves from space, the dipole is placed at the focal

point of a parabolic reflector of metal or metallic network. Other antennas are constructed with many dipoles mounted in rows along the ground, such as the Mills cross antenna. (Fig. A7.)

Antlia (Air Pump) A faint constellation in the southern hemisphere at 10h right ascension ($\alpha = 10h$), 35° south declination ($\delta = -35°$).

apastron The point in the orbit of a binary star farthest from the companion star. In the relative orbit, apastron is the point where the secondary component is most distant from the primary.

aperture The clear diameter of an objective or mirror.

apex The point on the celestial sphere toward which the sun seems to be moving at 12 miles/sec relative to the nearby stars. The apex of the sun's way is located in the constellation of Hercules near the border of Lyra at 18h right ascension and 30° north declination.

aphelion The point in the orbit where a planet or a comet is at its greatest distance from the sun. The earth is at aphelion on about July 1.

apogalacticon In the orbit of a star, the most distant point from the center of the galaxy.

apogee The point in the orbit where a satellite is at its greatest distance from the earth.

Apollo 1. A minor planet, detected in 1932, whose perihelion lies within the orbit of Venus. Its closest approach to the earth is about three million miles. 2. An American project for launching a manned spacecraft to the moon.

Apollonius Greek mathematician of Perga who worked in Alexandria about 200 B.C. He was probably the first to use *epicycles* to describe complex periodic motion.

apparent diameter The angular diameter of a celestial body expressed in minutes and seconds of arc.

apparent distance The *angular distance* between two celestial bodies such as the components of a binary star system, expressed in degrees, minutes, and seconds of arc.

apparent libration A term used to describe geometrical and diurnal libration. See: *libration*.

apparent magnitude A measure of a star's observed brightness. The brightness of a star as seen on the celestial sphere. See: *magnitude*.

apparent noon The moment the center of the sun crosses the meridian.

apparent position The observed position of a celestial body corrected for *refraction* (bending of light in the earth's atmosphere) and reduced to the earth's center as the origin, i.e., corrected for diurnal parallax.

apparent solar time A time division of the *apparent solar day*, the time interval between two successive transits of the sun across the meridian. Apparent solar time is equal to the hour angle of the sun plus 12 hours.

apsides The points of intersection of the major axis with the orbit of a planet or comet. *Perihelion* = the apse located nearer the sun. *Aphelion* = the apse located farthest from the sun.

apsides, line of The line connecting the two *apsides*, i.e., the major axis of an elliptical orbit. (Fig. A8.)

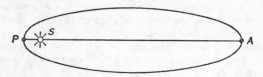

A8. Apsides. S = *sun*, P = *perihelion*, A = *aphelion*, PA = *line of apsides.*

Apus (Bird of Paradise) A constellation in the southern hemisphere at 16h right ascension (α = 16h), 75° south declination (δ = −75°).

Aquarids **1.** ETA AQUARIDS. A meteor shower that occurs early in May and apparently is associated with Halley's comet. **2.** DELTA AQUARIDS. A meteor shower that occurs early in August. Both swarms have their radiants in the constellation of Aquarius and are rather faint.

Aquarius (Water Bearer) An extensive constellation in the southern hemisphere at 23h right ascension (α = 23h), 10° south declination (δ = −10°). An inconspicuous constellation, it lacks stars brighter than the third magnitude. Aquarius is one of the signs of the Zodiac.

Aquila A constellation at the celestial equator in the Milky Way at 19h 30m right ascension (α = 19h 30m), 5° north declination (δ = +5°). The brightest star in Aquila is *Altair*.

Ara (Altar) A constellation in the southern hemisphere at 17h 30m right ascension (α = 17h 30m), 55° south declination (δ = −55°).

Archer A constellation in the southern hemisphere. See: *Sagittarius.*

Arctic The north polar area north of latitude 66° 33′ 8″ N.

Arcturus The star Alpha (α) Boötis (Herdsman), a red giant star of apparent visual magnitude 0.2 and spectral type K0.

Arend-Roland comet One of the more noteworthy comets of the present century, discovered by S. Arend and P. Roland at Uccle, Belgium, during the night of November 8–9, 1956. The comet reached perihelion on April 8, 1957, and came nearest the earth on April 20 at a distance of 53 million miles. The comet reached first magnitude and developed an anti-tail in addition to the normal tail pointing away from the sun. This secondary tail pointed toward the sun, appearing like a thin spearhead on April 25. Apparently, the abnormal tail consisted of substance from the comet that spread out along the orbit and was viewed edge-on when the earth passed through the plane of the comet's orbit. The primary tail had a maximum length of about 40° and the secondary tail was about half as long.

Argelander, Friedrich Wilhelm August (1799–1875) German astronomer who compiled the comprehensive star catalogue *Bonner Durchmusterung* in 1862.

Argo or **Argo Navis** (Ship Argo) An extensive constellation in the southern hemisphere at 9h right ascension (α = 9h), 55° south declination (δ = −55°). It has been divided into the constellations *Puppis* (Stern), *Vela* (Sails), *Carina* (Keel), and *Pyxis* (Compass). The brightest star is *Canopus*, or Alpha (α) Carinae, the next brightest star after Sirius with an apparent visual magnitude of −0.9 and of spectral type F0.

Ariel A satellite of the planet Uranus, discovered by Lassell in 1851. Mean distance to the planet is 119,000 miles; period of revolution, 2.52 days.

Aries (Ram) A constellation in the northern hemisphere at 2h 30m right ascension (α = 2h 30m), 13° north declination (δ = +13°); a sign of the Zodiac.

Aristarchus **1.** Aristarchus of Samos (310–230 B.C.). One of the foremost astronomers of antiquity. He was the first to propose a heliocentric system (sun in center). He also devised a method to determine the relative distance between the moon and the sun. **2.** A lunar crater in the northeast sector of the moon with a diameter of about 23 miles. Its central peak is the brightest spot on the moon's surface.

Arizona crater   See: *meteor craters.*

armillary sphere   An antique instrument used during the Middle Ages and later to determine positions of bodies on the celestial sphere. The armillary sphere consisted of a collection of rings corresponding to various circles on the celestial sphere. Tycho Brahe used an armillary sphere in his observations.

Arrhenius, Svante   (1859–1927) Professor of chemistry at Stockholm, Sweden. He devoted himself to astrophysics and published several books on popular astronomy. He was the originator of the *panspermia hypothesis.*

Arrow   Constellation in the northern hemisphere. See: *Sagitta.*

artificial horizon   A reflective surface, such as a surface of the element mercury, that is used on land to measure the altitude of a celestial body. The angle between the body and its reflection is equal to twice the apparent altitude.

artificial satellites   *Man-made moons,* launched from the earth. The first artificial satellite, Sputnik I, was launched by Soviet scientists on the night of October 4, 1957. With a velocity of 5 miles/sec, the satellite circled the globe at an altitude varying between 140 miles and 585 miles in a period of about 1½ hours. Since then, numerous artificial satellites have been launched by the Soviet Union and the United States. Primarily, these satellites are designed for scientific purposes, such as the study of radiation, scanning the earth's cloud layer, exploring the upper atmosphere and space near the earth. Telemetering devices and television scanners transmit reports to tracking stations on the earth. At the present time, several hundred artificial satellites have been launched.

ascending node   The point of intersection between the orbit of a planet or comet and the ecliptic where the planet or comet crosses the ecliptic moving from south to north (to pass from south to north celestial latitude). The celestial longitude of the ascending node is one of the *elements of an orbit.*

ashen light   **1.** At the new moon phase, the portion of the moon's surface that does not receive direct sunlight shines with a soft ashen light. This light is produced by sunlight reflected from the earth to the moon. It is called "earthshine" and occurs on the moon during "full earth." **2.** The faint glow occasionally observed on the dark hemisphere of Venus.

aspect   The positions of two celestial bodies with respect to one another. The most important aspects are: *conjunction,* when both bodies have the same astronomical longitude; *op-*

position, when the difference in longitude is 180°; *quadrature*, when the difference amounts to 90°. (Fig. A9.)

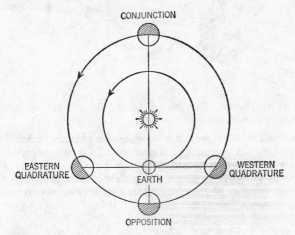

CONJUNCTION

EASTERN
QUADRATURE

EARTH

WESTERN
QUADRATURE

OPPOSITION

A9. Aspects.

associations Sparsely populated groups of stars with diameters between 40 and 400 light-years. Consisting mainly of very young stars, associations are believed to have evolved out of local condensations of interstellar matter. Associations are divided into two types: *O associations*, consisting of young stars of early spectral type (O and B stars), and *T associations*, consisting of young, red dwarf stars, often found to be variable (T Tauri stars). Associations are unstable formations whose members will eventually drift away from each other.

A stars Stars of spectral type A in the **Harvard classification* of stellar spectra. These are white stars at a temperature of about 10,000° K., whose spectra are dominated by the **Balmer series* of hydrogen lines.

asteroid A **minor planet*.

astigmatism An aberration in lenses and mirrors whereby light from a point source is imaged as a straight line, ellipse, or circle. The rays of light in two perpendicular planes appear as two lines at right angles. Astigmatic optics cannot produce a sharp image but the aberration can be suppressed with appropriate lenses. (Fig. A10.)

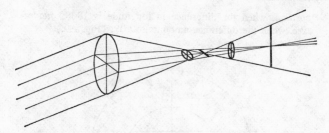

A10. Astigmatism. The images formed by a beam of light passing through astigmatic optics.

astrobiology The study of living organisms on other worlds.

astrograph A photographic instrument with high light-gathering power which is used to photograph a large field in a single exposure. To obtain a large field of good definition, a very complicated objective consisting of three or more lenses is required. Today, the astrograph is being replaced with the *Schmidt telescope.*

Astrographic Catalogue (*Carte du Ciel*) A catalogue containing the positions of about four million stars measured from 44,000 photographic plates prepared through a joint undertaking by a large number of observatories around the world. The same type of instruments were used by the various observatories, which were allocated particular areas of the sky. The work, proposed at the International Congress in Paris in 1887, started in 1896.

astrolabe An antique instrument used to measure positions on the celestial sphere. In its simplest form, the astrolabe consists of a graduated circular disc with a movable sighting device. The instrument, developed by the Arabians, was used for determining positions at sea. See: *prismatic astrolabe,* one of the most accurate instruments for the determination of right ascension of stars.

astrology A superstition that originated in Babylon about 3000 years ago. With the use of a *horoscope,* a person's fate as well as future events were predicted from the positions and motions of celestial bodies. Astrology was significant in the early history of astronomy. Since astrologers kept a very careful record of the motions in the sky for superstitious predictions, a technique of observation was developed which was later applied in astronomy. Astrology flourished in Europe as

late as the Middle Ages and was not recognized as a superstition until the 17th century. Even today, newspapers carry
astrological predictions, which must be regarded as pure
sham.

astrometry   A branch of astronomy that is concerned with the
determination of the apparent position and motion of celestial
bodies. Formerly, astrometry was referred to as spherical or
practical astronomy. Sometimes it is called positional astronomy.

astronaut   A trained space pilot.

astronautics   In a restricted sense, *space travel,* but in a broader
definition, the science that deals with the mechanical, technical, physiological, etc., requirements for space flight. Astronautics is a very young science in rapid development. During the International Geophysical Year, 1957–58, the Soviet
Union and the United States launched the first *artificial
satellites.* Space missions with living organisms were successfully carried out by 1960. In 1961, the first men were
launched into space, the Russian "cosmonauts" Y. Gagarin
(April 12) and G. Titov (August 6). The first American
"astronaut" to orbit the earth was John Glenn (February 20,
1962). In addition to orbital satellites, there have been various probes launched toward the moon and planets. For in-
stance, the far side of the moon has been photographed by
the Russian vehicles Lunik III (1959) and Zond III (1965);
close-range photographs of the moon were obtained by the
last three American "Rangers" of 1964 and 1965, showing
craters only a foot or so in diameter; and in December 1962
the U.S. Mariner II passed within 21,000 miles of Venus, so
providing us with our closest view yet obtained. The most re-
markable feat of the early years of space research was that of
July 1965, when another American probe, Mariner IV, obtained close-range photographs of Mars, showing the Martian
surface is covered with large craters apparently similar to
those of the moon. To escape the earth, a space vehicle must
attain a speed of 11.2 km/sec, or 7 miles/sec, relative to the
earth. Such velocities are reached with rocket propulsion
based on the reaction principle. Through the use of multi-
stage rockets, where each successive stage is fired in consecutive order after the previous stage burns out, high speeds are
obtained to orbit a satellite or send a probe to the moon.
Solid and liquid fuels are presently in use, but experiments
are under way to utilize atomic energy for rocket propulsion.

Ion and photon propulsion are also being considered to obtain high velocities.

astronomical clocks Precision clocks of various kinds for measuring time. The oldest precision clock is the pendulum clock, using a pendulum as a time regulator. A modern clock will have its pendulum in an evacuated case and is kept at a constant temperature. Errors amount to no more than a few thousandths of a second per day. Other types of astronomical clocks include the *quartz crystal clock,* which keeps time by the vibrations of a quartz crystal. Today, *atomic clocks,* which keep time by atomic and molecular vibrations of cesium and ammonia, are being used more frequently. Errors in these clocks amount to only one second in 3000 years.

astronomical constants Values of fundamental significance derived through precise measurements. The most important are: solar parallax, 8″79; nutation, 9″21; constant of aberration, 20″47; annual general precession, 50″27; obliquity of ecliptic, 23° 26′ 40″ (1960); sidereal day, 23h 56m 4.09s (mean solar time); synodic month, 29d 12h 44m 3s (mean solar days); sidereal month, 27d 07h 43m (mean solar days); tropical year, 365d 05h 48m 46s (mean solar days).

astronomical co-ordinates Values in a reference system used to relate the position of a body on the celestial sphere. Several different systems are utilized in astronomy: **1.** HORIZON SYSTEM. Reference plane: horizontal plane which intersects the celestial sphere along the horizon. Poles: zenith, equal to the extension of a plumb line to the sky, and the nadir, which is opposite of zenith. Co-ordinates: azimuth, A, the angle between the vertical circle through the celestial body (the great circle through the celestial body and the zenith) and the meridian (the great circle through the zenith and the north and south points); altitude, h, the angular distance along the vertical circle from the horizon to the object. (The complementary angle is called zenith distance.) Azimuth is measured from the south point westward from 0° to 360°, while altitude is measured positively above and negatively below the horizon from 0° to 90°. Azimuth is also measured from the north point eastward. **2.** EQUATOR SYSTEM. Reference plane: the plane of the earth's equator which intersects the celestial sphere along the celestial equator. Poles: celestial poles. Co-ordinates: right ascension, declination, and hour angle. *Right ascension* is the arc along the equator from the hour circle of the object (great circle through the poles and the object), measured eastward from the vernal equinox, i.e., the point of intersection of the ecliptic and the celestial equator where the sun changes from south to north declination. Right ascension is measured from 0h to 24h. *Declination* is the angular distance from the celestial equator to the object, measured along the hour circle of the object. Declination is measured positively from 0° to 90° toward the north celestial pole and negatively toward the south celestial pole. *Hour angle* is the angle between the hour circle through the object and the meridian. The hour angle is measured from the meridian westward from 0h to 24h. **3. ECLIPTIC SYSTEM.** Reference plane: plane of the ecliptic (the plane of the earth's orbit) which intersects the celestial sphere along the ecliptic, the sun's apparent path across the sky. Poles: poles of the ecliptic. Co-ordinates: celestial latitude and longitude. Longitude is measured along the ecliptic from the vernal equinox eastward from 0° to 360°, and is the angle between the great

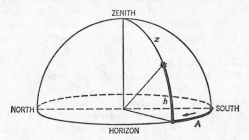

A11. Astronomical co-ordinates. Horizon system.

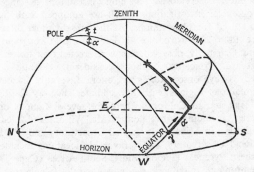

A12. Astronomical co-ordinates. Equator system.

circle through the object and the pole of the ecliptic and the great circle through the vernal equinox. Latitude is the angular distance between the ecliptic and the object, measured positively toward the north ecliptic pole and negatively toward the south ecliptic pole from 0° to 90°. 4. GALACTIC SYSTEM. Reference plane: galactic plane (the plane of the Milky Way). Poles: galactic poles. Co-ordinates: galactic longitude and latitude. Galactic longitude was formerly measured eastward from the point of intersection between the celestial equator and the galactic equator. (Now it is measured from the direction to the center of the Galaxy.) Latitude is measured positively toward the north galactic pole and negatively toward the south galactic pole. 5. POSITION ANGLE AND DISTANCE. Co-ordinates used in measurements of visual binaries. Position angle is the angle between the two components, measured from the hour circle through the primary eastward from the north celestial pole to the secondary star 0° to 360°. *Distance* is the angular separation of the two components measured in seconds of arc. Position angle and distance are measured with a special position micrometer attached to the telescope. (Figs. A11 and A12.)

astronomical instruments Instruments used to study the celestial bodies. There are two classifications: optical instruments that study the light radiated from the objects in the sky, and radio telescopes that receive radio frequency radiation. The various optical instruments, reflecting and refracting telescopes, meridian passage instruments, and others are included under their respective topics.

astronomical observatories Scientific institutions designed for astronomical investigations which are equipped with instruments used for observations. At the present time, there are more than 200 astronomical observatories throughout the world. Originally, observatories were erected near universities (Harvard, Princeton) without considering climatic conditions. Today, observatories are more favorably located in mountainous regions with dry climate, such as California and Arizona. In California there are several famous observatories, including Mt. Palomar, Mt. Wilson, and Lick observatories; in Arizona, the Lowell Observatory and Kitt Peak National Observatory. Other favorable locations include the northern Pyrenees (Pic du Midi), South Africa (Cape Town, Bloemfontein, Johannesburg), and Australia (Canberra). Radio astronomy is not dependent upon climatic conditions.

Radio observatories are found throughout the entire world. The largest radio telescopes include the 250-foot steerable receiver at Jodrell Bank, near Manchester, England, the 300-foot transit radio telescope at Green Bank, West Virginia, and the 1000-foot stationary disc near Arecibo, Puerto Rico. Other famous radio telescopes are found in Australia and Dwingeloo, Netherlands.

astronomical signs and symbols Letters or other symbols assigned to identify astronomical values or celestial bodies. The most important in the various branches of astronomy are as follows:

1. Spherical astronomy

α or R.A.	right ascension
δ	declination
a or A	azimuth
h	altitude
Z	zenith distance
λ	celestial longitude
β	celestial latitude
l	galactic longitude
b	galactic latitude
ϕ	polar distance
θ	sidereal time
t	hour angle
h	hour
m	minute
s	second
α	position angle
ρ	distance in seconds of arc
μ	proper motion
π	parallax in seconds of arc
ε	obliquity of the ecliptic

2. Orbit determination (theoretical astronomy)

k	constant of gravitation
m	planet's mass expressed in terms of the sun's mass as unity
T	time for perihelion passage
E	epoch
ω	angular distance from the ascending node to the perihelion point
Ω	longitude of the ascending node
ϖ	longitude of the perihelion point ($\varpi = \omega + \Omega$)
i	inclination to the ecliptic

e   eccentricity of the orbit
a   semi-major axis
q   perihelion distance
r   radius vector
P   period of revolution

3. Astrophysics

m   apparent magnitude
M   absolute magnitude
m_v apparent visual magnitude
m_{pg} apparent photographic magnitude
CI   color index
E   color excess
λ   wave length
μ   micron = 10^{-3}mm
Å   Ångstrom unit = 10^{-7}mm
JD   Julian day

4. Solar system

⊙   Sun
☿   Mercury
♀   Venus
⊕   Earth
♂   Mars
♃   Jupiter
♄   Saturn
♅ and ⯨   Uranus
♆   Neptune
♇   Pluto
☾   moon
🌑   new moon
🌓   first quarter
🌕   full moon
🌗   last quarter
⑥   minor planet (number in a circle)
☄   comet
♈   vernal equinox
☌   conjunction
□   quadrature
☍   opposition
☊   ascending node
☋   descending node

5. Constellations of the Zodiac

♈   Aries, the Ram
♉   Taurus, the Bull

♊ Gemini, the Twins
♋ Cancer, the Crab
♌ Leo, the Lion
♍ Virgo, the Virgin
♎ Libra, the Scales
♏ Scorpius, the Scorpion
♐ Sagittarius, the Archer
♑ Capricornus, the Sea Goat
♒ Aquarius, the Water Bearer
♓ Pisces, the Fish

astronomical societies Associations of astronomers or persons interested in astronomy found in most countries. Several are international, such as the *International Astronomical Union*. Other associations include the American Astronomical Society, British Astronomical Association, Royal Astronomical Society of Canada, Royal Astronomical Society, and the Astronomical Society of the Pacific.

astronomical triangle The spherical triangle formed by the arcs of the great circles joining the celestial pole, zenith, and a celestial body. This triangle is used for transformations between co-ordinate systems in spherical astronomy. (Fig. A13.)

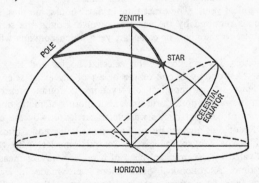

A13. Astronomical triangle.

astronomical tube *Kepler's telescope.* In its simplest form, a telescope consisting of two positive lenses. One, the objective, has a long focal length and forms an image of a distant object observed through the other lens, the ocular, used as a loupe. See: *refractor.* (Fig. A14.)

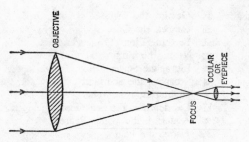

A14. Astronomical refractions telescope.

astronomical twilight From sunset to the time when the sun is 18° beneath the horizon.

astronomical unit A.U. The mean distance between the earth and the sun, 93 million miles.

astronomical units of distance The distance between the earth and the sun, 93 million miles, is used as a unit of measurement within the solar system. In the stellar system, the *parsec*, the distance at which the radius of the earth's orbit subtends an angle of 1″ of arc, or *light-year,* the distance that light travels in one year, is used. One parsec is equal to 3.26 light-years, or about 20 million million miles.

astronomical year The exact time in days, hours, minutes, and seconds required by the earth to revolve around the sun in contrast to the civil, or calendar, year which contains whole days.

astronomy The science of the celestial bodies and the universe. Astronomy is one of the oldest of the exact sciences. Evidence of astronomical observations is found preserved from the oldest prehistoric times, but more systematic observations of celestial bodies were later carried out by the civilized people of ancient Egypt, Babylonia, India, and China, as well as the Mayan Indians of Central America, who were motivated by the practical need of a regular way of measuring time. Astronomical observations were made in Egypt more than 5000 years ago and these observations made it possible to predict the overflow of the Nile. Astronomy reached a high position in Babylon, where systematic studies of the motions of the sun, moon, and planets were made primarily for astrological forecasts and predictions. In China, observations of the heavens can be traced back to the third century B.C., where interest was concentrated on unusual phenomena such as solar eclipses, comets, and novae. The astronomy of ancient Greece consisted mainly of philosophical and cosmological speculations. Through the influence of Babylon, observations became more significant. The Greeks began to make careful measurements of the length of the year, the period of revolution of the moon and the planets, and derived the earth's dimensions as well as the distance to the moon. Foremost among the ancient Greek astronomers was Hipparchus (second century B.C.), who is considered to be the greatest astronomer of antiquity and the founder of astronomy as a science. The classical concept that the sun, moon, and planets revolve about the earth (geocentric system) originated with the Greeks and dominated European thinking during the entire Middle Ages. Nicolaus Copernicus (1473–1543) revised this view by interpreting the motions as a result of the earth's rotation and revolution about the sun as the central body. The invention of the telescope in the beginning of the 17th century led to a revolutionary change in techniques of observation. Methods of measurement were refined and noteworthy discoveries followed in rapid succession. The announcement of the law of gravitation (Newton, 1687) ushered in a new era in astronomy and gave birth to theoretical astronomy, or celestial mechanics, which was dominant during the 18th and 19th centuries. In the 19th century, *photography* and spectral analysis began to be used in astronomy, which prompted a new branch, *astrophysics*, relating astronomy more intimately with physics. During the 20th century, a new field of exploration was opened by Jansky's discovery (1931) that radio waves can be received from space. A new branch of astronomy was founded, *radio astronomy*, which deals with the investigation of cosmic radio waves. This new field has become an extremely important complement to optical astronomy. The most important branches of astronomy are: **1.** ASTROMETRY, or spherical astronomy, which includes the determination of position and motion. It is also called *practical astronomy*. **2.** CELESTIAL MECHANICS is the study of the motions of celestial bodies and the determination of their orbits. **3.** ASTROPHYSICS, the study of the physical characteristics of the celestial bodies. **4.** STELLAR ASTRONOMY, the study of the composition and size of the stellar system. Other branches include *cosmogony*, which deals with the origin of the universe, and *radio astronomy*. Most of these branches are interrelated.

astrophotography The photographing of celestial objects. Today, photography is used in practically all observations. The
photograph is the most objective of all recording methods.
Since the effect of light upon photographic emulsions is additive, fainter stars are recorded by increasing exposure time.
Photography in different colors is possible through the use of
various filters and different emulsions. Astrophotography has
many applications in photometry, the measurement of the
intensity of light from the stars. Special cameras such as the
Schmidt telescope have been constructed with a wide usable
field. In this way thousands or hundreds of thousands of star
images can be obtained on one exposure. Photography is es-
sential in the study of nebulae and galaxies. Using special
instruments, photography of the sun in the light of one spectral line is possible (monochromatic photography). As yet,
the fine details of the planets have not been photographed,
since exposure times of several seconds are necessary and
atmospheric turbulence frequently blurs the image. Spectral
analysis is carried out almost exclusively with the aid of
photographic methods. Photography is responsible for the advanced development of astrophysics. Photography came into
use in astronomy in the middle of the 19th century, and is
now extensively used for astrometric purposes, for the determination of accurate positions of the stars, trigonometric
parallaxes, proper motions, etc.

astrophysics The branch of astronomy that treats of the physical characteristics and composition of the celestial bodies.
Astrophysics is based primarily upon the study of the radiation from these celestial bodies with respect to quantity (intensity) and quality (composition). By means of known
physical laws, it is possible to draw conclusions regarding the
physical condition and chemical composition of these bodies.
Using mathematics, theoretical astrophysics seeks to determine the conditions existing in the interior of stars, their
radiation, origin, and evolution on the basis of physical laws.

asymmetrical star stream See: *Strömberg's asymmetrical star
stream.*

Atlas One of the brighter stars in the *Pleiades* (Seven Sisters).

atmosphere The gaseous envelope surrounding a celestial
body. **1.** EARTH'S ATMOSPHERE. The earth's atmosphere contains 78% nitrogen, 21% oxygen, 0.9% argon, some carbon
dioxide, and several other substances in relatively insignificant quantities. In addition, water vapor is present in varying

amounts. The earth's atmosphere is divided into different layers. The *troposphere* is nearest the surface and extends to an altitude of between 5 and 10 miles. Above the troposphere, the *stratosphere*, to an altitude of 50 miles, then the *ionosphere*, where atoms are ionized. There are several electrically charged layers that reflect radio waves, including the Kennelly-Heaviside, or *E layer*, at about 65 miles, the Appleton or F_1 and F_2 layers at about 125 miles and 185 miles respectively. The ionosphere reaches an altitude of about 370 miles to the *exosphere*, which gradually merges into interplanetary space. The density of the atmosphere diminishes rapidly with altitude. At the surface, atmospheric pressure averages 760 mm Hg (one atmosphere) but by 30 miles altitude, the pressure has decreased to 0.5 mm Hg and with increasing altitude becomes exceedingly low. **2.** PLANETARY ATMOSPHERE. If a planet does not have sufficient mass, its gravity will be too low to sustain an atmosphere and the gas molecules will disappear in space. At high temperatures, the loss will occur more rapidly as a result of the greater molecular motion. The moon and Mercury lack an appreciable atmosphere because of these conditions. The composition of the planets' atmospheres has been determined through spectral analysis. Venus has a dense atmosphere containing carbon dioxide and very little water vapor. The atmosphere of Mars is very tenuous and also contains carbon dioxide and traces of water vapor. The giant planets, Jupiter, Saturn, Uranus, and Neptune, have extensive atmospheres containing methane, ammonia, and molecular hydrogen. The condition of Pluto's atmosphere is unknown. Titan, the satellite of Saturn, has an atmosphere of methane and ammonia. Triton, the satellite of Neptune, is presumed to have an atmosphere of methane. **3.** STELLAR ATMOSPHERE. The sun and stars are surrounded by atmospheres of densities considerably lower than the remainder of these gaseous bodies. The solar and stellar spectra show dark absorption lines that reveal important information about the nature of stars. The lower layer of the sun's atmosphere is called the **chromosphere* and is surrounded by a more tenuous envelope, the **solar corona*. Some stars have very extensive atmospheres which are studied by spectroscopic methods. Often, the spectra of stellar atmospheres contain emission lines, as in the case of Wolf-Rayet and P Cygni stars.

atmospheric extinction See: *absorption*.

atmospheric refraction The bending of light while passing
through the earth's atmosphere. Since the density of the atmosphere decreases with altitude, a ray of light from space
will bend more as it continues down through the atmosphere.
As a result, a star will appear higher in the sky than its true
direction. In the zenith, atmospheric refraction is zero while
at the horizon it amounts to 34′ 50″. Thus, the sun and the
moon are actually below the horizon when they appear to be
rising. Allowance must be made for atmospheric refraction
when determining positions. (Fig. A15.)

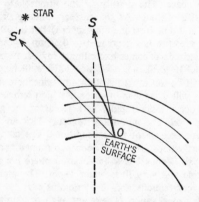

A15. Atmospheric refraction.

atmospheric turmoil Turbulence in the earth's atmosphere
which causes fluctuations in the direction and brightness of
the starlight passing through to the surface. The image of a
star is seldom motionless and bright, but rather unsteady and
fuzzy. As a result, stars appear to twinkle. See: *seeing* and
scintillation.

atmospheric windows Gaps in atmospheric absorption. The
atmosphere absorbs practically all radiation from space with
the exception of the region of visible light (wave lengths
0.0004 to 0.0008 mm) and the adjoining ultraviolet and infrared regions. This *optical window* extends from about
3000 to 30,000 Å. Radiation of shorter wave lengths is absorbed by the ozone in the atmosphere while radiation of
longer wave lengths is hindered by molecular absorption.
Within the short-wave radio region between a few millimeter
wave lengths to about 15 meters is another atmospheric win-

dow through which radio radiation from space can penetrate
to the surface; the so-called *radio window*. (Fig. A16.)

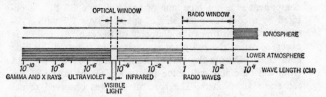

A16. Atmospheric windows.

atom The smallest stable unit forming the basic elements. An
atom consists of a nucleus that contains most of the mass and
is positively charged. Negatively charged electrons move
around the nucleus. The nucleus contains two kinds of particles; protons with a positive charge, and neutrons with no
charge. If an electron jumps from an outer to an inner orbit,
energy is released and the atom radiates light of a frequency
proportional to the energy lost, producing a specific emission
line in the spectrum. If the atom receives energy so that an
electron jumps from an inner to an outer orbit, a corresponding wave length in the spectrum will be lacking, producing
an absorption line. The radius of an atom is 10^{-8}cm, while
the nucleus is 10^{-5} or 10^{-6} times smaller.

atomic clock A type of modern clock in which the characteristic frequencies of certain atoms and molecules are utilized
for precision time measurement. Several kinds have been constructed, including *ammonia* and *cesium* clocks which attain
a stability ratio of $1:10^{11}$.

atomic weight The mass number or atomic weight of an atom
is equal to the sum of the protons and neutrons in the nucleus (the sum of the nucleons). Atomic weight varies from
1 for hydrogen to 254 for nobelium.

Aura An acronym for Association of Universities for Research
in Astronomy, operating agent for Kitt Peak National Observatory in Arizona and for a southern station in Chile.

Auriga (Charioteer) A conspicuous constellation in the northern hemisphere at 5h 30m right ascension (α = 5h 30m),
40° north declination (δ = +40°). The brightest star is
Capella.—Epsilon (ε) *Aurigae* is a double star with an infrared component with a diameter 3000 times the diameter of
the sun, or 2500 million miles. It is the largest known star.

Zeta (ζ) *Aurigae* is an interesting eclipsing binary (*photometric double star*) with a period of 972 days. The main component is a hot blue star of spectral type B8 that is orbited by a cool red giant star of spectral type K5 with a diameter over 200 times the diameter of the sun. An eclipse is observed when the red giant star passes in front of the blue component. During the partial phase of the eclipse, the light from the blue star will shine through different layers of the red star's atmosphere. The spectral changes observed reveal the structure of the atmosphere of the red giant.—*Zeta Aurigae variables* are eclipsing binary stars consisting of a relatively cool *supergiant of late spectral type and a smaller hotter star of early spectral type. The prototype is the star Zeta Auriga. The periods of these stars often amount to several years.

auroras Northern and southern lights. Luminous arcs, rays, and streamers that appear in the earth's atmosphere in the night sky with greatest frequency in two ringed belts about 1600 miles from the earth's magnetic poles. They are subject to rapid changes, appearing as rays, curtains, and luminous arcs. Colors vary from green-white to dark red. The aurora occurs most frequently at altitudes of between 50 and 100 miles and, in rare instances, as high as 600 miles. Appearing quite frequently during the time of sunspot maximum, the aurora has a definite relationship to *solar flares* (eruptions on the sun). Clouds of charged particles (positive and negative ions) from the sun reach the earth about a day after the eruption of a solar flare. Influenced by the earth's magnetic field, these particles penetrate the atmosphere, collide with and ionize molecules of the air to cause the glow. Auroras are also believed to occur in the atmosphere of Venus.

autumn A season of the year; the time interval between the autumnal equinox and the winter solstice, from September 23 to December 21.

autumnal equinox One of the points of intersection between the equator and the ecliptic. The sun reaches the autumnal equinox when it crosses from north to south and passes the celestial equator on about September 23. The autumnal equinox is located in the constellation of Virgo.

axis 1. AXIS OF ROTATION of a celestial body or star system is an imaginary line about which rotation takes place. 2. CELESTIAL AXIS is the extension of the earth's axis to the celestial poles. 3. OPTICAL AXIS is the straight line connecting the midpoints of the lenses or mirrors in astronomical instruments.

azimuth One of the co-ordinates of a star in the **horizon system*. The angle formed by the vertical circle of a star (the great circle through the star and the zenith) with the meridian of the position. Azimuth is measured from the south point of the horizon westward from 0° to 360°, or from the north point eastward.

azimuthal mounting See: *altazimuth*.

azimuth error An error found in a transit instrument when the horizontal axis is not aligned exactly east–west.

B

Baade, Walter (1892–1960) German-American astronomer who was active at Mt. Wilson and Palomar observatories for almost three decades. One of the foremost observers of his time, he discovered the two categories of stellar populations (1944) and in 1952 found that the distance measurement to the galaxies was incorrect and had to be at least doubled.

Bailey's Beads A phenomenon that occurs during a total eclipse of the sun. Just prior to and after totality, sunlight shines through the lunar valleys on the moon's limb, causing the dark face of the moon to appear to be surrounded by a shining necklace of pearls.

balloon satellite See: *Echo satellites*.

Balmer jump The intensity drop at the limit of the Balmer series of discrete lines in the hydrogen spectrum at about λ3650.

Balmer series A distinctive series of lines mainly in the visible spectrum of hydrogen, produced when electrons jump from an outer orbit to the second orbit measured from the nucleus. The most prominent lines are Hα(6563), Hβ(4861), Hγ(4340), Hδ(4102), Hε(3970), etc. The spectra of type A stars are characterized by the presence of the Balmer series.

band spectrum A spectrum originating from molecules and characterized by bands consisting of a series of very closely situated lines. Bands caused by titanium oxide, zirconium, and carbon compounds occur in the spectra of low-temperature stars.

Barlow lens   A plano-concave lens placed in the telescope between the objective and ocular to increase magnification.

Barnard's star   A star with the largest known proper motion, amounting to 10″3 per year, discovered in 1916 by the American astronomer E. E. Barnard.

barred spiral   A type of spiral galaxy that is characterized by a bar-shaped nucleus.

barycenter   The center of mass.

basic elements   Substances all atoms of which have similar chemical properties. Investigations of the atmospheres of the sun and stars, interstellar matter, etc., have shown that the *relative distribution* of the elements in the universe is about the same as found on the earth and in meteorites, with the exception of the lighter elements (hydrogen and helium). The following table shows the number of atoms of each element per million parts of atomic matter for the ten most common elements found in the universe:

Hydrogen	839,000	Carbon	130
Helium	159,000	Iron	64
Oxygen	680	Magnesium	42
Neon	640	Silicon	35
Nitrogen	200	Sulphur	12

As the result of nuclear processes in the interior of stars, the original composition of stellar matter is changed through the fusion of hydrogen to helium. Young stars of Population I contain more of the heavier elements in relation to hydrogen than the older stars of Population II. The *origin of the elements* has been a topic of extensive speculation. Very high temperatures are required to form elements. Hydrogen is transformed to helium through nuclear processes at temperatures of 10 million to 15 million degrees Centigrade. At 100 million degrees Centigrade, three helium atoms can fuse into a carbon isotope resulting in a series of other elements. Assuming that the entire universe was situated in a primeval atom at the beginning of time, Gamow suggests that a short time after the start of expansion, extremely high temperatures made the creation of heavy elements possible from the protons, neutrons, and electrons constituting the primordial matter. According to another hypothesis, the basic elements are formed in the interior of supernovae where temperatures of several thousand million degrees prevail. During the explosion of a supernova, these elements are hurled into space, accounting for the presence of heavy elements in interstellar matter from which additional stars, the sun, and planets were created.

Bay of Rainbows (*Sinus Irridium*) A semicircular formation in the *Mare Imbrium* (Sea of Showers) on the surface of the moon.

BD Abbreviation for **Bonner Durchmusterung*.

Bellatrix The star Gamma (γ) Orionis, one of the brightest stars in Orion, of apparent visual magnitude 1.7 and spectral type B2.

Berenice's Hair Coma Berenices. An open star cluster located near the north galactic pole at a distance of 260 light-years. It is visible to the unaided eye as a patch of light.

Bessel, Friedrich Wilhelm (1784–1846) German astronomer. An outstanding observer who made fundamental contributions to positional and spherical astronomy. In 1838, he successfully determined the first satisfactory stellar parallax (the star 61 Cygni).

Besselian year The point of time from which the tropical year is measured. According to Bessel, the tropical year should be measured from the point where the mean sun has a right ascension of 18h 40m, which is approximately the start of the calendar year.

Beta (β) The second letter in the Greek alphabet. Beta Lyrae stars; see: *Lyra*.

Betelgeuse The star Alpha (α) Orionis, a red giant variable with an apparent visual magnitude between 0.1 and 1.2 and spectral type M2. Betelgeuse is a **supergiant* star whose diameter was measured with an interferometer. Its maximum diameter is equal to approximately 400 solar diameters.

Biela's comet A short-period comet discovered by W. von Biela, of Austria, in 1826. Biela's comet was one of the most interesting comets observed. Determination of the orbital elements showed that the comet had a period of 6.7 years. During its closest approach, the comet could not be seen but was observed again on its return in 1845. Strangely, toward the end of 1845, the comet divided into two parts. By March 1846, the distance between the two components amounted to 180,000 miles. By the comet's return in 1852, the distance had increased to 1.5 million miles. Thereafter, the comet disappeared. The comet was expected again in 1872, but instead, on the evening of November 27, a remarkably brilliant meteor shower occurred that caused a sensation around the entire world. The shower was caused by the debris which spread out over the orbit of the now completely disintegrated comet. See: *Bielids.

Bielids Meteor shower originating from Biela's comet, most frequently referred to as *Andromedids.

Big Dipper The seven bright stars of the constellation Ursa Major. The names of these stars are Alkaid, Mizar, Alioth, Megrez, Phecda, Merak, and Dubhe.

binary stars Double stars. Stars that consist of two components mutually revolving around a common center of gravity. Modern investigation has shown that binary stars are very commonplace, perhaps every other or every third star is a double. Many stars have more than two components and are triple or *multiple stars*. Binary stars are divided into three categories: *visual, spectroscopic,* and *photometric*. **1.** If the angular separation or distance between the components is greater than about 0.″1, the star can be observed as a VISUAL BINARY. At present, more than 40,000 visual binaries are known. Orbital motion has been established for about 10% of the stars, while orbits have been determined for about 1%. Periods of revolution vary from several years to several hundred years and the true distance between the components is generally about 5 to 30 times the earth's distance from the sun. Orbits are elliptical and, as a rule, eccentricity is greater than found in the orbits of the planets. When the period and the size of the orbit are known, the total mass of the system is determined by the law of gravitation. **2.** SPECTROSCOPIC BINARIES. If the apparent distance between the stars is too small to be separated visually, the stars can be observed as spectroscopic binaries. As the components revolve about a common center of gravity, they alternately approach and recede from the earth. This motion is reflected in the spectral lines of the stars as a *Doppler effect*. Periodically, the spectral lines appear to double. If the stars are of different magnitudes, occasionally only the spectrum of the bright star can be seen. In such a case, spectral lines will appear to oscillate about an average position. Radial velocities are determined from the displacement of the spectrum lines and a *velocity curve* is developed to show the relationship of the radial velocity with respect to time. The orbit of the star can be calculated when the velocity curve is known. Several thousand spectroscopic binaries are known and orbits have been calculated for more than 500 systems. The periods of the spectroscopic binaries are much shorter than those of the visual binaries, ranging from a few hours to a few years, with orbits of generally small eccentricity. **3.** PHOTOMETRIC BINARIES (eclipsing variables). If the plane of the orbit lies in or near the line of sight, the stars will mutually eclipse one another and cause variations in the brightness. If the brightness is plotted on a graph as a function of time, a *light curve* is generated that illustrates the progress of the eclipse. The characteristics of the eclipse can be found from the shape of the light curve and the orbits, and the sizes of the components determined. Several thousand photometric binaries have been discovered. The first eclipsing binary discovered was Algol (β Persei). Spectral changes such as the appearance of emission lines have been detected among photometric binaries, which seems to indicate that some systems are surrounded by an expanding gas shell or extensive atmosphere that encloses one or both components. This is the case with the star Beta (β) Lyrae. A detailed study of the light curve will also show if the components of a close pair have become flattened or deformed. **4.** ASTROMETRIC BINARIES. Irregularities in the proper motion of stars caused by unseen companions have also been found. Such perturbations have made it possible to determine the orbits and the mass of the components. In this way, unseen components have been discovered with masses of only 10 to 20 times that of Jupiter. At one time, close binaries were assumed to have originated through the division of rapidly rotating stars. Today, it is believed that the components were formed as nearby condensations within the same nebulosity.

binocular An ocular arrangement adapted for both eyes. Binoculars are used in microscopes and astronomical instruments.

Bird of Paradise Constellation in the southern hemisphere. See: *Apus.*

birefringent filter A filter based upon the polarization of light which can isolate a narrow spectral band (1 Å or smaller). These filters permit monochromatic photography of such solar phenomena as flares and prominences. See: *monochromator.*

black-body radiation Radiation from a body capable of absorbing all radiation received. Black-body radiation is an idealized condition that does not actually occur in nature, although stars are approximately black bodies. In the laboratory, a close approximation to a black body can be made by shining a ray of light through a small hole in a heated ceramic tube. Laws describing black-body radiation are based on the theory of thermodynamic equilibrium.

blink microscope A *blink comparator*. An instrument used to observe small differences between two photographs of the same part of the sky. By means of a mechanical device, the photographic plates are seen alternately in rapid succession so that small differences can be distinguished in the luminosities or positions of stars. Using a blink microscope, variable stars or stars with large proper motions are easily detected in a star field. See: *stereocomparator*.

blue clouds Cloud formations on the planet Mars that appear on blue and ultraviolet photographs, but are invisible on yellow or red plates.

Bode's law An empirical law for the planets' distances from the sun. If a is equal to the mean distance from the sun, Bode's law gives the distances of the planets in astronomical units by the following expression: $a = 0.4 + 0.3 \times 2^n$, where $n = -\infty, 0, 1, 2, \ldots$. The following results are obtained:

Planet	n	a	Actual Distance
Mercury	$-\infty$	0.4	0.39
Venus	0	0.7	0.72
Earth	1	1.0	1.00
Mars	2	1.6	1.52
Ceres (minor planet)	3	2.8	2.77
Jupiter	4	5.2	5.20
Saturn	5	10.0	9.54
Uranus	6	19.6	19.18
Neptune	—	—	30.06
Pluto	7	38.8	39.52

bolide A fireball. A large *meteor* that is exceptionally bright. It sometimes explodes with a loud detonation, with fragments falling to the ground as meteorites.

bolometer An instrument to measure infrared radiation from celestial bodies. It is primarily a platinum wire coated with lampblack that changes in electrical resistance as temperatures vary, making measurements possible.

bolometric magnitude A measure of the total radiation of a star over the entire spectrum. Determination of bolometric magnitude has been possible for only a few bright stars from measurements by means of a *radiometer* or *thermocouple*, corrected for atmospheric absorption. Theoretically, bolometric magnitude can be estimated from a star's visual magnitude when the temperature is known. Bolometric magnitude is used as a measure of luminosity in theoretical investigations of stellar structure.

Bonner Durchmusterung A star catalogue and charts of the positions and magnitudes of about 325,000 stars, prepared by Argelander and Schönfeld and completed in 1862—includes stars brighter than 9th magnitude in the northern hemisphere and to 10th magnitude including stars to 23° south declination ($\delta = -23°$). Bonner Durchmusterung has been extended to stars at the south celestial pole through an analogous work at the Cordoba Observatory in Argentina (Cordoba Durchmusterung). A star is identified by its number in the Bonner Durchmusterung. For example, BD +31° 3932 refers to star 3932 in the 31° north declination zone in the Bonner Durchmusterung.

Boötes (Bear Keeper or Herdsman) A constellation in the northern hemisphere at 14h 30m right ascension ($\alpha = 14h$ 30m), 30° north declination ($\delta = +30°$). The brightest star in Boötes is Arcturus.

Boss' Catalogue A catalogue containing the proper motions of 33,342 stars, prepared by B. Boss (Washington, 1937).

Bradley, James (1692–1762) English astronomer. A distinguished observer who discovered the *aberration* of light.

Brahe, Tycho (1546–1601) Danish nobleman and astronomer. He constructed the observatories of Uranianborg and Stjärneborg on the island of Hven and carried out extensive observations with precision not previously attained. His observations of the planet Mars were adapted by his pupil, J. Kepler, and led to the discovery of *Kepler's laws* of planetary motion.

bridges of matter See: *matter, bridges of*

bright nebulae See: *galactic nebulae.*

brightness The intensity of starlight. With respect to their apparent brightness, stars are classified according to magnitude. See: *magnitude* and *absolute magnitude.*

B stars Stars of spectral type B in the *Harvard classification* of stellar spectra. These are blue-white stars of high absolute magnitude at temperatures of about 20,000° C. Spectra are characterized by lines of neutral helium.

Bull Constellation in the northern hemisphere. See: *Taurus.*

bursts Violent variations in the intensity of solar radio radiation which often occur during the eruption of a **flare*.

butterfly sunspot diagram The diagram developed by W. W. Maunder in 1904 to illustrate the **sunspot cycle*. In the diagram, time is the abscissa, and heliographic latitude (angular distance from the sun's equator) is the ordinate. When sunspots are plotted on the diagram, the curve generated resembles two butterfly wings located symmetrically about the sun's equator as the result of the advance of the sunspots from higher (northern and southern) latitudes toward the equator.

C

Caelum (Chisel) A faint constellation in the southern hemisphere at 4h 40m right ascension ($\alpha = 4h\ 40m$), 40° south declination ($\delta = -40°$).

calcium A basic element that is found in the atmospheres of stars and in interstellar space. The two H and K lines in the solar spectrum originate from ionized calcium. These lines are very pronounced in spectral type F and later type stars. Interstellar calcium lines originate in gas clouds found in space and are observed superimposed on the spectra of more distant stars. These narrow lines do not partake in the stars' motions and were, accordingly, referred to as *stationary calcium lines*.

calcium stars A name previously applied to **F stars* because calcium lines dominate their spectra.

calendar The chronological division of the civil year into days, weeks, and months. In a restricted sense, the calendar includes the dates of the phases of the moon and religious festivals. See: *chronology*.

Calendar of the French Revolution (French Republican Calendar) The calendar reform that took place in France during the French Revolution at the end of the 18th century. The year contained 12 months of 30 days with 5 or 6 leap days. The month was divided into three parts of 10 days each, replacing the weeks of 7 days. The epoch was the autumnal equinox of 1792. Each day was divided into 10 hours, the hours into 100 minutes, and minutes into 100 seconds. The Gregorian calendar was reinstated on January 1, 1806.

calendar reform   Recurrently, proposals have been made to simplify the present calendar. Disadvantages in the present calendar are that the year is not evenly divided into weeks, a given date occurs on a different day in the following year, months and quarters are of unequal length, and Easter always falls on a different Sunday each year. As yet, the advantages of a calender reform have not been realized.

calibration error   A systematic error in the graduated scale of an instrument.

Callisto   The most distant of the four moons of Jupiter, discovered by Galileo. Its period of revolution is 16.7 days.

Camelopardalis   (Giraffe) An extensive but faint constellation in the northern hemisphere near the north celestial pole at 5h right ascension ($\alpha = 5h$), and 70° north declination ($\delta = +70°$).

canals   Controversial surface phenomenon on the planet Mars, studied in detail in 1877 and in the years following by the Italian astronomer Schiaparelli. On his charts, the canals form a geometric network over the planet. The maps of Percival Lowell, the American astronomer, show over 500 narrow geometrical canals. Other investigators and distinguished observers with access to superior telescopes have been unable to see canals but instead have found the surface of Mars to be covered with an abundance of details at the threshold of vision. Because of technical difficulties in photographing details of the planet, no one has been successful in establishing with certainty the existence of canals. Nevertheless, some of the most prominent structures have been photographed and probably represent faults in the surface. Today, it is believed that the geometric network of canals should be attributed to an optical illusion caused by the tendency of the eye to give a geometric structure to distinctive, faint details.

Cancer   (Crab) A small constellation of the *Zodiac,* located in the northern hemisphere at 8h 25m right ascension ($\alpha = $ 8h 25m), and 20° north declination ($\delta = +20°$). The famous star cluster *Praesepe* is found in Cancer and is visible to the unaided eye as a faint patch of light. The star Zeta (ζ) Cancri is an interesting multiple star. Its primary star consists of two components, *A* and *B*, with a period of 60 years. The third component, *C*, is also a double star revolving about the other two stars in a period of between 600 and 700 years. The companion star of the *C* component is invisible and has a period of 18 years.

Canes Venatici (Hunting Dogs) A small constellation in the northern hemisphere at 13h right ascension (α = 13h), 40° north declination (δ = +40°). The famous spiral galaxy Messier 51 is in the constellation, as well as the globular cluster Messier 3.

Canis Major (Greater Dog) A constellation in the southern hemisphere at 7h right ascension (α = 7h), 20° south declination (δ = −20°). The brightest star in the sky is *Sirius*, Alpha (α) Canis Majoris, a famous binary star whose component is a *white dwarf* star.

Canis Minor (Lesser Dog) A small constellation in the northern hemisphere at 7h 30m right ascension (α = 7h 30m), 5° north declination (δ = +5°). The brightest star in Canis Minor is Alpha (α) Canis Minoris, or *Procyon*, which is of apparent visual magnitude 0.5 and has a *white dwarf* companion.

Cannon, Annie Jump (1863–1941) American astronomer who carried out extensive spectral classification at Harvard Observatory and, in addition, developed the Henry Draper Catalogue containing the spectra of over 225,000 stars.

Canon der Finsternisse Canon of eclipses. The great work by T. Oppolzer (1841–1886), of Germany, containing the elements of all solar and lunar eclipses occurring between 1200 B.C. and A.D. 2160.

Canopus The star Alpha (α) Carinae, the second brightest star in the sky, with an apparent visual magnitude of −0.9 and spectral type F0.

Cape Kennedy Formerly Cape Canaveral, the American rocket testing grounds in Florida; the launching area for artificial satellites.

Capella The star Alpha (α) Aurigae (Charioteer), a spectroscopic binary with a period of 104 days. With the aid of an interferometer, it has been possible to study the system's orbital motion. Capella is a giant star with absolute magnitude −0.6, with an apparent visual magnitude 0.2 and spectral type G0.

Capricornus (Sea Goat) A sign of the *Zodiac*. A constellation of faint stars in the southern hemisphere at 21h right ascension (α = 21h), 20° south declination (δ = −20°).

carbon cycle The *carbon-nitrogen cycle*. A type of nuclear reaction that is believed to take place in the interior of the stars. Helium is formed by the fusion of four hydrogen nuclei, releasing an enormous amount of energy. The process produces a chain reaction with carbon playing the role of a catalyst. These reactions were discovered independently by C. F. von Weizsäcker and H. Bethe. The reaction occurs at a temperature of 15 million to 20 million degrees Centigrade.

carbon dioxide   (CO_2) A gas found in the earth's atmosphere, as well as the atmospheres of Venus and Mars.

carbon-nitrogen cycle   See: *carbon cycle.*

Carina   (Keel) A part of the constellation *Argo.*

Carpenter, Malcolm Scott   (1925–   ) American astronaut. On May 24, 1962, he completed three orbits around the earth in a Mercury capsule launched from Cape Kennedy, formerly Cape Canaveral, Florida.

Carrington, Richard Christopher   (1826–1875) English astronomer. Compiled a catalogue of more than 3700 circumpolar stars and carried out extensive observations of the sun.

Carte du Ciel   A star catalogue and photographic atlas of the heavens developed through the combined efforts of 18 observatories around the world. The work was started in 1887 and is still in progress. See: *Astrographic Catalogue.*

Cassegrainian telescope (Cassegrainian system)   An arrangement frequently used in instrument construction. The parabolic primary mirror is furnished with a hole bored through the center. The light rays from the primary are reflected back again by a hyperbolic convex secondary mirror to a point located beyond the hole in the primary where the ocular or the photographic plate, spectrograph, photoelectric photometer, etc., are placed. (Fig. C1.)

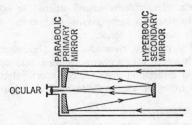

C1. Cassegrainian telescope.

Cassini   Italian-French family of astronomers. **1.** GIOVANNI DOMENICO (1625–1714), born in Nice, professor at Bologna and later active as astronomer in Paris. Derived the rotation periods of Mars and Jupiter, discovered four satellites of Saturn and the gap in Saturn's ring which was later named after him. **2. JACQUES** (1677–1756), son of Giovanni, director of Paris Observatory. **3. CÉSAR FRANÇOIS** (1714–1784), son of Jacques, director of Paris Observatory.

Cassini's division A gap 1800 miles wide which divides the rings of Saturn into two parts; discovered by G. D. Cassini in 1675.

Cassiopeia A constellation in the northern hemisphere at 1h right ascension (α = 1h), 60° north declination (δ = +60°). Its five brightest stars form a W.

Cassiopeia A The strongest radio source (radio stars), identified as faint nebulous filaments at a relative speed of 3000 km/sec, causing the intense radio frequency radiation.

Cassiopeia B A radio source in the constellation of Cassiopeia that constitutes the remains of Tycho Brahe's star, the supernova of 1572.

Castor Alpha (α) Geminorum is the second brightest star in Gemini, the Twins, with apparent visual magnitude 1.6 and spectral type A0. Castor is an interesting multiple star. The system consists of two nearby visual components with a revolutionary period of 380 years. Each component is, in itself, a double. A third component, also a double star, is located at a distance 16 times greater than the distance between the main components.

cataclysmic hypothesis The origin of the solar system by a collision, or near collision, of a star with the sun. Accordingly, a tidal wave of matter was torn from the stars to form the planets. (Jeans, Jeffreys, and others.) In other versions, the nearby star was a supernova. At present, these theories have only historical interest.

cathode The negative electrode. In a photoelectric cell, the cathode is coated with a photosensitive substance. When light strikes the cathode in a photoelectric cell, electrons are released, forming an electron stream. See: *photoelectric photometry*.

celestial Heavenly.

celestial axis The earth's axis extended to the celestial poles.

celestial bodies A term encompassing the sun, moon, planets, stars, and other objects in the universe.

celestial equator A great circle on the celestial sphere halfway between the *celestial poles*.

celestial mechanics The branch of astronomy that deals with the problems of mass and motion of celestial bodies through the mathematical application of the laws of gravitation.

celestial meridian The great circle on the celestial sphere through the poles, zenith, and nadir, intersecting the horizon at the north and south points.

celestial poles The points on the sky where the earth's axis, if projected to infinity, will intersect the celestial sphere.

celestial sphere The apparent sphere on which celestial bodies appear projected. The position of the observer is at its center. As a result of the earth's rotation from west to east, the celestial sphere seems to turn from east to west. (Fig. C2.)

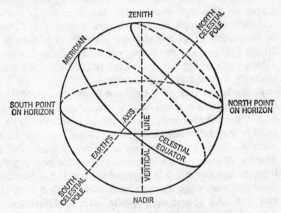

C2. Celestial sphere.

Celsius, Anders (1701–1744) Swedish astronomer. Participated in the French expedition to Tornedalen in 1736–37 to determine the oblateness of the earth by measuring the distance of one degree change of latitude. He was the first to try to determine stellar magnitude by photometric methods. From 1739–42, he constructed an observatory at Uppsala. Celsius is known for his construction of the Centigrade thermometer.

Centaurus (Centaur) An extensive constellation in the southern hemisphere at 13h right ascension ($\alpha = 13$h), 50° south declination ($\delta = -50°$). The brightest star is *Alpha* (α) *Centauri*. The famous globular cluster *Omega* (ω) *Centauri* is located in the constellation. *Alpha (α) Centauri* is the nearest star beyond the sun. Its distance amounts to 4.3 light-years, the equivalent of 270,000 times the distance between the earth and the sun. Alpha Centauri is a multiple star with two components which are like the sun in many ways. One component has the same color as the sun but is somewhat greater in volume. The other component is somewhat redder than the sun (spectral types G0 and K5, respectively, and apparent magnitudes 0.3 and 1.7). Its period is 80 years and mean distance 23 A.U., or about 2,240,000,000 miles. Another star belonging to the system, a faint dwarf called *Proxima Centauri,* orbits at a distance of 10,000 A.U. This star is a red dwarf, flare type variable star, with absolute magnitude 15.4 and spectral type M5. Proxima C is about 0.15 light-years from Alpha Centauri. *Omega (ω) Centauri* is the nearest of all the globular clusters, at a distance of 20,000 light-years. This cluster, visible to the unaided eye as a faint patch of light, contains over 100,000 stars and is considerably flattened at the poles.

central diaphragm method   An out-of-focus photograph of the stars taken in two colors with a *central opaque diaphragm* placed over the objective lens. Invented independently by N. Tamm, of Sweden, and G. A. Tikhoff, of Russia, the method is based upon *chromatic aberration* present in all objectives. When an orthochromatic plate is focused in yellow light, each stellar image is surrounded by a ring of blue light. Since red stars have a pronounced center with a faint ring, and blue stars appear the opposite, stars of different colors may be distinguished by their relative intensities.

central line   The center of the path of totality during a total eclipse of the sun.

central motion   A motion caused by the action of a force that is directed toward a central point. An example of central motion is the revolution of the planets around the sun.

central peak   A mountain summit with one or more peaks often found in the center of lunar craters.

centrifugal force   A force which impels an object away from a center; the opposite of *centripetal force.*

centroid of motion   Vector quantity describing the mean velocity and position of stars in a **moving cluster* without regard to mass.

cepheids (Cepheid variable stars)   A very interesting group of variable stars that vary in brightness as the result of pulsations of their surfaces and atmospheres. In 1912, at Harvard Observatory, Miss H. Leavitt discovered a relationship between the period of the light variation and the star's absolute magnitude, the so-called *period-luminosity relation*. From this important relationship, the distances to the stars can be derived. When the period of variation is known, the absolute magnitude can be found. The apparent magnitude of the star is observed and distances evaluated by the relationship between absolute magnitude and apparent magnitude. Since cepheids have been discovered in other galaxies, these stars have become the most important yardsticks in measuring distances to the remote galaxies. Cepheids are classified according to the length of the period into *short-period cepheids* with periods less than one day (they are also called cluster type variables or RR Lyrae stars) and *long-period cepheids*, or *classical cepheids*, with periods between one and fifty days. One type of classical cepheid is the W Virginis stars. Like the cluster type variables, these stars belong to *Population II* (old stars) while the classical cepheids belong to *Population I* (young stars). A different period-luminosity relationship applies to each population. See: *period-luminosity relation*.

Cepheus A constellation in the northern hemisphere at 22h right ascension ($\alpha = 22$h), 73° north declination ($\delta = +73°$). The star, Mu (μ), an irregular variable with a pronounced red color, is called the *Garnet star*. The star Delta (δ) is also a variable and the prototype of the so-called *cepheid* type pulsating stars. See: *cepheids*. *Delta* (δ) *Cephei* varies regularly between 3.7 and 4.4 magnitudes in a period of 5.366 days. (Fig. C3.)

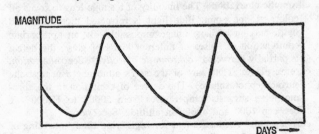

C3. Light curve for cepheid variable (δ Cephei).

Ceres The first *minor planet* discovered, on January 1, 1801, by Piazzi. Ceres is the largest of the minor planets with a diameter of 427 miles at a distance of 2.8 A.U. from the sun.

Cetus (Whale) A large constellation at the celestial equator at 1h 30m right ascension (α = 1h 30m), 10° south declination (δ = $-10°$). The star Omicron (o) Ceti, or Mira (the Wonderful), is a long-period variable star discovered by Fabricius in 1596.

Chamaeleon (Chameleon) Faint constellation near the southern celestial pole at 11h right ascension (α = 11h), 80° south declination (δ = $-80°$).

Chandrasekhar's limit (Chandrasekhar–Schönberg limit) The limiting mass of the helium in the core of a star named after S. Chandrasekhar, an Indian-born American astronomer. In the evolution of a star, hydrogen in the core is converted to helium until all available hydrogen has been used and an isothermal condition is produced. Energy continues to be produced by the star in a shell surrounding the helium core. As more helium is produced, the shell wanders outward but the process can only continue until the mass of the core has reached about 12% of the total mass of the star. This critical limit is called Chandrasekhar's limit. See: *stellar evolution.*

characteristic curve The relationship between the density of the photographic image and the intensity of the light causing it. (In astronomy, synonymous with the relationship between the image and magnitude.) See: *photographic photometry.*

Charioteer Constellation in the northern hemisphere. See: *Auriga.*

Chisel Constellation in the southern hemisphere. See: *Caelum.*

Chondrite A type of meteorite. See: *meteorite.*

chromatic aberration The inability of a single lens to focus all colors at one point. Blue light is refracted more than red light, making a sharp image impossible. By an appropriate combination of lenses of different kinds of glass, the defect is partially corrected (*achromatic objective*). See: *aberration.*

chromosphere That part of the sun's atmosphere nearest the surface (photosphere). The degree of excitation in the chromosphere suggests temperatures from 5000° to 15,000° C. between 1000 and 4000 km altitude. See: *sun.*

chronograph An instrument for registering time, consisting of a moving sheet of paper on which clock-beats are marked. In addition to regular clock-beat marks, there is a mechanism to allow the recording of the time that a star crosses the meridian. The observer presses a key activating a pen to record the time the star was seen in the cross-wire of a transit or meridian circle. Today, a transit micrometer is used to give automatically an electric signal for marking time.

chronology The science of time division and time measurement. Since antiquity, regularly recurring astronomical phenomena have been used to measure time. The change between night and day is responsible for probably the oldest time measure, the day. In more advanced cultures, the phases of the moon and the change of the seasons were used to measure time over a longer period. However, these ways of measuring time are not commensurable. The moon completes one lunation in a period of about 29.53 days (*the synodic month*) and the tropical year, or the year of the seasons (two consecutive passages of the vernal equinox by the sun), has a length of 365.24 days. A lunar year of 12 months has a length of 354 days, or 11 days shorter than the tropical year. In order to have the lunar year coincide with the solar year, a leap month was introduced every third year. Since the year is actually almost 365¼ days long, a leap year of 366 days must be introduced every fourth year (**Julian calendar*) so that the tropical year and the civil year remain in step. See: *Gregorian calendar*. The lunar year was used by the Babylonians, while the Egyptians measured time by the solar year. Hebrew and Moslem calendars are based on the lunar year.

chronometer A portable precision clock with spring drive, used primarily in navigation. To remain independent of rolling motion, the chronometer is fastened to a pair of concentric rings, i.e., **gimbal mounting*.

Circinus (Compass [dividers]) A faint constellation in the southern hemisphere at 15h right ascension ($\alpha = 15$h), 60° south declination ($\delta = -60°$).

circle of longitude A great circle from the pole of the ecliptic at right angles to the plane of the ecliptic.

circummeridian altitudes Altitudes of stars measured on both sides of the meridian, providing a convenient method for determining the latitude for a position.

circumpolar stars Stars that are always seen above the horizon from a given position. They are located between the celestial pole and a diurnal circle with an angular distance equal to the altitude of the pole. (Fig. C4.)

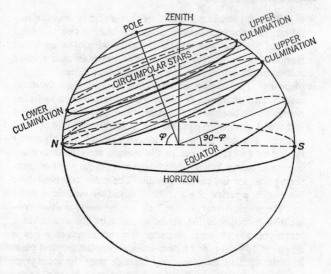

C4. Circumpolar stars.

Cirrus Nebula The *Veil Nebula* in *Cygnus.*

cislunar Between the earth and the moon.

civil time Mean solar time. In the United States, the term Greenwich civil time (GCT) is used. In Great Britain, Greenwich mean time (GMT) refers to the civil day. Civil time is measured from the 0° meridian, Greenwich. The United States and Canada lie between 4 and 11 hours west of Greenwich. Australia and New Zealand are between 8 and 12 hours east of Greenwich. The date changes at local civil midnight.

Clepshydra A water clock.

Clock Constellation in the southern hemisphere. See: *Horologium.*

clocks Astronomical precision clocks; among the most important components of an observatory's instrumentation. Various types include *pendulum clocks* where time is kept by means of a pendulum; *quartz crystal clocks,* based on the oscillations of quartz crystals; *atomic clocks,* based on the oscillations of atoms or molecules.

cluster A *star cluster.*

cluster variables Short-period *cepheid variables* with periods less than one day, which are found in globular clusters. In

the Galaxy, they are called RR Lyrae stars after the prototype RR in the constellation of Lyra.

Coal Sack A *dark nebula* in the constellation of the Southern
Cross (Crux). The Coal Sack is easily observed with the unaided eye. At a distance of about 500 light-years, its *absorption of light* is approximately one magnitude.

coelostat *Siderostat* or *heliostat*. A movable mirror with a
clock-drive mounted in such a way that light from a celestial
body is reflected in one direction. Since the image remains
fixed in the focal plane, instruments such as a horizontal
camera can be permanently mounted. Often, two mirrors are
used, where one is movable while the other remains fixed. A
coelostat used in solar observations is called a heliostat.
Sometimes, coelostat refers to an instrument with two mirrors
and a siderostat to an instrument with only one mirror. (Fig.
C5.)

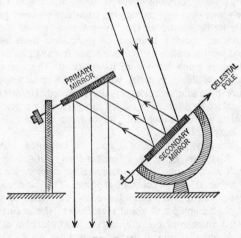

C5. Coelostat.

collimation error The error in a telescope of a transit or meridian circle that occurs when the angle between the *line of
collimation* and the axis of rotation is not correct. See: *collimation, line of.*

collimation, line of The straight line in a telescope connecting
the optical center of the objective lens and the middle wire
of the reticle. If this line is not perpendicular to the horizon-

tal axis of a meridian circle, a transit, or a theodolite, a *colli-mation error* will be encountered. See: *collimation error.*

collimator A lens which changes light from a point source (or slit) to a parallel beam. The source of light is placed at the focal point of the lens. A collimator is used in a **spectroscope.* (Fig. C6.)

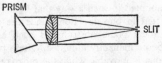

C6. Collimator.

collisions between galaxies It was formerly thought that some of the remote radio sources might be due to colliding galaxies. According to this theory, the radio waves were produced not by actual collisions between stars—which would be extremely rare—but by the constant collisions between particles of interstellar matter as the two galaxies "passed through" each other, moving in opposite directions. Such an idea seemed very plausible at the time when it was first advanced, but later research has led to its rejection. The energy produced by colliding material would not be great enough to produce the radio emission actually recorded. Unfortunately, no satisfactory alternative theory has yet been proposed, and the origin of the strong radio waves from certain galaxies is still unexplained.

color Formerly, the color of a star was expressed in a scale with white stars equal to 0^c and red stars 10^c where c = color. Today, a numerical measure called *color equivalent* is used rather than the color of the star. The most common color equivalent is the *color index*, the difference between a star's photographic and visual magnitudes. The ordinary unprepared photographic emulsions are most sensitive at about 4400 Å and the human eye at about 5500 Å. As a result, blue-white stars appear brighter on photographic plates than red stars. The opposite is true when the stars are viewed with the eye (visual magnitudes). Color index is so devised that a star of spectral type A0 has a color index of 0. Blue-white stars have negative color indices, while yellow and red stars have positive values. (The color index of a K0 star = $+1^m0$.) Today, visual magnitude is replaced by photovisual magnitude arrived at through the use of color-sensitive pho-

tographic plates and yellow filters. Blue and red magnitudes
are obtained by combining different filters. Color index is always defined as the difference between the short-wave length
magnitude and the long-wave length magnitude, i.e., the *UBV*
system with ultraviolet, *U*, blue, *B*, and visual, *V*, magnitudes
and the color combinations *U* minus *B* (*U* − *B*) and *B* minus
V (*B* − *V*). Various color indices can also be obtained from
monochromatic magnitudes (intensity in a narrow spectral
region). Color is intimately related to the temperature of a
star.

color equivalent   A measure of a star's color. Usually color
index is used. See: *color.*

color excess   The difference between the measured color index
of a star and the mean color index for the spectral type to
which the star belongs. If the color index is too high and the
color of the star is redder than normal for its spectral type,
then the light from the star has passed through interstellar
matter that scatters the short blue and violet wave lengths
more than the longer wave lengths of red. Color excess is a
measure of the amount of absorbing matter between us and
the stars. See: *interstellar matter.*

colorimetry   Determination of the colors of the stars. See:
color.

color index   A measurement of color of the stars expressed as
the difference between the star's magnitude in two colors.
See: *color.*

color-luminosity diagram   A diagram whose abscissa is the
color of the stars and whose ordinate is the absolute magnitude. See: *Hertzsprung-Russell diagram.*

color temperature   The temperature obtained for a star through
the study of energy distribution for given wave lengths. Color
temperature is determined by means of *Planck's radiation
laws.*

Columba   (Dove) A small constellation in the southern hemisphere at 5h 50m right ascension (α = 5h 50m), 37° south
declination (δ = −37°).

colures   The great circles on the celestial sphere through the
celestial poles and the equinoxes, the *equinoctial colure,* and
through the solstices, the *solstitial colure.*

coma   **1.** The nebulous cloud surrounding the nucleus of a
comet. Together, the coma and nucleus form the comet's
head. See: *comets.* **2.** An error in an optical image that ren-
ders a cometlike appearance to points of light. Occurring

most frequently in mirrors, a coma is noticeable just beyond the optical axis. This error can be corrected with special optical systems.

Coma Berenices (Berenice's Hair) An open star cluster located near the north galactic pole and visible to the unaided eye.

Coma cluster A large cluster of galaxies containing about 1000 members located near the north galactic pole in the constellation of *Coma Berenices*. At a distance of about 220 million light-years, its diameter is approximately 20 million light-years.

cometary swarm A cloud of comets surrounding the sun containing 100,000 million members with a mass between $\frac{1}{10}$ and $\frac{1}{100}$ times the mass of the earth. The radius of the cloud extends beyond 100,000 astronomical units. Originally proposed by Schiaparelli, the cometary swarm hypothesis has been more extensively developed by the Dutch astronomer J. Oort. See: *comets*.

comet seeker A low-power, large-field telescope used in the search for new comets. A comet seeker is often equipped with an altazimuth mounting to sweep the sky conveniently.

comets Small bodies that are members of the solar system and move in very elongated orbits. A comet consists of a nucleus with a diameter less than a few miles made of small solid particles of dust, sand, and stone in frozen gases. When a comet nears the sun, the gases, consisting of water, ammonia, carbon monoxide, and methane, vaporize to form a cloud ranging in diameter between 6000 and 60,000 miles (coma). These gases reflect sunlight which is observed as a continuous spectrum. An emission spectrum originating from ionized and neutral compounds of carbon, hydrogen, nitrogen, and oxygen (CN, CH, OH, $OH+$, $CO+$, and N_2+) is caused by ultraviolet radiation from the sun. The molecules of dust and gases of the comet are subjected to the corpuscular radiation of protons and electrons from the sun. This radiation pressure causes the material of the comet to be continuously driven off to form a *tail*. Generally, these tails are pointed away from the sun and may reach lengths of almost 100 million miles. A comet is an unstable body that gradually disintegrates and distributes particles in its wake. When the earth passes through a swarm of comet debris, a brilliant meteor shower results. Comets are classified into two groups: the short-period comets with periods of about seven years and orbits of small eccentricity, and the long-period comets with periods approaching one million years and orbital eccentricity near a value of 1. Jupiter's *family of comets* is made up of short-period comets. According to recent interpretations, the solar system is surrounded by an extensive *cometary swarm* several light-years in diameter that contains 100,000 million comets. From time to time, the disturbing influence of a passing star changes the orbits of some comets to bring them into the central parts of the solar system where they can be observed. Several comets are detected annually, but the majority are not visible without optical aid. Orbits have been determined for over 760 comets.

comets, family of Short-period comets with orbits altered by the disturbing influence of the more massive planets. More than 25 comets have orbits closely related to Jupiter's orbit, indicating that these comets have been "captured" by the planet. There are other giant planets, each with a family of comets. For example, *Halley's comet* belongs to Neptune's family of comets.

communication satellite American artificial satellite supplying radio and television connection between the United States and Europe (e.g., *Telstar I*, launched July 10, 1962).

companion The fainter one of the two components in a double star.

Companion of Sirius See: *Sirius, Companion of*

comparator An instrument which allows two photographs of the same region of the sky (or two spectra of the same star) to be compared at the same time. Comparators are often equipped with a *blink microscope*. See: *stereocomparator*.

Compass (dividers) Constellation in the southern hemisphere. See: *Circinus*.

components The individual stars forming a binary star system. The primary star, the brighter, is designated *A,* and the fainter member, *B*. In a multiple system, the additional stars are designated *C, D,* etc., in order of brightness.

concave grating A reflection grating ruled on a concave mirror. A sharp image of the spectrum is formed without resorting to special lenses. Thus, the grating is especially suitable in the ultraviolet region.

concave lens A negative lens that causes the entering parallel rays of light to diverge. A concave lens is used as an ocular in a Galilean telescope.

conic sections The curves generated by the intersection of a cone by a plane. If the plane is perpendicular to the axis of the cone, the section is a *circle*. An *ellipse* is generated when the plane is oblique to the axis of the cone. If the plane is parallel to one of the elements of the cone, the section is a *parabola*. To generate a *hyperbola,* rotate the plane further in the same direction. (Fig. C7.)

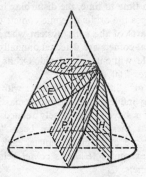

C7. Conic sections.

conjunction When two celestial bodies have the same longitude. The sun and the moon are in conjunction at new moon. The planets Mercury and Venus are in conjunction twice in one revolution; *inferior conjunction* when they are between the earth and the sun, and *superior conjunction* when the sun is between the earth and the planets.

constellation A grouping of conspicuous stars named after gods, heroes, animals, and mythological beings by ancient astronomers. Ptolemy listed 48 constellations located in the northern hemisphere and in the equatorial zone. During the age of discovery, when voyages were made to the southern hemisphere, new stars were discovered and new constellations were named after practical objects related to navigation. Since Ptolemy, 40 constellations have been added, mainly during the 17th century. The sky is divided into 88 constellations, 32 of which lie entirely or partly in the northern hemisphere. The division of the sky into constellations is helpful for the purposes of orientation.

continuous radio radiation The general continuous radio frequency radiation from space, earlier referred to as *galactic radio noise,* found in addition to discrete *radio sources* ("radio stars"). Investigations have been made at various wave lengths, and isophote charts generally follow the structure of the Milky Way. The origin of the radiation is unknown. Several theories have been proposed which explain the radiation as thermal emission from interstellar gases or syncrotron radiation emitted by charged particles moving at high velocity in interstellar magnetic fields. A component of the radiation is evenly distributed over the sky and may originate either in the *galactic halo* or in extragalactic space. See: *Milky Way system.*

continuous spectrum   An emission spectrum consisting of an unbroken band of color from infrared to ultraviolet within the optical region or an unbroken emission band in the radio frequency region. Continuous spectra occur in stars through (1) the capture of free electrons by ionized atoms (recombination) emitting kinetic energy as radiation; or (2) the release of a portion of kinetic energy by one atom passing another (free-free transitions). A continuous spectrum results, since the kinetic energy of electrons may assume all values.

contraction theory   A theory proposed during the latter half of the 19th century whereby the source of solar energy was explained as the potential energy released during the sun's contraction. Later investigations have shown that this energy source is entirely inadequate to account for the loss of solar energy by radiation. See: *energy production.*

convective core   A small portion of the central core of a star where radiant energy is generated through nuclear processes. In this region, energy is exchanged by *convection currents* in the substance of the star.

convergent point   The point in the sky toward which the stars of a *moving cluster seem to recede. The paths of the stars are actually parallel and the apparent convergence is the effect of perspective. The distance to the cluster can be determined from the positions and motions of the stars. (Fig. C8.)

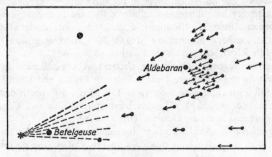

C8. Convergent point (Hyades).

convex lens   A positive lens which bends parallel light rays to a point called the focus. Used as an integral part of the objective and ocular lenses in astronomical telescopes.

Copernican system   The theory of planetary motion formulated by *Nicolaus *Copernicus* in 1543. The basic principles assumed by the system are that the apparent daily motion of the sky is caused by the earth's rotation and that the earth and other planets revolve around a central sun (heliocentric theory). The Copernican system led to present-day concepts.

Copernicus   One of the larger craters on the moon, located in the *Oceanus Procellarum*. The crater extends to about 18,300 feet above the lunar surface and has a diameter of about 56 miles. Several central peaks are observed, as well as a ray system emanating from the crater.

Copernicus, Nicolaus   (1473–1543) Born in Thorn, Poland, died in Frauenburg. In his work, *De Revolutionibus Orbium Coelestium* (On the Revolutions of the Celestial Bodies), 1543, he set forth the principles of the earth's axial rotation and its revolution around the sun as the central body (the heliocentric system), which began a new epoch in the history of astronomy.

Cor Caroli   (Heart of Charles) The star Alpha (α) in the constellation *Canes Venatici*. A double star named in honor of the English king Charles II.

coriolis   An effect of the earth's rotation discovered by C. G. Coriolis, a French physicist. As a result of inertia, an object moving north from the equator will retain its greater peripheral velocity and appear to curve toward the right as seen from the surface. A correction for the rotation of the earth is necessary to calculate the true path of a satellite with respect to the surface.

corona   The outermost layer of the sun's atmosphere, visible as a silvery halo during an eclipse of the sun. See: *solar corona*.

Corona Australis   (Southern Crown) A faint constellation in the southern hemisphere at 18h 30m right ascension (α = 18h 30m), 40° south declination (δ = −40°).

Corona Borealis   (Northern Crown) A constellation in the northern hemisphere located between Boötes and Hercules at 15h 35m right ascension (α = 15h 35m), 30° north declination (δ = +30°). The brightest star, Alpha (α) Coronae Borealis, is called Gemma (the Gem).

coronagraph   An instrument invented by the French astronomer B. Lyot which produces an artificial eclipse permitting the study of the solar corona without a total eclipse of the sun. (Fig. C9.)

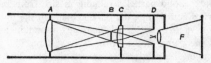

C9. Lyot's coronagraph. A = *lens which forms the image of the sun on the blackened occulting disc,* B. C = *lens which forms the image of the objective on the diaphragm,* D, *which blocks out light from the edge.* F = *camera that photographs* B *and the surrounding corona.*

coronal condensations Occasional condensations in the solar corona (a type of activity center) that produces short-wave radio frequency radiation at about 60 cm.

coronal lines Emission lines in the spectrum of the solar corona which for a long time defied interpretation. The strongest are a green line ($\lambda 5303$ Å) and a red line ($\lambda 6374$ Å). In 1941, the Swedish physicist B. Edlén showed that the lines originated from highly ionized iron, nickel, and calcium. The green coronal line is produced by iron that has lost 13 of its 26 electrons. In order to explain this highly ionized state, a coronal temperature of about one million degrees must be assumed.

coronium A hypothetical element formerly believed to be the cause of emission lines within the corona's spectrum. Later investigations have shown these lines to emanate from highly ionized iron, nickel, and calcium. See: *coronal lines.*

corpuscles Charged particles.

corpuscular radiation Radiation emitted by the sun and stars consisting of charged particles (protons and electrons).

correcting plate A lens or lens system of special curvature used to correct optical errors in spherical or parabolic primary mirrors. A correcting plate is found in a **Schmidt telescope* to remedy the spherical aberration of the spherical primary mirror. A parabolic mirror can be corrected for coma, thereby increasing the usable field with a suitably figured lens system.

correction The cancellation of the error of a clock determined by means of time signals transmitted by radio or by astronomical observations.

Corvus (Crow) A small constellation in the southern hemisphere at 12h 20m right ascension ($\alpha = 12\text{h } 20\text{m}$), 18° south declination ($\delta = -18°$).

cosmic dust Solid particles ranging in size from molecules to meteorites constituting the dark nebulae in the universe (*interstellar matter* and *dark nebulae*) found in an extensive belt in the plane of the Milky Way system. The particles of 10^{-5}cm in size scatter and absorb the blue and violet light more effectively than the red, causing starlight to be reddened (*color excess*) in passing through a cloud of cosmic dust. The density of a cloud is low, amounting to only 10^{-25} to 10^{-26}g/cm.

cosmic radiation A *corpuscular radiation* from space consisting of nuclear particles of unusually high energy. Upon entering the earth's atmosphere, secondary cosmic rays are produced by the release of energy through nuclear processes. Astronomically, there is greater interest in primary radiation, which is caused by protons with energies in the order of 10^9 to 10^{17} electron volts. Primary cosmic rays are investigated by means of high-altitude balloons, rockets, and artificial satellites. Several theories have been proposed regarding the origin of cosmic rays. One of the sources of cosmic rays may be the sun. There is an increase in cosmic radiation during the eruption of *solar *flares*. A nova, or especially a supernova explosion, probably releases an enormous amount of cosmic radiation. See: *exploding stars*.

cosmic radio noise A term previously used to describe the continuous radio frequency radiation received from the cosmos.

cosmogony The study of the origin and development of the universe. **1.** SOLAR SYSTEM. Several theories for the origin of the solar system have been proposed. These can be divided into two groups: (a) the formation of planets by internal forces; and (b) the formation of planets by external forces. Kant (1755) proposed that the planets were formed out of a rotating mass of dust (nebular hypothesis). Laplace (1796) suggested that the planets condensed out of gaseous rings which spiraled from the sun or a primordial nebula. According to the theory of Jeans and Jeffreys (1917), a close approach between the sun and another star caused the outer layers of the sun to be torn away by tidal action to form the planets. Recently, other theories have been developed by G. P. Kuiper, C. von Weizsäcker, H. Alfvén, and others. At one time, astronomers assumed that planets were created under high-temperature conditions. Today, many believe that the planets were born out of a cold cloud of gases and particles (99% hydrogen and helium and 1% other elements). Mutual gravitation caused the material in the cloud to collapse into a central condensation (the sun) surrounded by a flat disc. Within the disc, there were eddies which eventually formed into planets. In *Alfvén's theory, electric and magnetic forces account for the motions of the planets around the sun. 2. UNIVERSE. The *red shift in the spectra of galaxies, and the relationship between the amount of displacement and the distances to the galaxies (Hubble effect), were discovered by Hubble and Humason. These discoveries led astronomers to believe that the universe is expanding and has continued to expand for 10,000 million years or more. The initial stage is explained in several theories (Lemaître, Gamow) as a "primeval atom" containing all the matter and energy in the universe. Through a cosmic explosion, the substance in the atom spread out in all directions and is now observed as receding galaxies. Theories based upon Einstein's relationship between matter and energy suggest that the universe began as a concentration of thermal radiation at temperatures reaching 15,000 million degrees. The temperature decreased very rapidly to form giant clouds of gas which developed into galaxies. Condensations within these "protogalaxies" evolved into "protostars" which in turn became the stars and the planetary systems. A universe of energy was transformed into a universe of matter. The universe may be pulsating, expanding, and contracting, alternating between matter and energy. (The theories for the expansion of the universe are based upon Einstein's theory of relativity.) According to other viewpoints (Hoyle, Lyttleton, Bondi, Gold), the universe is in a "steady state" with respect to time and space. As the galaxies recede and the universe expands, new matter is created to maintain a constant mean density of matter in the universe. Other theories and speculations regarding the cosmos have been proposed. But at the present time, there is no agreement among astronomers regarding the validity of these different theories. Still lacking is an accurate determination of the velocity of expansion at great distances (over 2000 million light-years) and a more reliable relationship between distance and the velocity of expansion.

cosmography A literal description of the universe.

cosmology Study of the universe.

cosmonaut   The Russian name for a space pilot. See: *astronaut*.
cosmos   Universe.
coudé system   An optical system in which the beam of light
from the primary mirror of a reflector or the objective lens
of a refractor is reflected down through the instrument's polar
axis by means of secondary mirrors. Since a fixed position is
maintained with respect to the earth, light can be analyzed
with permanently installed apparatus. In addition, very long
focal lengths are obtained. (Fig. C10.)

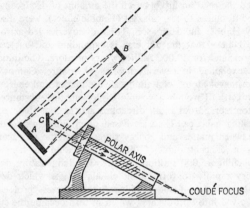

C10. Coudé system. A = *primary mirror,* B and C = *secondary mirrors.*

Crab   Constellation in the northern hemisphere. See: *Cancer.*
Crab Nebula   Messier 1, a *gaseous nebula* located in the constellation of *Taurus,* the Bull. The Crab Nebula is the remains of an explosion of a supernova which was seen in the
year 1054. During the past several decades, the Crab Nebula
has been the subject of detailed investigation. The nebula is
expanding at a velocity of about 1100 km/sec, or about 70
million miles each day. The distance to the nebula has been
estimated from measurements of the changes in its diameter
and rate of expansion to be about 4000 light-years. Spectral
investigations have revealed a continuous as well as an emission spectrum. The continuous spectrum originates from the
light in the diffuse central regions, which are pronounced on
photographs in blue light. The bright line emission spectrum
is produced by a luminous filamentary structure that sur-

rounds the nucleus, which appears prominent on photographs in red light. The continuous spectrum is attributed to synchrotron radiation, which occurs when energetic electrons move in a magnetic field. In addition, the Crab Nebula emits an intensive radio frequency radiation and is a conspicuous "radio star" (radio source Taurus A).

Crane Constellation in the southern hemisphere. See: *Grus.*

crape ring The inner ring of Saturn, discovered in 1850. The crape ring is much fainter and more difficult to observe than the outer rings. It is 11,500 miles wide and the inner edge is about 7000 miles above the surface of Saturn.

Crater (Cup) A small constellation with faint stars in the southern hemisphere at 11h 20m right ascension ($\alpha = 11$h 20m), 15° south declination ($\delta = -15°$).

crater pits (craterlets) As seen from the earth, the smallest crater formations on the moon. They generally lack a circular wall and appear to be hemispherical depressions. Their diameters vary from a few hundred yards to about 1000 yards.

craters, lunar Ring formations on the moon with dimensions that vary from a few hundred yards to over 125 miles in diameter. See: *moon.*

crochet A disturbance of the earth's magnetic field caused by the eruption of a *solar *flare.*

Crow Constellation in the southern hemisphere. See: *Corvus.*

Crown The names of constellations: **1.** In the northern hemisphere, see: *Corona Borealis.* **2.** In the southern hemisphere, the Southern Crown, or *Corona Australis.*

crown glass A kind of glass that has about the same refractive power as *flint glass* but only half as great dispersive power. Crown glass is used in combination with flint glass to construct an achromatic prism, or *achromatic objective.*

Crux (Cross, or Southern Cross) A small but brilliant constellation in the southern hemisphere at 12h 30m right ascension ($\alpha = 12$h 30m), 60° south declination ($\delta = -60°$). The four brightest stars form a cross.

culmination Meridian passage of a celestial object. A passage above the celestial pole is called *upper culmination.* A passage between the celestial pole and the north point on the horizon is called *lower culmination.* Only circumpolar stars are observed in both culminations.

Cup A faint constellation in the southern hemisphere. See: *Crater.*

curve of growth   The relationship between the equivalent width
and the number of atoms producing the spectral line. The
equivalent width, the width of a dark rectangular line equivalent to the energy absorbed by the original line from the continuous spectrum, is a measure of the intensity of a spectral
line. The curve of growth is of fundamental importance in
quantitative analysis of stellar spectra.

cyanogen absorption (cyanogen bands)   Bands of molecular
cyanogen in the spectra of stars. The cyanogen bands at
$\lambda 4180$ Å serve as a measure of absolute magnitude for stars
of spectral type G0 and later types. A Swedish astronomer,
B. Lindblad, has shown that cyanogen absorption is more
pronounced in giants than in dwarfs of the same spectral
class. Cyanogen absorption is one of the important *luminosity criteria.*

Cygnus   (Swan) A constellation located in the northern hemisphere in the Milky Way at 20h 20m right ascension ($\alpha =$
20h 20m) and 40° north declination ($\delta = +40°$). The stars
α (Deneb), β, δ, ε, and γ form a large cross called the
Northern Cross. The star Beta (β), or Albireo, is a beautiful
double star that can be resolved in a small telescope. The
constellation contains several gaseous nebulae such as the
North American Nebula, as well as dark nebulae. The star
61 Cygni, an interesting double, was the first star to have its
trigonometric parallax measured (Bessel, 1838). *P Cygni
stars,* named after the star P in Cygnus, are variable stars
with irregular periods. Their spectra contain emission lines
originating from an expanding shell around the central star.
SS Cygni stars are variables named after the first known star
of this kind, SS Cygni. These stars are at minimum brightness
for a long period of time, suddenly increase to maximum,
and slowly return again to minimum.

Cygnus A   The second strongest radio source in the sky, located in the constellation of Cygnus, the Swan. It once was
believed to have been caused by the collision of two member
galaxies of a cluster of galaxies located at a distance of 700
million light-years, though the *colliding-galaxy* hypothesis
has now been abandoned.

cylindrical lens   A lens that is placed in the light path in a
spectroscope to broaden the spectrum of a star which other-
wise would be a narrow filament.

D

dark nebulae Extensive clouds of fine-grained dust found in the disc of the Milky Way system (spiral arms). These clouds appear as dark patches in rich star fields, obscuring the light from the stars that lie beyond. Dark nebulae appear in other galaxies as a dark band through the plane of symmetry when viewed edge-on. See: *interstellar matter* and *Wolf diagram*.

day The 24-hour period of time equal to one rotation of the earth on its axis. The day is measured in several ways. **1.** THE SIDEREAL DAY. The interval between two successive meridian transits of a star which coincides with the rotation of the earth. **2.** THE SOLAR DAY. Since, for all practical purposes, daily life is regulated by the sun's apparent motion, it becomes inconvenient to use the sidereal day. The period between two successive meridian transits of the sun is called an *apparent solar day*. The sun appears to move eastward about 1° each day as a result of the orbital motion of the earth, so that the solar day is about four minutes longer than the sidereal day. **3.** MEAN SOLAR DAY. For various reasons, the sun's apparent motion is not uniform, resulting in a solar day of varying length during the course of the year. To avoid a variation in the length of the solar day, the average for the year, the *mean solar day,* was introduced. See: *chronology*.

daylight saving time In some countries during the late spring and summer, the clock is moved forward one hour. Sometimes, the clock is moved forward two hours for double daylight saving time.

daytime The time interval when the sun is above the horizon for a given position. The length of the daylight period varies with the time of year and the latitude of the position.

declination The co-ordinate in the equator system (Delta δ) which is the measure of the angular distance of a body from the celestial equator. Declination is measured positively (+) north and negatively (−) south of the celestial equator from 0° to 90°.

declination axis The axis to which the telescope tube is fastened in an equatorial mounting. The declination axis is at right angles to the polar axis, which is pointed toward the celestial pole. When the instrument is turned on the declina-

tion axis, the optical axis follows an hour circle across the
sky.

declination circle A graduated circle mounted on the *declination axis* of a telescope, which is set to the declination of a
star.

deferent According to the *Ptolemaic system,* a planet revolves
in a small circle (epicycle), whose center scribes a larger
circle with the earth at its center. The larger circle is called
the deferent. (Fig. D1.)

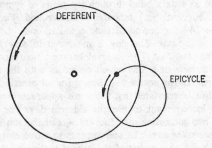

D1. Deferent.

degenerate matter A gaseous state of matter partially characterized by enormous density. The constituents of the gas are
completely ionized atomic nuclei and the freed electrons. In
white dwarfs and in the cores of red giant stars, only the
electron component of the gas may be degenerate. The positions and the momenta of electrons must be considered simultaneously in the quantum theory of a degenerate gas, for
the momenta are allowed only discrete values which depend
on the locations of neighboring electrons. As the density of
an electron gas increases, individual electrons become more
limited in the number of momentum states each may occupy.
Ultimately, no electron may change from its momentum state
until another state is vacated. In particular, all of the low-
value states are occupied and changes may occur only among
the topmost states; thus the gas is also characterized by a
high temperature, and densities of the order of 100,000 (water = 1) are common. At extremely high temperatures, momenta may be so great as to need relativistic corrections for
proper description. A further stage of degeneracy occurs
when the gas composed of atomic nuclei becomes degenerate.

degree $\frac{1}{360}$ part of a circle.

Deimos The more distant of the two satellites of Mars. Deimos makes one revolution in 30 hours and 17 minutes. Its diameter has been estimated at 5 miles.

Delphinus (Dolphin) A small constellation in the northern hemisphere at 20h 40m right ascension (α = 20h 40m), 12° north declination (δ = +12°).

Delta (δ) The fourth letter in the *Greek alphabet*. Delta Cephei; see: *Cepheus*.

Demon Star A former name for the star Algol [Beta (β) Persei], the Winking Demon.

Deneb The star Alpha (α) Cygni in the constellation of Cygnus, the Swan, of apparent visual magnitude 1.3 and spectral type A2p.

Denebola The star Beta (β) Leonis of apparent visual magnitude 2.2 and spectral type A2.

depression Dip of the horizon. The difference between the visible horizon and the astronomical horizon. As a result of the earth's curvature, an observer above the surface can see below the true horizon. The amount of dip depends upon the observer's elevation. At sea, allowances must be made for horizon dip when determining the positions of the stars, since observations are made at a distance above the sea-line. (Fig. D2.)

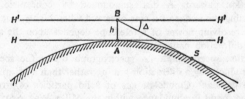

D2. *Dip of the horizon.* HH (H′H′) = *astronomical horizon,* BS = *visible horizon from* B *at altitude* h *above the surface,* Δ = *dip.*

desert regions The bright orange-colored areas on the planet Mars, called continents in contrast to the dark areas that have been called "seas" since early times. It is now known that large craters occur on them.

deuterium Isotope of hydrogen (heavy water).

deuteron The nucleus of a deuterium atom, consisting of one proton and one neutron.

dew cap A cylindrical tube placed in front of the objective of a refracting telescope to avoid the formation of dew or frost on the objective.

diameters, stellar The diameters of eclipsing variable stars may be determined from the light curve. The diameter of some stars may be measured by a method based upon the principle of interference of light. In addition, stellar diameters can be calculated from the star's absolute magnitude and temperature by means of the *Stefan-Boltzmann law*. The star with the largest known diameter is the infrared component of the eclipsing binary Epsilon (ε) Aurigae, which amounts to 3000 times the diameter of the sun. Another supergiant star, Alpha (α) Herculi, has a diameter equal to 800 solar diameters (as measured by the interference method). In contrast, white dwarf stars are planetary in size, with the smallest known barely larger than the moon.

diaphragm A device placed in the light path of an optical instrument to reduce the aperture. In photoelectric photometry, diaphragms are placed in the focal plane to eliminate stray light and isolate the star whose brightness is being measured.

diffraction The bending of light when passing a sharp edge.

diffraction grating A grating consisting of a large number of finely ruled lines. Used in the spectrograph instead of a prism to produce a spectrum.

diffraction pattern A disc surrounded by concentric rings, forming the image of a star observed when highly magnified. The resolving power of a telescope depends upon the size of the diffraction pattern.

diffraction spectrograph A spectrograph where the spectrum is produced by a diffraction grating rather than a prism.

diffuse nebulae Clouds of gas or solid particles of irregular shape found in abundance within the Milky Way. See: *interstellar matter, dark nebulae*, and *galactic nebulae*.

diffuse reflection The scattered reflection of light from an uneven surface where the irregularities are greater than the wave lengths of light, causing reflection in all directions.

Dione One of Saturn's satellites, discovered by Cassini in 1684.

diopter 1. A sighting apparatus previously used in astronomical observations. A kind of theodolite. 2. A unit of measure used in optics: the reciprocal of the focal length of a lens, measured in meters.

dip of the horizon The angle made by the horizontal line from the eye of the observer and the tangent to the surface of the earth, which is the difference between the visible horizon and the true horizon. In determining position, allowance must be made for dip. See: *depression*.

dipole antenna A type of antenna often used with radio telescopes where the element consists of a metal rod whose length is commonly equal to one half the wave length of the radio frequency under investigation. The rod is divided in half, forming a dipole.

direct motion Motion from west to east across the sky (the opposite of daily motion). The planets revolve in direct motion most of the time. The reverse is called *retrograde motion*.

discontinuous spectrum The same as a line spectrum, produced by low-pressure luminous gases.

Discoverer A series of American satellites designed to return to the surface of the earth after a predetermined or prescribed number of orbits.

discrete radio source A particular small area on the sky from which radio waves are received; formerly called *radio "stars."*

dispersion The separation of light into its primary colors. Dispersion occurs when a beam of white light is passed through a prism where it will separate into different colors. Projected on a screen, light will emerge as a band of colors, a spectrum, since longer wave lengths of light deviate less than shorter wave lengths.

distance Angular separation between two stars. When measuring the positions of binary stars, distance is used together with the *position angle.

distance-finding The determination of distances to the celestial bodies is one of the fundamental problems of astronomy. Several methods are presently in use. The following overview describes the more important. **1.** TRIGONOMETRIC. (a) To determine trigonometric *parallax*, triangulation is used and the celestial body is sighted from the end points of a base line. When observing objects in the solar system, a base line on the earth that is as large as possible is used. When determining stellar parallax, the diameter of the earth's orbit, 186 million miles, is used as a base line. The first stellar parallax (the angle made by the radius of the earth's orbit as seen from the star) was determined by Bessel in 1838 (the star 61 Cygni). At distances greater than a few hundred light-years, trigonometric measurements of parallax become very uncertain. (b) *Star stream parallax*. If a group of stars have common motion in space, their distances can be derived from their proper motions and radial velocities. (c) *Dynamic parallax*. The determination of the distance to a binary star system from the period of revolution, semi-major axis, and the masses of the components by means of *Kepler's third law*. (d) *Statistical parallax*. The determination of the mean distance of a great number of stars from the parallax, resulting from the motion of the solar system through space. **2. PHOTOMETRIC.** (a) By means of luminosity criteria (giving the relationship between the intensity of spectral lines and bands of the star's atmosphere and the absolute magnitude), it is possible to derive the absolute magnitude, M, of a star. By assuming that space is completely transparent, the distance, r, expressed in parsecs, can be determined from the apparent magnitude by the expression: $\log r = \dfrac{m-M}{5} + 1$.

(b) The distance to the *cepheid* variable stars can be derived from their light variations by means of the *period-luminosity relation*, which describes the relationship between the period of light variation and the absolute magnitude of the star. Distances are derived from the apparent magnitude as in 2(a) above. **3. GALAXIES.** The distances to the galaxies can be derived by photometric methods when the galaxies can be resolved into stars. Another method is based upon the amount of *red shift*, the displacement of the spectral lines toward the red. According to the investigations of Hubble and Humason, there is a relationship between the amount of red shift and the distance to a galaxy. The red shift is regarded as a *Doppler effect*, indicating recession. The greater the amount of red shift, the greater the distance to the galaxy.

distance modulus A measurement of distance to a star derived from the relationship between the apparent magnitude, m, and the absolute magnitude, M. $(m - M) = 5 \log r - 5$, where r is the distance expressed in parsecs.

distortion An aberration whereby the image produced is not proportional to the object. For example, if the image of a square diminishes in size toward the edges, "barrel distortion" will result, with the sides bulging outward. If, on the other hand, the image increases in size toward the edges, "pincushion" distortion will occur, with the sides appearing concave. (Fig. D3.)

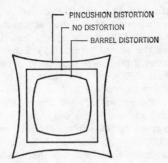

D3. Distortion in the image of a square figure.

diurnal circle The apparent path of a heavenly body across the sky during the daylight hours because of the earth's rotation.

diurnal motion The apparent motion of celestial bodies across the sky from east to west caused by the earth's rotation from west to east.

diurnal parallax See: *parallax.*

D layer Electrically charged layer in the ionosphere at an altitude of between 35 and 40 miles.

Dog Star The star *Sirius.*

Dollond, John (1706–1761) English optician who was the first to construct an *achromatic objective.* See: *Klingenstierna, Samuel.*

dome A movable hemispherical roof of an astronomical observatory possessing an observing slit stretching from the lower edge of the dome to a point beyond the top to allow zenith stars to be observed.

Donati's comet An unusually bright comet discovered by the Italian astronomer G. Donati, of Florence, in 1858. In addition to a wide, curved tail, over 30° long when fully developed, envelopes of gas emanated from the nucleus to form several straight rays adding to the tail.

Doppler broadening The broadening of spectral lines caused by the motions of atoms in the high-temperature stellar atmospheres. Small displacements of the lines toward the longer and shorter wave lengths result in the spreading of the lines.

Doppler, Christian (1803–1853) Austrian physicist after whom the *Doppler effect* is named.

Doppler effect The apparent change in the wave length of electromagnetic radiation or other wave motion (sound waves) when the source of radiation approaches or recedes from the observer. If the source approaches, the number of waves received per second (frequency) increases, while the number decreases if the source recedes. With respect to light, the spectral lines shift toward the violet end of the spectrum if the source approaches and toward the red if the source recedes. From the amount of shift, the relative velocity between the earth and a celestial body can be determined in km/sec. At a speed of 100 km/sec, the shift will amount to 1.7 Å for λ5000 Å. The Doppler shift not only makes it possible to determine *radial velocity*, the velocity in the line of sight of stars, but also rotation. Unless the axis of rotation is in the line of sight, one edge of the star will approach as the other recedes. Spectral lines will show a slight shift from which the speed of rotation can be determined.

Doppler-Fizeau principle The fundamental phenomenon on which the *Doppler effect* is based; first applied by Fizeau with respect to the displacement of spectral lines.

Dorado (Swordfish) A large constellation in the southern hemisphere at 5h right ascension (α = 5h), 60° south declination (δ = −60°). Part of the Large Magellanic Cloud is located in Dorado. The star *S* Doradus in the Magellanic Cloud is one of the most luminous stars known, radiating at more than one half million times greater than the sun.

Double Cluster in Perseus *h* and χ Persei. A well-known double cluster in the constellation of Perseus that appears as a patch of light to the unaided eye. The distance to the double cluster is about 7000 light-years. It contains a *stellar association* containing about 50 supergiants of spectral type B, A, and M.

double galaxy Two galaxies located near each other that are physically joined. This phenomenon is quite common among galaxies.

double stars See: *binary stars.*

Dove Constellation in the southern hemisphere. See: *Columba.*

Draco (Dragon) A constellation that coils around the north celestial pole between 9h 20m and 20h 40m right ascension (α = 9h 20m to 20h 40m), 47° to 86° north declination (δ = +47° to +86°).

Draconids Two meteor showers with radiants in the constellation of *Draco.* One appears early in October and the other late in June.

draconitic month The *nodical month*. The time required for the moon to complete one revolution with respect to one of its nodes. The draconitic month is equal to 27.2122 days.

Draper classification A classification of stars' spectra according to *spectral types*, developed by *Annie Cannon*, at the Harvard Observatory, giving positions, magnitudes, and spectral classification for 225,300 stars in nine volumes of the *Henry Draper Catalogue* (1924). See: *Harvard classification.*

Dubhe The star Alpha (α) Ursae Majoris, with an apparent visual magnitude 1.9 and spectral type K0.

Dumb Bell Nebula A gaseous nebula (planetary nebula) in the constellation *Vulpecula* (Fox), Messier 27.

dwarf cepheids Very short period *cepheids* with periods less than ⅕ of a day and absolute magnitudes between +1.5 and +4.0. Generally, these are low apparent magnitude stars with a light variation of small amplitude.

dwarf galaxies A type of galaxy, generally elliptical or irregular, that is decidedly smaller than the normal galaxies. A number of dwarf galaxies have been discovered in the vicinity of the Milky Way and in the Virgo cluster.

dwarf stars Stars with small diameters. Two distinct kinds of stars of late spectral types G, K, and M are found, i.e., the *giant stars* and *dwarf stars*. Dwarf stars have low absolute magnitudes and comparatively high mean densities. Dwarf stars are identified with a *d* before the spectral classification, such as dG0. By means of *luminosity criteria,* it is possible to determine from its spectrum whether or not a star is a giant or a dwarf. See: *Hertzsprung-Russell diagram.* A special type of dwarf, the *white dwarfs,* are about ten magnitudes fainter than normal stars of the same spectral type (A or F).

Dwingeloo Famous radio astronomy observatory in the Netherlands. Its largest instrument has a diameter of 25 meters.

dynamic parallax Parallax of double stars, determined from the masses of the stars, the period, or revolution, and the apparent length of the semi-major axis of the orbit using Kepler's third law of motion.

E

Eagle A constellation on the celestial equator. See: *Aquila.*

earth Earth, the third planet from the sun, has an equatorial radius of 3963.35 miles; polar radius, 3950.01 miles; oblateness, $\frac{1}{297}$; period of rotation, 23h 56m 4s; inclination of the axis, 66° 33' to the plane of the ecliptic. At a mean distance of 93 million miles from the sun, the earth's period of revolution is 365.2564 days (sidereal year). The earth is a spheroidal body with a solid crust surrounded by a mantle of atmosphere. Its average density is 5.52 times that of water and its mass is 6.0×10^{21} metric tons. Seismological investigations of the interior of the earth at various depths reveal a zone of discontinuity. Therefore, conclusions are that a thin crust is supported by a mantle of silicates which surrounds a central core of iron and nickel. The earth is shrouded by a gaseous envelope, the *atmosphere,* whose composition by volume at the surface is 78% nitrogen, 21% oxygen, 1% argon, and 0.03% carbon dioxide. In addition, the atmosphere contains water vapor in varying amounts. Air pressure, which averages 760 mm, or 30 inches, at the surface, is reduced by one half for every 3 miles of increase in altitude. The atmosphere is divided into separate layers: *troposphere* (0 to 5 miles at the poles, 0 to 11 miles at the equator); *stratosphere* (to 50 miles); *ionosphere* (50 to 400 miles) containing electrified (ionized) layers that reflect radio waves; *exosphere,* above the ionosphere, gradually merges into interplanetary space. The earth is surrounded by the *Van Allen radiation belts* of charged particles originating in the sun. Using radioactivity methods, the age of the earth has been estimated to be about 5×10^9 years.

earthshine At the new moon phase, the dark side of the moon is illuminated by an ashen light produced by sunlight reflected from the earth. The moon is enjoying "full earth" and the surface of the moon is bathed in earthshine, or light from the earth.

Easter A religious holiday. The Christian celebration of Easter has its origin in the Hebrew *Passover.* According to a decree by the Council of Nicaea in 325, Easter is celebrated on the first Sunday after the first full moon after the vernal equinox. Determination of the date of Easter is difficult since a complete understanding of the moon's complicated motion is required.

ebb tide Low tide. See: *tides.*

eccentric anomaly See: *anomaly.*

eccentric circle The circular orbit which the sun was supposed to describe around the earth. In ancient times, in order to explain the irregularities in the sun's annual motion, it was believed that the earth was located off the center of the circular orbit followed by the sun.

eccentricity The measurement of the elongation of an **ellipse* expressed as the value obtained by dividing distance between the focal points by the length of the major axis. Expressed as *e*, the eccentricities of the orbits of the major planets lie between 0.0068 (Venus) and 0.249 (Pluto). The eccentricity of the earth's orbit is 0.0167. The orbital eccentricities of the minor planets lie between 0 and 0.78; comets between 0.5 and 0.9.

Echo satellites American satellites: *Echo I* launched on August 12, 1960, consisting of an aluminum-coated plastic balloon with a diameter of 100 feet, and *Echo II* launched on January 25, 1964, with a diameter of 135 feet. Radio waves are reflected from their surfaces, making long-distance communications possible. Echo II is the brightest artificial satellite sent aloft, appearing as one of the brightest stars in the sky, and it circles the earth in a near-polar orbit.

eclipse The phenomenon that occurs when one celestial body is concealed by another. (When the moon or a planet passes in front of a star, the phenomenon is called an *occultation*.) *Solar eclipses* are seen when the moon passes between the earth and sun at new moon phase. On the surface of the earth where the moon's center is seen crossing the center of the solar disc, the eclipse is *central*. If the moon's apparent diameter is greater than the sun's apparent size, the eclipse will be *total* for all areas traversed by the umbra of the moon's shadow. If the apparent diameter of the moon is less than the sun's apparent size, the eclipse is *annular*, the dark disc of the moon surrounded by a bright ring. All portions of the surface of the earth within the penumbra of the shadow have a *partial* eclipse. Predictions of eclipses for the year are given in the *Nautical Almanacs*, ephemerides, and handbooks including the beginning and end of the eclipse for various positions, path of totality, and the regions where a partial eclipse is visible. A total eclipse is eagerly awaited by the astronomer for the opportunity to study the **solar corona*, the outer layer of the sun's atmosphere. Totality can last a maximum time of 7.5 minutes, but usually duration is only a few minutes. *Lunar eclipses* occur when the sun, the earth, and the moon are nearly in a straight line, with the moon immersed in the earth's shadow. If the entire moon enters the shadow, the eclipse will be *total,* and *partial* if only part of the moon passes into the shadow. The eclipse can last for

1½ hours. During totality, the moon is illuminated in a copper-red color, caused by sunlight refracted in the atmosphere of the earth. A lunar eclipse is visible from all parts of the earth where the moon is above the horizon. If the orbits of the moon and earth were in the same plane, eclipses would occur every month. However, the moon's orbit is inclined 5° to the ecliptic and an eclipse can only occur when the moon is near a node, which is one of the intersections of the two orbits. Since the nodes advance along the ecliptic and return to the same point in 18 years, 11 days, eclipses will repeat in this interval, called the *Saros*. Discovered by the Babylonians, the Saros was used by astronomers of antiquity to predict eclipses. On the average there are one or two lunar eclipses (maximum two) and two or three solar eclipses (maximum five) each year. *Jupiter's satellites* are considered to be in eclipse whenever they pass into the shadow of the planet. (Fig. E1.)

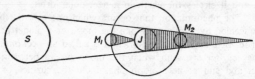

E1. *Eclipses.* S = *sun,* J = *earth,* M_1 = *moon's location during a solar eclipse,* M_2 = *moon's location during a lunar eclipse.*

eclipsing variables The same as photometric double stars. See: *binary stars.*

ecliptic The great circle on the celestial sphere which is the sun's apparent annual path. The ecliptic is inclined 23½° to the celestial equator.

ecliptic system Co-ordinate system with the plane of the ecliptic as the fundamental plane. See: *astronomical co-ordinates.*

E corona The portion of the *solar corona originating from the emission lines of highly ionized gases of iron, nickel, and calcium constituting only 1% of the total light of the corona.

Eddington, Sir Arthur Stanley (1882–1944) English astronomer who made extensive measurements of stellar motions and pioneered in theoretical investigations of the internal constitution of the stars.

effective temperature The temperature of a star calculated by the radiation laws based upon the star's observed radiation. Radiation laws (Stefan-Boltzmann law and Planck's law) are valid for a perfect radiator, a "black body," that absorbs all radiation that falls upon it at every wave length. In deriving effective temperature, the stars are assumed to radiate as black bodies.

effective wave length The effective wave length of a source, or of the receiver, or of the combination, is that wave length dividing the spectral curve so that the total energy from all light of longer wave length equals the total energy from all light of shorter wave length. The light from a star possesses various intensities at various wave lengths. A red star will be more intense at long wave lengths than short wave lengths. A receiver, such as the eye or a photographic emulsion, will have various sensitivities, or responses, at various wave lengths, a factor biasing the observed spectral intensities of the source of light. (Fig. E2.)

E2. Effective wave length. Schematic diagram of an objective grating spectrum of a red (R) and a white (V) star.

Einstein, Albert (1879–1955) German-born physicist. Probably the most brilliant scientist of our time, whose investigations, especially the theories of relativity, have been exceptionally significant to astronomy.

Einstein effects Consequences of Einstein's theories of relativity. The astronomical effects are as follows: **1.** ADVANCE OF THE PERIHELION OF MERCURY. The major axis of the orbit of Mercury slowly advances 43″ of arc per century. This advance was predicted by Einstein in his General Theory of Relativity. **2.** CURVATURE OF LIGHT IN A GRAVITATIONAL FIELD. When a light ray passes near the limb of the sun, the ray will be displaced 1″.75 at the limb. Observations during total eclipses of the sun have verified this prediction. **3.** DISPLACEMENT OF SPECTRAL LINES. The light emitted from a star will have its spectral lines shifted to the red by an amount which is proportional to the mass of the star divided by the radius. The *red shift* is insignificant in the case of the sun and other normal stars, but is readily measurable in *white dwarfs*. The phenomenon was confirmed by observations of the faint white dwarf companion of Sirius.

Einstein's theories of relativity The theories developed by Albert Einstein regarding space and time (*Special Theory of Relativity*, 1905, and the *General Theory of Relativity*, 1916). According to the theory, classical mechanics is a special case of a more general mechanics and is valid only for low velocities (low with respect to the velocity of light in a vacuum). At high velocity, mass is no longer constant but increases with velocity. Mass is regarded to be a form of energy and is therefore the equivalent of a given amount of energy. According to relativity, no distinction can be made between gravity and inertia. (A more comprehensive treatment of relativity lies outside the scope of this work.) See: *Einstein effects*.

E layer An electrically charged layer in the ionosphere at an altitude of about 65 miles, from which radio waves are reflected. The E layer is also called the *Kennelly-Heaviside layer*.

electromagnetic radiation A general term used to describe all radiation of electromagnetic nature with wave lengths from the shortest gamma (γ) radiation (10^{-10} cm), to X ray, ultraviolet, visible light, infrared, to radio waves with wave lengths to 30,000 meters.

electromagnetic spectrum The complete range of electromagnetic energy arranged according to wave length.

electron Negatively charged atomic particle with a mass equal to $\frac{1}{1837}$ the mass of a proton. See: *atom*.

electronic telescope See: *image converter*.

electron-multiplier tube A photoelectric cell in which the current is amplified within the cell through an emission from a series of secondary electrodes. The electron-multiplier is used in photoelectric photometry.

electron stream The electric current emitted when light falls on a photosensitive substance. See: *photoelectric photometry*.

electron volt (eV) The energy required by an electron to move through a potential of one volt in a vacuum.

element See: *elements of an orbit* and *basic elements*.

elements of an orbit The numerical quantities that describe a body's orbit. The size and form of an elliptical orbit are specified by the semi-major axis, *a,* and eccentricity, *e.* The orientation of the orbit in space is specified by the longitude of the ascending node (the angular distance from the vernal equinox to the point where the body intersects the ecliptic moving from south to north) (Ω), and its inclination to the ecliptic, *i.* The orientation of the orbit in the orbital plane is

specified by the angular distance between the perihelion point
and the ascending node, ω. In addition there is the time of
perihelion passage, T. If the orbit is parabolic, the semi-
major axis is replaced by perihelion distance, q. In a parabolic orbit, the eccentricity is equal to 1. (Fig. E3.)

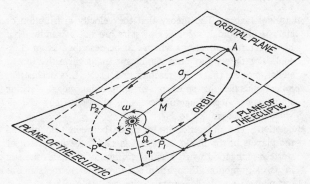

E3. Elements of an orbit. A = *aphelion*, P = *perihelion*, a =
semi-major axis = MA, e = *eccentricity* $\frac{MS}{a}$, i = *inclination*,
Ω = *longitude of the ascending node*, P_1 = *ascending node*,
P_2 = *descending node*, ♈ = *vernal equinox*, ω = *angular distance
of perihelion from ascending node.*

elephant trunks Dark serpentine nebulae found among bright
  hydrogen clouds (H-II regions) that are probably the result
  of cooler neutral hydrogen (H-I).

ellipse A plane curve such that the sum of the distances from
  a point on the curve to two fixed points within the curve
  (foci) is constant and equal to the length of the major axis
  of the ellipse. The ellipse is a conic section. The distance between the focal points, expressed in terms of the major axis,

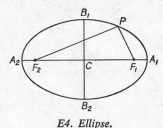

E4. Ellipse.

is called the *eccentricity*. The larger the eccentricity, the more elongated the ellipse. If the eccentricity is 0, the ellipse becomes a circle; if the eccentricity is 1, the ellipse becomes a parabola. According to Kepler's first law, every planetary orbit is an ellipse with the sun located at one focal point. (Fig. E4.)

ellipsoidal theory The theory that the velocity distribution of stars is ellipsoidal; velocities of stars are not at random but have preferred directions which can be described as an ellipsoid. The theory has been significant in the investigation of stellar motion (K. Schwarzschild and C. V. L. Charlier).

elliptical galaxies A spherical or ellipsoidal galaxy lacking spiral arms. According to increasing ellipticity they are divided into classes E0 to E7.

elongation The difference in longitude between the sun and the planets or the moon. A planet is said to be in eastern or western elongation when it either follows or precedes the sun in its daily motion. Elongation is approximately the same as the planet's angular distance to the sun. (Fig. E5.)

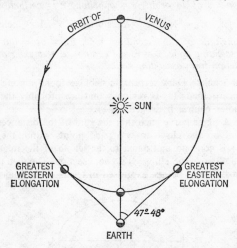

E5. Elongation (Venus).

emersion The reappearance of a celestial body after an eclipse, or the reappearance of a star after an occultation by the moon.

emission lines Bright lines in the spectrum of an incandescent gas. They occur when electrons in the atoms of the gas change from an outer to an inner orbit and the energy released is emitted as light of the same wave length as the gas in question.

emission nebula A bright gas cloud. See: *galactic nebulae*.

Encke's comet An interesting comet discovered in 1786 and later named after the German astronomer J. F. Encke (1791–1865), who made comprehensive theoretical investigations of the motions of this comet. The comet has the shortest known period of revolution (3.3 years). Encke found that the period was shortened by 2.5 hours for each revolution. Later, Backlund, of Sweden, found that this retardation was not uniform. The reason for this phenomenon is unknown.

energy production Energy is produced in the interior of the sun and stars by means of nuclear reactions. The high temperatures in the sun and stars (10 million to 15 million degrees and more) is sufficiently high to convert four hydrogen nuclei to helium, liberating a vast amount of energy which can be maintained for thousands of millions of years. There are two chain reactions that are presently under consideration. In the *proton-proton reaction,* two protons (hydrogen nuclei) fuse into a nucleus of deuterium, releasing a positron. In the next phase, another proton collides with the deuterium nucleus, forming the helium isotope $2He^3$, releasing energy and two protons. Two helium isotopes combine to form an ordinary helium nucleus. Another reaction which occurs at a somewhat higher temperature is called the *carbon-nitrogen cycle,* or the *carbon cycle.* This cycle is more complicated than the *proton-proton reaction,* but the results are the same in each case; helium is produced through the fusion of hydrogen nuclei with the release of an enormous amount of energy. At temperatures of 200 million degrees Kelvin, a new nuclear process can begin where helium is transformed into heavier elements (*Salpeter process*). At higher temperatures (thousands of millions of degrees) other processes occur where heavier metals (iron, nickel) are formed through the fusion of lighter elements.

English mounting A method of mounting an astronomical telescope where the polar axis is a rectangular yoke supported by two piers, as shown in Fig. E6. See: *equatorial mounting.*

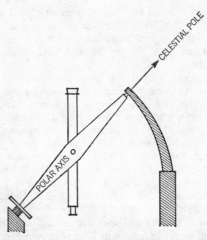

E6. English mounting.

epact 1. ANNUAL EPACT. The time that must be added to the lunar year (12 lunations) to make it coincide with the solar year (about 11 days). **2.** The moon's age at the beginning of the calendar year. **3.** LUNAR EPACT. The difference between the calendar month and the lunar month.

ephemeris 1. A table of the positions of a planet for a series of dates derived from the planet's orbital elements. **2.** Annual publication of the positions of the sun, moon, and planets during the course of the year, circumstances of solar and lunar eclipses, information regarding certain stars, listing of astronomical constants, etc. Generally used in navigation, the most important publications are *The American Ephemeris and Nautical Almanac, The Astronomical Ephemeris* (Great Britain), and the French *La Connaissance des Temps.*

epicycle According to Ptolemy (A.D. 150), a planet revolves at a constant velocity in a smaller circle whose center, in turn, revolves in a larger circle, with the earth at its center. The smaller circle is called an epicycle and the larger, the *deferent.* (See Fig. D1.)

epicycle theory An attempt to explain the apparent motion of the planets by means of epicycles. (Ptolemy, about A.D. 150.)

epoch A precise date to which the co-ordinates and other data for a heavenly body are referred or from which a new period (or **era*) is measured. In a star catalogue, the epoch is indicated for stellar co-ordinates by a date such as α_{1950}, δ_{1950}. For variable stars, the epoch gives the date for maximum or minimum magnitude. In determining orbits, the epoch is included as an *element of an orbit* (time of perihelion passage).

Epsilon (ε) The fifth letter in the *Greek alphabet. Epsilon Aurigae, Epsilon Lyrae;* see: *Auriga, Lyra.*

equal altitudes Similar altitudes of a star before and after meridian passage. If the time is recorded with a sidereal clock and the star's right ascension is known, clock errors can be found without the declination of the star or the latitude of the position. The method can also be used to determine the location of the meridian.

equation of light The time interval required by light to pass through space to the earth from a celestial body within the solar system. An object is seen not as it is at the time of observation but as it was the moment when the light left the body. If distance is known, the equation of light can be solved. The position of a celestial body must be corrected for the equation of light. See: *light-time effect.*

equation of the center An irregularity of the moon's motion known in ancient times. Since the orbit of the moon is eccentric, orbital motion will vary so that in one revolution, the moon will alternately be ahead of or behind the position it would have if its speed were constant. This deviation has a maximum value of about 6° in both directions in a period equal to the moon's revolution, and can be defined as the difference between the true and mean anomaly. See: *anomaly.*

equation of time The difference between apparent solar time and mean solar time. Fig. E7 shows how the equation of time

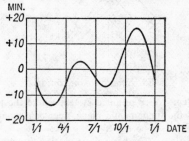

E7. Equation of time.

varies during the year. These variations are due to the eccentricity of the earth's orbit and the inclination of the ecliptic.

equator 1. The great circle on the surface of a celestial body whose plane passes through the center of the celestial body and is perpendicular to the axis of rotation. **2.** Celestial equator; the circle on the celestial sphere in the plane of the earth's equator extended to the celestial sphere.

equatorial horizontal parallax The angle formed by the earth's equatorial semi-diameter as seen from a celestial body. See: *diurnal parallax.*

equatorial mounting A telescope mounting consisting of a *polar axis* pointed toward the celestial pole (and therefore parallel to the earth's axis), and a *declination axis* supporting the instrument at right angles to the polar axis. The telescope is turned on the polar axis at the same speed as the diurnal motion of the sky by means of a clock-drive. There are several kinds of equatorial mountings, including the *German mounting* with a short polar axis placed on the top of a vertical pier, and the *English mounting* with a long polar axis resting on two piers. In a *fork mounting,* which is often used with reflecting telescopes, the telescope tube is suspended and moved freely in a short fork placed on the top of the polar axis. (Fig. E8.)

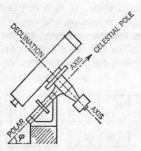

E8. Equatorial mounting.

equator system A co-ordinate system where the plane of the equator is the fundamental plane. See: *astronomical co-ordinates.*

equinoctial colure The hour circle passing through both *equinoxes.*

equinoxes The two points of intersection between the ecliptic and the celestial equator on the celestial sphere. The *vernal equinox* (in the constellation of Pisces) is the point of intersection where the sun changes from south to north declination. The opposite point is the *autumnal equinox* (in the constellation of Virgo). When the sun reaches the equinoxes on about March 21 and September 23, respectively, day and night are of equal length. (Equinox means equal day and night.)

equivalent width A measure of the absorption of a spectral line. The width in Ångstroms of a completely absorptive rectangle whose area is equal to that of the true spectral line. (Fig. E9.)

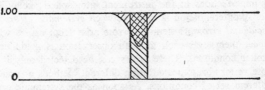

E9. Equivalent width.

Equuleus (Little Horse) A small, insignificant constellation in the northern hemisphere at 21h 10m right ascension ($\alpha =$ 21h 10m), 5° north declination ($\delta = +5°$).

era A system for measuring years. In Rome, the years were originally measured from the founding of Rome. Today, in western culture, the *Christian era* is used counting the years from the birth of Christ. This system originated in the middle of the 6th century with the abbot Dionysius Exiguus. According to Dionysius, Christ was born on December 25, A.D. 1. (This date is very uncertain.) The Christian era is also used to indicate the years before Christ. Historians use the year 1 B.C. to mark the year prior to the birth of Christ. This method is unsuitable since 0 year is not included, causing a discontinuity in the numbering system. For astronomical time measurements, the following is valid: Year 0 = 1 B.C.; Year −1 = 2 B.C.; Year −2 = 3 B.C.; etc.

Eratosthenes (275–192 B.C.) Greek astronomer. Eratosthenes was the first to determine the actual size of the earth and was the founder of geodesy. He also compiled a star catalogue.

Eridanus (River) An extensive constellation in the southern hemisphere that meanders between 1h 20m and 5h 10m right ascension (α = 1h 20m to 5h 10m), 0° and 58° south dec-lination (δ = 0° to −58°).

Eros A minor planet which makes a close approach to the earth during favorable oppositions (about 16 million miles). On these occasions, through the international co-operation of many observatories, the minor planet's motion is studied to give a more accurate determination of the earth's distance from the sun. The asteroid's period of revolution is 1.76 years and its mean distance from the sun is 135,600,000 miles. Eros's brightness varies, indicating an axial rotational period of 5h 16m.

errors All astronomical observations are beset with errors, due to imperfections in the instrument, atmospheric conditions, etc. A differentiation is made between *systematic errors* and *accidental errors*. Systematic errors arise from causes which repeat themselves each time an observation is made under similar conditions. These errors can be detected only if the observations are repeated using different methods or under a different set of conditions. As soon as the systematic errors are known, observations are corrected accordingly. The re-maining errors are of an accidental nature. From a large number of observations, the mean error is calculated to give the size of the error. Errors are treated mathematically by means of the *method of least squares*.

eruptive prominence A type of *solar *prominence* character-ized by rapid changes of an explosive nature.

escape velocity The velocity required by a body to achieve a parabolic orbit. Escape velocity for the members of the solar system is as follows: Mercury, 2.0 miles/sec; Venus, 6.3; earth, 6.95; Mars, 3.1; Jupiter, 37.0; Saturn, 22.0; Uranus, 13.0; Neptune, 15.0; Pluto, 6.9 (?); and the moon, 1.5 miles/sec. In order for a planet to retain an atmosphere, the average velocity of the molecules of gas must be substantially below the velocity of escape.

ESO (European Southern Observatory) A co-operative Eu-ropean project to construct and maintain a large astronomical observatory in the southern hemisphere. At present, five countries are connected with the project: Belgium, France, the Netherlands, Sweden, and West Germany. The main in-strument will be a 3.5-meter reflecting telescope, a large Schmidt telescope, and a number of smaller instruments for photoelectric and spectrographic purposes. The observatory will be built in Chile at a mountain region about 300 miles north of Santiago near the American AURA observatory.

ESRO (European Space Research Organization) The European astronautical association in which twelve countries are participating. ESRO will include a space science center, research laboratories, bases for the launching of satellites and high-altitude rockets. One base for high-altitude rockets will be constructed in Sweden.

Europa One of Jupiter's four brightest satellites, discovered by Galileo in 1610.

evection An irregularity in the moon's motion caused by perturbations of the sun and planets, resulting in a displacement of the moon from its true position by a maximum value of $\pm 1°16'$ in a period of 32 days.

evening The time between sunset and the end of twilight.

evening star (Hesperus) The name describing the planet Venus when it is east of the sun and is visible in the western sky after sunset.

excess Spherical excess. The amount to which the sum of the angles of a spherical triangle is greater than $180°$.

exosphere The outer portion of the earth's atmosphere beyond the ionosphere.

expanding gaseous envelopes Gaseous envelopes have been discovered around many exploded stars including *P Cygni* stars and novae. Their spectra contain emission lines. The velocity of expansion of the envelopes can be calculated from the displacement of the lines by the **Doppler effect*.

expansion The expansion of the universe. See: *universe*.

exploding stars (erupting stars) Irregular variable stars that rapidly increase in luminosity. Several different types are found. 1. NOVAE (new stars). In normal novae, luminosity increases in a few hours or days, reaches a maximum, and gradually declines. Several months or years may go by before the star returns to the same luminosity it had before the outburst. During the outburst, luminosity may increase 100,000 times, or an increase of 10 to 13 magnitudes. During the change in brightness, many interesting spectral changes take place. The gas shell is observed to rush toward us at speeds of several thousand km/sec, or over six million miles an hour. In several instances, the expanding shell can be observed as a small nebula around the star after the novae eruption. The expanding gases are extremely tenuous and are believed to amount to no more than ⅟₁₀,₀₀₀ of the star's mass. In the Milky Way, there are apparently 20 to 30 nova outbursts each year, but only a few are discovered. Novae have also been observed in other galaxies. Since the maximum absolute magnitude of novae is fairly constant (about −7.0 magnitude), they can be used to determine the distances to other galaxies. Occasionally, *supernovae* will appear with a maximum absolute magnitude −16. While novae rise more than 10 magnitudes, supernovae increase 20 magnitudes with a brightness equal to 100 million suns. The gases expand with a velocity of 10,000 km/sec, or over 20 billion miles per hour. The erupted matter is equal to 0.1 to 1 solar masses. Supernovae are very rare phenomena. In the Milky Way, supernovae evidently occurred in 5 B.C., A.D. 185, 369, 1006, 1054 (*Crab Nebula*), 1572 (Tycho's star), and 1604 (Kepler's star). The debris of supernovae can often be detected as radio sources. About 50 supernovae have been observed in other galaxies. There are two types of supernovae: Type I, with a mean absolute magnitude −14.3; Type II, with a mean absolute magnitude −12.2. **2.** RECURRENT NOVAE. Stars that have nova type outbursts more than once, such as RS Ophiuchi and T Pyxidis. SS Cygni stars are also included. **3.** FLARE STARS. Certain type M stars show an occasional outburst, increasing their luminosity several magnitudes in a few minutes or hours. It is believed that these outbursts are caused by powerful eruptions of radiation on the surface of the star similar to the *solar *flares* seen on the sun.

Explorer I   The first artificial satellite launched by the United States on January 31, 1958. It was designated 1958α.

extinction   The absorption of light in the earth's atmosphere. See: *absorption.*

extragalactic nebulae   Remote stellar systems located beyond the Milky Way. Today, they are referred to as **galaxies.*

eyepiece   (ocular)   A lens system through which the observer views the image formed by the objective of a telescope.

F

Fabricius, David   (1564–1617)   German clergyman and astronomer. On August 3, 1596, he discovered the light variations of the star Mira (o Ceti). He also observed the comet of 1607, the star Nova Ophiuchi, and sunspots.

Fabry lens A lens or lens system used in photoelectric photometry to focus the image of the objective on the light-sensitive surface of a photoelectric cell.

faculae Bright areas on the sun that are about 10% brighter than the surrounding photosphere. Usually found near *sunspots*, faculae are visible on ordinary photographs (*photospheric faculae*). They appear very conspicuous at the limb of the sun as bright cloudlike formations swaying in the solar atmosphere. Faculae show structural details remindful of *solar granulations* but are brighter and last for a longer period of time. Recently, small, sparse patches near the poles, *polar faculae,* have been discovered during sunspot minimum and apparently are related to coronal streamers. Faculae are subject to the same 11-year cycle as the sunspots and other solar phenomena. *Spectroheliograms* taken in the K line of calcium show the entire solar disc covered with faculae. Spectroheliograms of the chromosphere show formations called *chromospheric faculae.* These appear conspicuous in photographs taken in the H line of hydrogen.

fade outs Disturbances in long-distance radio communications, most often caused by the eruption of a *solar *flare.*

falling stars Bright streaks of light caused by small cosmic particles entering the atmosphere at speeds of up to 45 miles/sec. See: *meteors.*

F corona The outer portion of the solar corona where sunlight is scattered and reflected by dust particles. The spectrum of the F corona is similar to the solar spectrum and contains *Fraunhofer lines.* It has been detected at a distance of 10 solar diameters from the sun's limb and forms a transition to the interplanetary dust observed as the *zodiacal light.* See: *solar corona.*

Fechner's law A physiological law which states that the stimulus producing a sensation increases in proportion to the logarithm of the intensity of stimulation (the psychophysical relation). The division of stars into a scale of magnitudes is based upon Fechner's law.

filamentary nebula A gaseous nebula in the constellation of Cygnus (Swan) that resembles a cirrus cloud.

filaments Dark threadlike markings visible on monochromatic photographs of the sun taken in the light of one spectral line

such as a calcium line. Filaments are the projections of
prominences on the solar surface.

filters Colored glass discs placed in the light path to study
starlight in various colors. Special filters based upon the principle of the interference of light are used to obtain colors in
a very narrow band (monochromatic light).

finder A low-power telescope with a wide field of view that is
fitted to a larger telescope with the optical axes of both telescopes parallel. In order to set the main instrument, the object to be observed is first brought into view in the finder.

fireball A brilliant meteor. See: *bolide.*

fission theory The theory for the origin of binary stars
through the division of a single star. A star, formed out of
the gaseous matter in space, will rotate more rapidly and
contract into a spheroid with two identical axes. With further
increase in rotation, the star may become an ellipsoid with
three axes; more lenticular and, finally, at a critical point,
pear-shaped. With continued increase in the rate of rotation,
separation into two unequal parts takes place. According to
G. H. Darwin, spectroscopic binary stars may have evolved
in this manner. The theory cannot be accepted in its present
form, since the stars are assumed to have constant density.
The density of a star increases toward the center.

fixed stars The name given to the stars since antiquity when
the stars were believed to be firmly fastened to a crystal
sphere.

Flammarion, Camille (1842–1925) French astronomer who
received world-wide recognition through his books on popular astronomy. He actively promoted the study of astronomy.

flare, solar flare, solar eruption Powerful eruption of radiation
on the sun, associated with sunspots. Photographed in the
light of the hydrogen lines, flares are among the brightest
phenomena on the sun, occurring very rapidly, lasting only
15 to 20 minutes and, in rare instances, a few hours. Sometimes, a type of prominence called a *surge* will develop rapidly above a flare. Flares emit intensive short-wave and corpuscular radiation that can reach the earth in about 26 hours
and cause brilliant displays of aurora and magnetic storms.
The short-wave radiation from the flare affects the layers of
the ionosphere in the earth's atmosphere, resulting in "fade
outs" of radio communication. Flares also bring about a

powerful increase in radio frequency radiation as well as the intensity of cosmic radiation.

flare star A type of variable (red dwarf star) that shows rapid and irregular changes in light which probably are caused by the eruption of a *flare.

flash spectrum The emission spectrum of the chromosphere of the sun observed an instant before the beginning and after the end of totality during an eclipse of the sun. When the photosphere disappears behind the disc of the moon, the absorption spectrum suddenly changes to an emission spectrum. The phenomenon lasts for only a few seconds. When the flash spectrum is recorded by a spectroscope without a grating, or with an *objective prism, the emission lines are curved, since every line records an image of the visible portion of the solar atmosphere in a specific wave length. The distribution of the elements in the various layers of the solar atmosphere can be studied from the length and width of these "chromosphere arcs." Over 3000 lines have been measured in the flash spectrum.

F layers Layers in the ionosphere (F_1 and F_2 at about 125 miles and 185 miles, respectively) also called the *Appleton layers* after their discoverer.

flint glass A type of glass with high dispersive power that is used together with crown glass in the construction of an *achromatic objective.

flocculi Light and dark markings that are prominent in monochromatic photographs of the sun in the light of the K line of calcium and the hydrogen alpha line, $H\alpha$. They are masses of gases that are hotter (the bright) or cooler (the dark) than the surrounding region. *Calcium flocculi* are generally bright, cloudlike markings and form a torchlike expanse in the higher regions of the sun's atmosphere. *Hydrogen flocculi* are often dark, elongated, and often appear as curved filaments in the vicinity of sunspots. Also called plages.

flood tide High tide. See: *tides.*

fluorescence The property of certain elements when illuminated to emit light of a longer wave length than the original light. In this way, invisible X rays can be observed on a fluorescent screen. When light shines through a gas, the atoms of the gas become excited and emit radiation of a different wave length than the entering light. An analogous radiation is produced in nebulae. See: *nebulae.*

Fly Constellation in the southern hemisphere. See: *Musca.*

Flying Fish Constellation in the southern hemisphere. See: *Volans.*

flying saucers Alleged observations of moving light phenomena or objects which have not been identified as meteors. An extensive literature on the subject has emerged since World War II.

f-number Nominal focal ratio. The ratio between the diameter of the entrance pupil and the focal length of an object lens. If the objective has an aperture of 10 cm and a focal length of 150 cm, the ratio is equal to $\frac{1}{15}$, the f-number = 15 and designated as f/15. Refractors work at a speed of f/15 to f/20 and reflectors at f/4 to f/5. Schmidt telescopes have f-numbers between f/2 and f/3 and sometimes f/0.5.

focal distance The distance from the objective lens or primary mirror of an astronomical instrument to the *focal point* or focus.

focal plane The plane at the *focus* at right angles to the optical axis.

focal point The *focus.* The point to which parallel light rays near the optical axis are bent by a convex lens or lens system or the point to which light rays are reflected by a concave mirror.

focal surface A surface containing focal points of all parts of the object. The surface may be a plane or a curve. In some instances the curvature is great, as in a Schmidt telescope, and curved photographic plates are necessary to insure sharp images over a large area.

focus The *focal point.* The point to which the parallel rays of light in an optical system are refracted or reflected.

Fomalhaut The star *Alpha* (α) *Pisces Austrini,* the brightest star in the constellation *Pisces Austrinus,* Southern Fish, of apparent visual magnitude 1.3 and spectral type A3.

forbidden lines Spectral lines that normally are produced only under special physical conditions, i.e., in the rarefied gases found in space. Some of the intense spectral lines of gaseous nebulae are the forbidden lines of oxygen and nitrogen.

force The product of the mass and acceleration of a body.

fork mounting A type of mounting that is used primarily with reflecting telescopes, with the telescope turning around a short declination axis that rests in a fork mounted on the polar axis. See: *equatorial mounting.* (Fig. F1.)

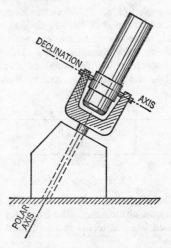

F1. Fork mounting.

Fornax (Furnace) A constellation in the southern hemisphere at 3h right ascension ($\alpha = 3$h), 30° south declination ($\delta = -30°$).

Foucault knife-edge test A method used to test the optical quality of mirrors and lenses, developed by J. B. L. Foucault. An artificial star is placed at the center of curvature of a concave mirror to be tested. By placing a knife edge in the light beam, shadows formed on the mirror will indicate the quality of the surface. In addition, it is possible to measure the surface profile directly. The method has gained wide application in optics.

Foucault pendulum A heavy weight suspended by a long wire mounted to swing freely with a minimum amount of friction. The Foucault pendulum will swing in the same plane as it started for a long period of time. The earth's rotation is reflected in the slow turning of the plane of the pendulum's motion. The experiment was performed for the first time by the French physicist Foucault in 1851.

Fox A constellation in the northern hemisphere. See: *Vulpecula*.

Franklin-Adams charts Photographic atlas of the entire sky reproduced on 206 charts containing stars brighter than 16th magnitude.

Fraunhofer, Joseph (1787–1826) German optician. He measured and studied the dark lines in the solar spectrum that
now bear his name. See: *Fraunhofer lines.*

Fraunhofer lines Dark absorption lines that were discovered
in the solar spectrum by Wollaston and mapped by Fraunhofer in 1814, and in stellar spectra by Wollaston in 1823.
(Fig. F2.)

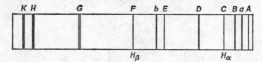

F2. Fraunhofer lines.

frequency The number of cycles per second of a wave motion
or other periodic phenomenon. The frequency of electromagnetic radiation is equal to the speed of light divided by the
wave length.

F stars Stars of spectral type F in the *Harvard classification*
of stellar spectra. These are yellow-white stars whose spectra
are dominated by H and K lines of ionized calcium as well
as metallic lines. Their surface temperature reaches about
7000° C.

full moon The phase when the moon's "age," measured from
new moon, is 14½ days. The moon is opposite the sun with
its fully lighted surface facing the earth.

fundamental catalogue A catalogue of *fundamental stars* giving positions in right ascension and declination for a given
epoch.

fundamental stars A number of stars distributed over the entire sky whose positions have been determined with the greatest possible accuracy. These stars serve as a standard for the
determination of the positions of the other stars.

Furnace Constellation in the southern hemisphere. See: *Fornax.*

G

Gagarin, Yuri (1934–   ) Soviet "cosmonaut," the first man
to orbit the earth. The feat was accomplished in the space-

ship Vostok I, on April 12, 1961, in 108 minutes, with a landing in a predetermined target area.

galactic co-ordinates *Galactic latitude* and *longitude* are co-ordinates in a system where the plane of the Milky Way is the fundamental plane.

galactic equator The great circle in the sky defined by the plane of the Milky Way, or the galactic plane. At an angle of about 62°, the galactic equator intersects the celestial equator at two points located in the constellations of Monoceros and Aquila.

galactic nebulae Extensive clouds of dust and gas located in the arms of the Milky Way. Local concentration of *interstellar matter,* these clouds are classified as *bright nebulae* and *dark nebulae.* Bright nebulae are grouped into *emission nebulae* and *reflection nebulae.* Emission nebulae are mainly clouds of hydrogen that are ionized by the intense short-wave radiation of nearby stars of high temperature (O and B stars). When ions reunite with free electrons, radiation is emitted which is observed as a bright nebulae with an emission spectrum. These nebulae are very tenuous (10 atoms/cm^2), and are also referred to as H-II regions. The spectra of the nebulae also contain *forbidden lines* of ionized oxygen and nitrogen. In reflection nebulae, the light from nearby stars is reflected by dust particles within the nebulae. Dark nebulae primarily consist of dust particles about 10^{-5} cm in size and are metallic or possibly ice. Since light from remote stars is dimmed by intervening dust clouds, dark nebulae are prominently seen in rich star fields in the Milky Way. The particles disperse blue light more than red so that starlight appears redder (color excess) after passing through a dark nebula. Distances to dark nebulae can be determined by a statistical star count within successive magnitudes in the regions of the nebulae with an absorption-free comparison region. See: *Wolf diagram.* In addition, vast regions of neutral hydrogen (H-I regions) have been found with radio telescopes tuned to a wave length of 21 cm. New stars are believed to be created through the condensation of galactic nebulae.

galactic poles The poles of the Milky Way. The north galactic pole is located at about 12h 40m right ascension (α = 12h 40m), and 28° north declination (δ = +28°). The south galactic pole is the diametrically opposite point. Since 1959, the co-ordinates of the north galactic pole have been considered to be at α = 12h 49m, δ = +27°4, a value that is in accordance with the results derived for the location of the galactic plane in radio astronomy investigations.

galactic rotation Rotation of the Milky Way Galaxy. The motion of the individual stars depends upon their relative distance from the center of the Galaxy. At the sun's distance from the center, rotational velocity is more than 262 km/sec and the period of rotation is 225 million years.

galactic star clusters Star clusters confined to or near the Milky Way. These *open clusters* are classified according to concentration toward the center and the number of stars contained. The nearer clusters are more sparsely populated *moving star clusters* (such as the Hyades) with parallel paths through space determined from the proper motions and radial velocities of the individual stars. Other *open star clusters* (such as the Pleiades and Praesepe) are at greater distances than the moving clusters. Among many clusters, proper motion has not been determined. Several hundred open clusters are known. Various types of clusters are found; some are

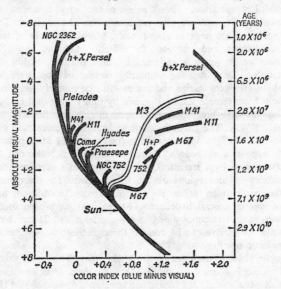

G1. Schematic Hertzsprung-Russell diagram for galactic star clusters.

more highly concentrated toward the center while others have stars more evenly distributed. There are clusters with a few very bright stars and clusters of stars with little variation in luminosities. A cluster may consist of a few scattered stars or thousands of stars in a rich, compact cluster. A study of the magnitudes and colors (spectral types) of the stars using the *color-luminosity diagram,* or *Hertzsprung-Russell diagram* (the abscissa is the color or spectral type, the ordinate is the *absolute magnitude*), has provided information regarding the age and distance of these clusters. See: *stellar evolution* and *Hertzsprung-Russell diagram.* Distances to the clusters vary from 150 to 15,000 light-years and diameters are found to lie between 5 and 60 light-years. The ages of the open clusters vary between a few million years to several thousand million years. Some clusters, such as the Pleiades, are surrounded by nebulosity. The stability of a cluster depends upon the mutual attraction of the individual member stars and must therefore be greater than the gravitational attraction of the stars in the Milky Way. If the cluster is sparsely populated, the stars will disperse. A more highly concentrated cluster will be more stable. Random collisions of stars are considered in the study of the dynamics within a star cluster. (Fig. G1.)

galactic system Our stellar system. See: *Milky Way system.*

galactic windows Openings in the dust clouds that shroud the plane of the Milky Way, through which distant galaxies can be observed. See: *zone of avoidance.*

galaxies *Extragalactic nebulae.* Star systems analogous to the Milky Way. The distribution of galaxies in the sky is characterized by an apparent concentration toward the galactic poles. The region along the plane of the Milky Way is practically devoid of galaxies because of the presence of obscuring dust clouds (*zone of avoidance). Galaxies are classified into two categories according to their physical structure: *regular systems* and *irregular systems.* About 97% of the galaxies are regular systems. These symmetrical galaxies are divided into two groups, *elliptical* and *spiral galaxies.* Spiral galaxies are grouped as *normal spirals,* with a symmetrical nucleus from which spiral arms extend, and *barred spirals,* where the arms begin from opposite sides of an elongated nucleus shaped like a bar. These galaxies are further divided into subgroups. The nearer galaxies can be resolved into stars. As a result, these galaxies have been found to contain the same objects as the Milky Way system, including cepheid variables, novae, open and globular clusters, and nebulae. With the help of these stars, distances to the galaxies, measured in millions of light-years, have been calculated. By means of spectroscopic observations, the rotation of some of the galaxies has been determined. The total mass of a system can be found from its rotation. These galaxies are of the same size as the Milky Way, or about 100,000 million solar masses. When galaxies cannot be resolved into stars, indirect methods based upon the total luminosity are used to determine distances. Measurements of radial velocities show that the galaxies are receding at velocities that increase with distance. (Spectral lines are displaced toward the red, the so-called *red shift.) Distances are determined by the amount of red shift. The elliptical galaxies and the central portions of the spiral galaxies consist of old stars (*Population II), while the spiral arms contain young stars (Population I), as found in the spiral arms of the Milky Way. Galaxies often appear in groups. The Milky Way has two satellite galaxies (the two Magellanic Clouds), and the Andromeda Galaxy has two companions. The local group consists of 17 galaxies including the Milky Way within a sphere of about two million light-years' radius. Among the galaxies there are double and multiple systems as well as clusters or clouds of galaxies containing thousands and tens of thousands of members. Bridges of galactic matter connecting one galaxy with another have been observed among the nearby galaxies. See: cosmogony for the evolution of galaxies. The galaxies visible to the unaided eye include the two *Magellanic Clouds and the *Andromeda Galaxy. Radio astronomy techniques have been used to study the motions of the galaxies.

galaxies, cluster of   An aggregation of galaxies held together by gravity. Several thousand clusters have been discovered. One of the largest is the Coma cluster, in the constellation of Coma Berenices, near the north galactic pole. It consists of about 10,000 galaxies at a distance of 120 million light-years.

Galaxy   (galactic system) The great stellar system of which the sun is a member. See: Milky Way system.

Galilean moons   The four brightest satellites of Jupiter, discovered by Galileo in 1610 and named Io, Europa, Ganymede, and Callisto. They can easily be observed with binoculars.

Galilean telescope (opera glass) A telescope with a positive objective lens (or lens system) and a negative ocular. The optical system is illustrated in Fig. G2. This telescope con-

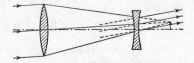

G2. Galilean telescope.

struction, invented by Galileo in 1609, is no longer used in astronomy. See: *astronomical telescope* (Kepler's telescope).

Galilei, Galileo (1564–1642) Italian physicist and astronomer. He constructed a telescope in 1609 and made many important discoveries, including lunar mountain ranges, star clusters, the four brightest satellites of Jupiter, and the phases of Venus.

Ganymede Jupiter III, one of the four Galilean moons of Jupiter, discovered in 1610. Its distance to the planet is 666,000 miles; period of revolution, 7.16 days; and diameter, 3200 miles.

Garnet star The name given to the deep red variable star μ Cephei by W. Herschel.

gaseous nebula See: *galactic nebulae.*

Gauss, Karl Friedrich (1777–1855) German mathematician and astronomer. He devised methods for determining the orbits of planets and applied the method of least squares to his observational results.

Gegenschein (Ger., counterglow) A very faint glow of light in the sky which is an extension of the *zodiacal line* that occasionally can be observed in the opposite direction from the sun.

Gemini (Twins) One of the more striking constellations in the northern hemisphere at 7h right ascension ($\alpha = 7h$), 22° north declination ($\delta = +22°$). *Castor,* Alpha (α) Geminorum, and *Pollux,* Beta (β) Geminorum, are its brightest stars.

Geminids A meteor shower that occurs in the first half of December with its radiant in the constellation of Gemini.

Gemma The star Alpha (α) Coronae Borealis (Northern Crown) with an apparent visual magnitude 2.3 and spectral type A0.

general precession The combined effect of *luni-solar* and *planetary precession*. See: *precession*.

geocentric position The position of a celestial body in the geocentric co-ordinate system which has as its origin the center of the earth.

geocentric universe A universe with the earth at its center, such as the *Ptolemaic System* (Ptolemy, about A.D. 150).

geodesy The study of the earth's shape and size and the methods used to determine its size.

geoid The earth viewed as a geometric solid whose entire surface at every point is perpendicular to the line joining the point to the center of gravity and, in general, coincides with the mean level of the oceans extended through the continents.

German mounting An equatorial mounting often used with refractors. The telescope is fitted to one end of the declination axis and a counterweight is placed on the other. The declination axis is fastened to the top of the polar axis. (Fig. G3.)

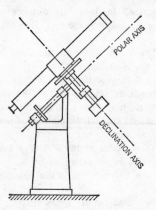

G3. German mounting.

ghost False image of spectral lines appearing in a diffraction grating, or the false image caused by reflection in an optical system; e.g., against the inner surface of the correcting plate in a Schmidt telescope.

giant planets The *Jovian planets:* Jupiter, Saturn, Uranus, and Neptune. The giant planets are enormous spheres with large masses (14 to 318 times the earth's mass), low densities

(0.13 to 0.29 times the earth's density), rapid axial rotation (9.9 to 15.8 hours), extensive atmospheres, and a large number of satellites (2 to 12). Spectroscopic investigations show the atmospheres to contain methane and ammonia. In addition, traces of molecular hydrogen have been found.

giant sequence The region of the *Hertzsprung-Russell diagram* where giant stars are grouped.

giant stars Members of the *giant sequence* of the *Hertzsprung-Russell diagram*. As early as 1907, E. Hertzsprung noted two different groups of stars of spectral type G to M, giant stars and *dwarf stars*. These giant stars have high absolute magnitude, enormous dimensions, and low mean density. From the investigation of the intensity of certain lines and bands (molecular cyanogen) it is possible to determine absolute magnitudes and separate giants from dwarfs. In giant stars, absorption by cyanogen is more pronounced, as is the intensity of certain lines of ionized elements such as strontium. See: *luminosity criteria*. A distinction is made between normal giants and *supergiants* with higher absolute magnitudes, as well as *subgiants* with lower absolute magnitudes than normal giants.

gimbal mounting A device for keeping a chronometer aboard a ship, horizontal, and independent of the rolling motion. The chronometer is fastened to a pair of concentric rings which swing on pivots that are situated at right angles to each other.

Giraffe Constellation in the northern hemisphere. See: *Camelopardalis*.

Glenn, John (1921–   ) The first American astronaut to orbit the earth. On February 20, 1962, he completed three orbits around the earth in a Mercury capsule and landed in a predetermined target area in the Atlantic Ocean.

globular clusters Star clusters containing between 10,000 and 100,000 stars in an almost globular system, with the stars strongly concentrated toward the center of the cluster. They consist primarily of stars belonging to Population II (old stars). Several clusters contain a large number of cepheid variable stars, principally short-period cepheids (*cluster type variables*). The distances to the clusters have been determined from the light variations of the cepheids. See: *cepheids*. The nearest globular cluster is Omega (ω) Centauri in the southern hemisphere (20,000 light-years) and Messier 13 in Hercules (30,000 light-years). Their diameters amount to several hundred light-years. Over 100 globular clusters are known. They form an almost spherical system with a diameter of 100,000 light-years about the center of the Milky Way. Globular clusters are very old systems with ages of 10,000 million or more years. Globular clusters have been discovered in other galaxies, such as the Andromeda Galaxy.

globule Very small dark nebulae that are seen projected against bright gaseous nebulae. They are believed to be protostars.

gnomon An instrument used in ancient times to measure the altitude of the sun. It consisted of a vertical shaft raised on a horizontal base. Since the height of the shaft was known, the altitude of the sun was calculated by measuring the length of the shadow cast on the base by the shaft. (Fig. G4.)

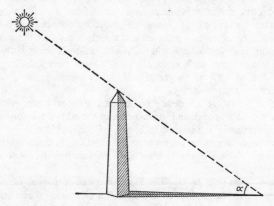

G4. Gnomon.

golden number The number giving the position of any year in the *Metonic cycle*. Meton (Greek astronomer, fifth century B.C.) found that the phases of the moon recurred at the same time and place in the sky every 19 years. Each year has a golden number, ranging from 1 to 19. The golden number is found by adding 1 to the given year and dividing by 19. The remainder in the division is the golden number. If the remainder is zero, the golden number is 19.

Göttinger Aktinometrie A catalogue of photographic magnitudes compiled by K. Schwarzschild at the Göttingen Observatory.

granulation A fine granular structure on the solar surface (photosphere). The grains are brighter than the surrounding area, indicating that gases are rising from the interior of the sun. Of short duration (about three minutes), these bright patches cause a continuous change in the granulation patterns. The grains are about 600 miles in diameter.

grating A large number of narrow rulings through which light is diffracted to form a spectrum, a *grating spectrum*. A *reflecting grating* consists of a large number of parallel rulings on a reflecting surface. In astronomy, gratings are used to obtain a large dispersion spectra. When a very coarse line grating is used in front of the objective (*objective grating*), the star images on the photographic plate form a central image with one or more spectra to either side. If the grating is very coarse, the spectra become points of light. See: *photographic photometry*.

gravitation The attraction between two bodies. Also called the force of *gravity*.

gravitation, constant of The attraction between two unit masses at unit distance apart. In the c.g.s. system, the constant of gravitation, $G = 6.673 \times 10^{-8}$.

gravitation, law of The law of gravitation developed by Newton in his *Principia* published in 1687. According to this law, every particle in the universe attracts every other particle with a force that is directly proportional to the product of their masses and inversely proportional to the square of the distance between them. The law is of fundamental significance in the study of the motions of the celestial bodies and their conditions of equilibrium. See: *celestial mechanics*.

gravity According to the law of gravity, the earth exerts a force of attraction on all bodies. This force is called the force of gravitation or gravity. The gravity affecting a mass, *m,* is $m \times g$, where *g* is the acceleration of a free-falling body (32.1 ft/sec²).

gravity, acceleration of The acceleration of gravity, *g,* of a falling body. At the equator, $g = 32.09$ ft/sec²; at the poles, $g = 32.26$ ft/sec². As a mean value, $g = 32.1$ ft/sec² is used.

great circle Intersection of a sphere and a plane through the center of the sphere. The intersection forms a circle that divides the sphere into two equal parts.

Great Cluster in Hercules (M13) A star-rich globular cluster in the constellation of Hercules. Its distance is about 30,000 light-years.

Greater Bear Constellation in the northern hemisphere. See: *Ursa Major.*

Greater Dog Constellation in the southern hemisphere. See: *Canis Major.*

Great Nebulae in Orion (M42 and M43) See: *Orion Nebula.*

Greek alphabet Used to identify stars within a constellation. The brightest star is called Alpha (α), the next brightest, Beta (β), etc.

α = Alpha	η = Eta	ν = Nu	τ = Tau
β = Beta	θ = Theta	ξ = Xi	υ = Upsilon
γ = Gamma	ι = Iota	o = Omicron	ϕ = Phi
δ = Delta	κ = Kappa	π = Pi	χ = Chi
ε = Epsilon	λ = Lambda	ρ = Rho	ψ = Psi
ζ = Zeta	μ = Mu	σ = Sigma	ω = Omega

green flash When the sun has set below the apparent horizon and only a small segment remains, under ideal conditions this segment is observed to change color from orange to green, so that the last glimpse is a flash of green or blue-green. The phenomenon is an effect of atmospheric dispersion of sunlight.

Greenwich Observatory The old English observatory located in Greenwich, a few miles from the center of London. Longitude on the earth is measured east and west from the Greenwich meridian (0° meridian). The Royal Greenwich Observatory instruments and staff have been moved to Sussex, and the original building has been turned into a museum.

Gregorian calendar The Julian calendar was based upon a tropical year, 365.25 days long, with each fourth year a leap year of 366 days. Since the actual tropical year has a length of 365.2422 days, an error of nearly 8 days will accumulate in 1000 years. The Gregorian calendar, named after Pope Gregory XIII, attempted to adjust the error by foreshortening the year 1582 by 10 days, whereby the day after October 4 that year became October 15. So that similar errors in time measurement will be avoided in the future, only century years which are evenly divided by 400 are leap years (1600, 2000). As a result, 3300 years will elapse before the calendar will be in error by one day.

Gregorian telescope A telescope designed by James Gregory (1638–1675). The parabolic primary mirror has a hole bored through the center. The light rays are reflected from the primary mirror to a concave secondary mirror where the light is reflected back to the primary mirror and through the central hole to an eyepiece mounted behind the primary mirror. (In a Cassegrainian telescope, the secondary mirror is convex rather than concave.)

Grus (Crane) Constellation in the southern hemisphere located at 22h 30m right ascension (α = 22h 30m), 45° south declination (δ = −45°).

G stars Stars of spectral type G in the *Harvard classification* of stellar spectra characterized by a great number of metallic lines. Temperatures are about 6000° C. The sun is a member of this spectral type; a subdwarf star of dG2 classification.

guide star A star conveniently located in the field of view to be photographed. The main instrument is adjusted so that the guide star appears in the cross-wires of the *guide telescope*. The guide star is used to control the tracking of the instrument during exposure.

guide telescope A telescope with cross-wires that is attached to a second telescope being used for photographic purposes. The guide telescope is mounted parallel to the optical axis of the main instrument. In practice, a guide star is centered on the cross-wire during exposure of the plate. Periodically, the position of the guide star is observed for possible irregularities in the clock-drive mechanism.

H

Hagen's cosmic clouds A faint, diffuse glow seen over many parts of the sky. Their existence was observed as early as 1811, by Herschel, and, since then, they have been studied systematically by Hagen at the Vatican Observatory (1931). Hagen found the glow more pronounced at the galactic pole than elsewhere. The phenomenon is very faint and, as a result, has been impossible to photograph. Opinions are divided regarding the nature of the glow; whether or not it is real or imaginary. Hagen believed that the faint glow originated with interstellar matter, while others have explained it as an electrical phenomenon related to the aurora.

Hale, George Ellery (1868–1938) American astronomer and outstanding solar observer. He invented the *spectrohelio-graph* and discovered the magnetic fields of sunspots. He took

an active part in the establishment of Yerkes, Mt. Wilson,
and Mt. Palomar observatories.

Hale telescope   The largest optical telescope in the world, at
Mt. Palomar, 5600 feet above sea level in southern California. This instrument is named after George Ellery Hale. The
mirror has a diameter of 200 inches. The prime focus is located at a distance of 54 feet from the primary mirror, where
an observing cage is located. Using secondary mirrors, focal
lengths to 492 feet can be obtained. The moving parts of the
mounting weigh over 500 tons. The revolving part of the
dome has a diameter of 137 feet and a weight of 1000 tons.
With this instrument, galaxies to a distance of 4000 million
light-years can be photographed.

Halley, Edmund   (1656–1742) Astronomer Royal and col-
league of Newton. Using Newton's law of gravitation, he derived the orbits of several comets, including *Halley's comet*
which was named after him. He discovered the proper motions
of some stars.

Halley's comet   A periodic comet revolving in 76 years, named
after *E. Halley*, who was the first to calculate the comet's orbit. Halley's comet has been visible from time to time as a
very striking object and reports regarding the comet have
been traced to 240 B.C. Since then, it has been observed 29
times, the last time in 1910. The comet is expected to return
to the vicinity of the sun in 1986.

halo   A spherical cloud of Population II stars (old stars) that
surrounds the Milky Way system and apparently other spiral
galaxies. The diameter of the Milky Way's halo is about
100,000 light-years.

H and K lines   The most conspicuous spectral lines, caused by
ionized calcium in type F and later type stars. The H line
has a wave length of 3969 Å and the K line has a wave
length of 3934 Å.

Hare   Constellation in the southern hemisphere. See: *Lepus*.

Harvard classification   A classification of stellar spectra published in the *Henry Draper Catalogue* which was prepared at
the turn of the century by E. C. Pickering and Miss A. J. Cannon and based on the characteristic lines and bands of the
chemical elements. The most important classes, in order of decreasing temperature, are as follows: O, B, A, F, G, K, M.
Additional classes include spectral type W, for Wolf-Rayet
stars, at the blue end of the spectrum, and R, N, and S, which
are low-temperature and extremely red stars. In the series

O to M, the colors of the stars change from white to yellow to orange to red. Among the O type stars (temperatures about 50,000° C.) lines of ionized helium are found. B type stars (about 20,000° C.) have absorption lines of hydrogen and helium. A type stars (white stars at 10,000° C.) have spectra dominated by the Balmer series of hydrogen lines. Among the F type stars (yellow to white stars at 7000° C.) metallic lines, notably of calcium, begin to appear. G type stars (yellow stars at 6000° C.), the class to which the sun belongs, have metallic lines of great intensity. In K type stars (yellow to red stars at 5000° C.), molecular bands begin to appear in the spectra. M type stars (red stars at 3000° C.) have distinct bands of titanium oxide in their spectra. Each class is subdivided with a numerical system or by letters of the alphabet, such as A5, G2, Ma, etc.

Harvard Observatory American observatory at Cambridge, Massachusetts, famous for its comprehensive classification of stellar spectra. See: *Harvard classification.* The observatory has both optical and radio telescopes.

Haute-Provence One of the largest observatories in France, located on a high plateau 650 meters above sea level at St. Michel about 100 km north of Marseilles. The observatory has a 74-inch reflector.

HD Abbreviation for the **Henry Draper Catalogue.*

Hebrew calendar In Hebrew chronology, the year consisting of 12 months alternating between 29 and 30 days, making a year of 354 days. In order to conform to the solar year, a leap month is included every third year. A month begins the day the new moon is first seen. The years are counted from the time of "creation," believed by Hebrew theologians to have occurred in the year 3761 B.C.

heliacal rising The time a star will rise shortly before the sun. The heliacal rising of Sirius played a significant role in ancient Egypt by presaging the annual flooding of the Nile.

heliocentric position The position of a planet or comet in a co-ordinate system with the center of the sun at the origin.

heliocentric system A planetary system, such as the Copernican system, with the sun at the center.

heliometer An astronomical instrument consisting of a refractor with a movable split objective lens. The two sections of the lens can produce images of separate stars. The angular distance between the stars is measured with precision by moving the two sections, bringing the images of the star together.

heliostat *Siderostat.* An equatorially mounted mirror with a clock-drive that can reflect the light from a celestial body in a constant direction for an extended period of time. See: *coelostat.*

helium (He) A basic element, first discovered in the sun, second only to hydrogen as the most abundant substance in the universe. Its atomic weight is 4.003. Helium is formed in a star's interior by the fusion of four hydrogen protons, which results in an enormous release of energy. See: *energy production.*

helium stars A term once applied to spectral type B stars whose spectra contain helium lines.

hemisphere Half of the earth or half of the celestial sphere.

Henry Draper Catalogue A catalogue containing the spectra of 225,000 stars published in Volumes 91 to 100 of the *Harvard Annals.* See: *Harvard classification.*

Herbig-Haro objects Small condensation of nebulosity with a central star found in regions where interstellar matter is concentrated. They are characterized by weak continuous spectra with intense emission lines. Named after their discoverers G. H. Herbig (United States) and G. Haro (Mexico), these objects are considered by some observers to be protostars, but may in fact be much more remote. If so, they must be classified as *quasars.*

Hercules A large constellation in the northern hemisphere at 17h 20m right ascension (α = 17h 20m), 25° north declination (δ = +25°). The globular cluster M13 is located in Hercules.

Hermes An asteroid that can pass within 221,000 miles of the earth, or less than the distance between the earth and the moon.

Herschel, Sir John (1792–1871) Son of William Herschel, who continued his father's study of double stars, star clusters, and nebulae, including investigations of the sky in the southern hemisphere. His catalogue contains over 5000 objects.

Herschel, William (1738–1822) Hanoverian astronomer, the founder of stellar astronomy. Constructed reflecting telescopes and was a pioneer in modern observational astronomy. Discovered the planet Uranus (1781) as well as a great number of double stars and nebulae. Most of his life was spent in England.

Hertzsprung, Ejnar (1873–) Danish astronomer active in Germany (Göttingen and Potsdam) and the Netherlands (as professor and director of the observatory at Leiden). Has made extensive investigations of stellar luminosity and color, variable stars, double stars, etc. Hertzsprung discovered the existence of giant and dwarf stars (1905). The *Hertzsprung-Russell diagram* is named after him.

Hertzsprung gap The empty region between the giant branch and the main sequence in the Hertzsprung-Russell diagram for Population I stars.

Hertzsprung-Russell diagram A graphic representation of the classification of stars according to spectral type (color or temperature) and absolute magnitude, originated by E. Hertzsprung and H. N. Russell. On the diagram, the spectral type (color or temperature) is the abscissa, and absolute magnitude (or luminosity) is the ordinate. (If color is used as the abscissa, which is necessary with faint stars, such as stars located in distant clusters, a *color-luminosity diagram* is produced.) Star positions plotted on the H-R diagram are concentrated in some areas and totally lacking in others. The greatest number of stars falls along a diagonal line stretching from the upper left corner to the lower right in the diagram, called the *main sequence*. (The sun is located about in the middle.) Another grouping from absolute magnitude +2 to −1 and spectral type G to M forms the *giant branch* (normal giants). A limited number of supergiants are found above this branch. In the diagram, there is a space called the *Hertzsprung gap* separating the giant branch from the main sequence stars (Population I) found in the spiral arms

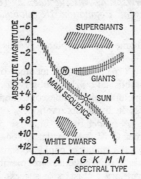

H1. Schematic Hertzsprung-Russell diagram for Population I type stars.

of our stellar system in the vicinity of the sun. The *white dwarf* stars are located in the lower left region of the diagram. The H-R diagram has a somewhat different character for the old stars (Population II) in the central regions of the galaxy, the halo, and the globular clusters. For these stars, the giant branch is divided into two parts and the Hertzsprung gap is lacking. The physical properties of a star, such as absolute magnitude, temperature, mass, etc., are correlated with its position on the H-R diagram. In addition, the H-R diagram has been significant in the study of stellar evolution (see: *cosmogony*) and the determination of distances to star clusters. (Figs. H1 and H2.)

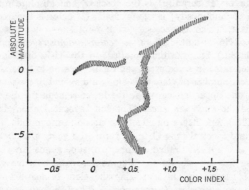

H2. Schematic Hertzsprung-Russell diagram (color-luminosity diagram) for stars of Population II (globular cluster Messier 3).

Hesperus   Greek name for the planet Venus as an evening star.

Hevelius, Johannes   (1611–1687) A member of the city council of Danzig. Established a private observatory with excellent instrumentation including large telescopes and quadrants. His primary work was in lunar observation.

hierarchy universe   A model of the universe proposed by the Swedish astronomer C. V. L. Charlier (1864–1934). According to the theory, the universe could be infinite in terms of distance and mass if the galaxies are members of clusters which in turn form larger clusters of successive higher order. The radius of each cluster is greater than the square of the radius of the preceding system of galaxies.

High-velocity stars Members of the galactic halo that are relatively near the sun but do not partake in the rotation of the spiral arms. Their high velocity as compared to the sun (greater than about 65 km/sec) is a result of the sun's motion around the center of the Milky Way (more than 250 km/sec). High-velocity stars are members of Population II (old stars). An example would be a subdwarf star.

Hipparchus (190–125 B.C.) Greek astronomer from Nicaea. Considered to be the greatest astronomer of antiquity and founder of the science of astronomy. Compiled a star catalogue containing over 1000 stars and, in addition, discovered the precession of the equinoxes.

H-I and H-II regions Regions in space containing interstellar hydrogen. The H-I regions consist of neutral hydrogen and are not visible in optical telescopes, but can be studied with radio telescopes by their radio frequency emission at 21 cm wave length. Temperatures are found to be about 100° K. H-II regions consist of ionized hydrogen surrounding very hot stars whose ultraviolet radiation ionizes the hydrogen gas. Consequently, a rearrangement of electrons and protons takes place. Electrons continuously recombine with protons, causing the hydrogen lines to emit in the visible spectrum. To study H-II regions, red filters allowing the H α line (located in the red) to pass through are used with photographic plates sensitive to red light. On these photographs, the H-II regions appear as cloudlike formations. Temperatures amount to about 10,000° K.

Hooker telescope The 100-inch reflecting telescope located at the Mt. Wilson Observatory in southern California. Prior to the Hale telescope on Mt. Palomar, the Hooker telescope was the largest in the world. Its focal length is 42 feet. The instrument was made possible through a donation by John D. Hooker of Los Angeles. The Hooker telescope has significantly increased our knowledge of galaxies and their motions.

horizon The great circle marking the intersection of the *horizontal plane* with the celestial sphere.

horizon system The co-ordinate system with the horizontal plane as the fundamental plane. The co-ordinates are altitude and azimuth.

horizontal parallax The maximum value of the *diurnal *parallax*. Horizontal parallax is the angular semi-diameter of the earth as it would appear from a celestial body.

horizontal plane The plane through the observer's position at right angles to the plumb line.

horizontal refraction The amount of refraction of a star on the horizon. Horizontal refraction is equal to about 35'.

Horned Goat Constellation in the southern hemisphere. See: *Capricornus.*

Horologium (Clock) A faint constellation in the southern hemisphere at 3h right ascension ($\alpha = 3$h), 55° south declination ($\delta = -55°$).

horoscope A schematic drawing which shows the positions of the sun, moon, and planets at the time of a person's birth. A horoscope is used by astrologers in their forecasts.

Horrebow-Talcott method A method used to determine latitude with great accuracy. Using a *zenith telescope,* two stars of nearly equal zenith distances, one just north and the other just south of the zenith, are observed to pass the meridian. The latitude of the position can be calculated from the declinations of the stars and the difference between their zenith distances.

Horse Head Nebula A dark nebula in the form of a horse's head that projects against a bright gaseous nebula. The Horse Head Nebula is located near the star Zeta (ζ) Orionis.

hour One twenty-fourth of a day.

hour angle The angle between the *hour circle* of a star and the celestial meridian. It is the arc measured westward from the meridian from 0^h to 24^h. (The hour angle measured eastward from the meridian is negative and called meridian angle.)

hour circle 1. A great circle in the equator system which passes through a specified point on the celestial sphere and the celestial pole. Declination is measured along the hour circles. 2. A graduated circle fastened to the *polar axis* of an equatorial mounting, used to show the hour angle of an object.

H regions Extensive regions of interstellar hydrogen. *H-I regions* of neutral hydrogen can be detected only with radio telescopes by observations of 21 cm radio frequency radiation. *H-II regions* of ionized hydrogen are studied optically. See: *hydrogen* and *interstellar matter.*

Hubble, Edwin (1889–1953) American astronomer. Hubble was a pioneer investigator of nebulae who found an important relationship between the dimensions of galactic nebulae and the brightness of the star responsible for the illumination. His main contribution was in the realm of the galaxies with his velocity-distance relation deduced from the large red shift of receding galaxies. He worked mainly at Mt. Wilson and Palomar observatories in California.

Hubble effect The same as the *red shift* in the spectra of galaxies.

Hubble's classification of galaxies A sequence of galaxies classified according to their structure. The sequence begins with the most spherical to the most elongated elliptical galaxies. From the elliptical group, the sequence divides into two branches of spirals, normal and barred. The classification is illustrated in Fig. H3.

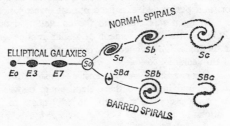

H3. Hubble's classification of galaxies.

Hubble's constant The spectra of the galaxies show a shift of the spectral lines toward the red (*red shift*) caused by the recession of the galaxies. Velocity increase is linear with respect to distance. *Hubble's constant* is the increase in velocity measured in km/sec for an increase in distance of one million parsecs. As yet, the value of Hubble's constant has not been precisely determined due to the difficulty in measuring the distances to the remote galaxies and systematic errors in the values of the radial velocities. The original value given by Hubble in the 1920s was 526 km/sec per 10^6 parsec. This amount was lowered to 180 km/sec in the 1950s, in view of the new distance scale. Latest investigations with corrections for systematic errors point to an even lower value of 90 km/sec and possibly 60 km/sec.

Hunting Dogs Constellation in the northern hemisphere. See: *Canes Venatici.*

Huygenian ocular An eyepiece that consists of two plano-convex lenses placed with the convex surfaces toward the objective. The light entering the objective produces an image between the two lenses where a cross-wire is necessary. (Fig. H4.)

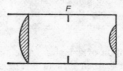

H4. Huygenian ocular.

Huygens, Christian (1629–1695) Dutch physicist and astronomer. He discovered the true nature of Saturn's rings, studied the planet Mars, introduced the pendulum as a time regulator, and performed extensive optical investigations.

Hyades An open star cluster in the constellation of *Taurus,* the Bull. By the measurement of stellar motion as well as other methods, its distance has been calculated to be about 130 light-years.

Hydra (Water Snake) An extensive constellation most of which is found in the southern hemisphere between 8h and 15h right ascension (α = 8h to 15h), 7° north to 35° south declination (δ = +7° to −35°). *Alphard,* Alpha (α) Hydrae, is the brightest star.

hydrogen The most abundant element in the universe. Chemical symbol, H; atomic weight, 1.008; density, 0.09×10^{-3}; melting point, −259°3 C.; boiling point, −252°8 C. Hydrogen is the most abundant substance in stars. The heavier elements are transmuted by the fusion of hydrogen nuclei accompanied by the release of energy. Extensive clouds of hydrogen abound in interstellar space. Hydrogen near hot stars is ionized and can be observed by optical methods (H-II regions). Neutral hydrogen is cold, invisible, and is detected with radio telescopes tuned to 21 cm wave length. (This radiation occurs when an electron changes its spin direction and emits a photon with a wave length of 21 cm.)

hydrogen ion The negative hydrogen ion (H^{-1}) is produced when a neutral hydrogen atom captures a free electron. The presence of negative hydrogen ions in the solar atmosphere is one of the principal reasons for the sun's lack of transparency, or its great opacity.

hydrogen lines The most prominent lines in the spectra of stars are the so-called *Balmer series of hydrogen lines.* In radio astronomy, the hydrogen line at 21 cm wave length is used to investigate the distribution of neutral hydrogen in the universe.

hyperbola The curve formed by points whose difference in distance from two points (foci) remains constant. The eccentricity of a hyperbola is always greater than 1.

hyperbolic mirror A mirror with a surface which is a hyperboloid of rotation, a curve formed by rotating a hyperbola about its axis. The secondary mirror of a Cassegrainian telescope is hyperbolic.

Hyperion One of the planet Saturn's satellites, discovered in 1848. Its mean distance from the planet is 920,000 miles and its period of revolution is 21.3 days.

I

IAF Abbreviation for *International Astronautical Federation.

Iapetus One of Saturn's moons, discovered by Cassini in 1671. Its mean distance from the planet is 2,200,000 miles and its period of revolution is 79.33 days.

IAU Abbreviation for *International Astronomical Union.

IAU number The designation for *radio sources (radio stars) of the *International Astronomical Union.

Icarus A minor planet whose perihelion lies within the orbit of Mercury.

IGY Abbreviation for *International Geophysical Year.

image converter An electronic apparatus whereby the image formed by an optical telescope is converted, amplified, and focused upon a fluorescent screen or a photographic plate. Attempts have been made with the electronic telescope to photograph the surfaces of the planets as well as other celestial objects. As yet, the method is not fully perfected. The electronic telescope is an example of an image converter.

image errors Aberrations occurring in optical systems. The most important are: **1.** Errors at the center of the image: (a) *chromatic aberration (in lenses), (b) *spherical aberration. **2.** Errors at the edges of the image: (a) *astigmatism, (b) curvature of field, (c) *coma, (d) distortion, (e) vignetting.

immersion The disappearance of one celestial body behind another (e.g., a satellite enters the shadow of a planet and is eclipsed); the disappearance of a star behind the moon or a planet. See: *occultation*.

impulse   The product of a particle's mass times its velocity.

inclination   One of the *elements of an orbit*. The angle formed by the plane of the orbit of a comet or a planet and the plane of the ecliptic.

index   An indicator or pointer attached to a graduated scale.

index arm   A movable arm (**alidade*) which is pivoted on a graduated arc. Found on the sextant and other angle-measuring instruments.

index error   An error caused by the improper positioning of the vernier with respect to the graduated arc. Index error must be carefully determined and corrected.

index of refraction   See: *refraction*.

Indian   A constellation in the southern hemisphere. See: *Indus*.

Indus   (Indian) A faint constellation in the southern hemisphere at 21h right ascension ($\alpha = 21$h), 50° to 70° south declination ($\delta = -50°$ to $-70°$).

inertia   The property of a body to remain in its state of rest or of uniform motion unless acted upon by an external force. The resistance to such a change of state is called inertia.

inferior culmination   The time interval when a star in its diurnal journey crosses the meridian between the celestial pole and the north point of the horizon.

inferior planets   Older designation for the planets Mercury and Venus, whose orbits are located within the orbit of the earth.

infrared radiation   Electromagnetic radiation at wave lengths beyond the red portion of the visible spectrum located from 0.75μ to 1 mm, or 10^{-4} cm to 10^{-1} cm, or about 10^4 Å to 10^7 Å.

inner planets   The planets that are closer to the sun than the asteroids, i.e., Mercury, Venus, Earth, and Mars.

insolation   The solar energy received by the earth.

instrument   See: *astronomical instruments*.

interference   A phenomenon occurring when waves of similar frequency are combined. The waves will either reinforce or interfere with each other depending upon phase difference. If the relative phase difference is one half wave length, the waves can be entirely nullified. When monochromatic light is passed through two adjacent, narrow slits, a pattern of light and dark fringes will result depending upon whether or not the difference between the rays is an odd or even number of half-waves. The wave length of the light is determined with high precision from the measurement of the interference image.

interference filter Filters constructed upon the principle of the interference of light. Using these filters, narrow spectral regions are isolated. Interference filters are used to take monochromatic photographs of the sun in the light of one spectral line such as Hα.

interferometer An instrument constructed on the principle of the interference of light which is used to measure small angles. In optical astronomy, A. A. Michelson, of the United States, used an interferometer to measure the distances between close binary stars, and also measured the diameters of a few giant stars. The interferometer principle is used extensively in radio astronomy to increase resolving power.

intergalactic matter Matter in space between the galaxies. Such matter has been observed in the form of bridges between galaxies.

International Astronautical Federation (IAF) A union of about 40 national societies which contribute toward the support of space exploration. IAF was organized in 1950.

International Astronomical Union (IAU) An international association of the world's astronomers founded in Brussels in 1919. It is divided into about 40 groups that cover the entire field of astronomical investigation. Conferences are held every third year with periodic symposiums to discuss current astronomical problems. The first conference was held in Rome in 1922, and the latest in Hamburg, Germany, in 1964. At present, the IAU has about 1000 members and issues the *Transactions of the International Astronomical Union.*

international date line The 180th meridian of longitude from Greenwich passing across the Pacific Ocean. A person traveling around the earth in an easterly direction will have gained a day upon his return to the starting point. Conversely, a day is lost if a person travels around the earth in a westerly direction. To avoid this situation, the 180th meridian was selected by international agreement as the line where the date will change. Although local time is the same on both sides of the line, the western side of the boundary is one day ahead of the eastern side. A mariner crossing the international date line from east to west will advance the date one day. When a crossing is made from west to east, the same day is counted twice.

International Geophysical Year   Abbreviated IGY, a world-wide scientific effort to study geophysical phenomena and their cosmic origin through the co-operation of over 50 nations from July 1957 to January 1959. The first *artificial satellites* were launched during the IGY.

interplanetary gas   Very tenuous gas (mainly neutral and ionized hydrogen) that exists within extensive regions of the solar system. See: *interplanetary matter*.

interplanetary matter   Matter in space between the planets. In addition to dust, space contains protons, electrons, and other particles ejected from the sun. The outer portions of the *solar corona* and the *zodiacal light* are evidences of the presence of interplanetary matter.

interstellar   Between the stars.

interstellar absorption   The absorption of light by interstellar matter during passage through space. Interstellar space contains minute particles of matter that absorb and scatter the light from the more distant stars. Not only is the light dimmed, but also reddened since blue and violet light are scattered more than red. See: *color excess*. In determining distances in space, this absorption must be considered. The stars seem to be at greater distances than they actually are as a result of absorption. The distribution of distant galaxies shows that interstellar absorption is concentrated in the plane of the Milky Way in a belt between 10° and 40° wide, where galaxies are hidden from view by the intervening matter. See: *zone of avoidance*.

interstellar gas   Gaseous matter found in space between the stars. See: *interstellar matter* and *H regions*.

interstellar lines   Absorption lines that can be observed in the spectra of stars but that do not share the spectral shift caused by the motion of the stars. These stationary lines are the result of gas clouds located between the stars and the earth. Since interstellar gas clouds are of low density, the interstellar lines are sharp and distinct, and are easily distinguished from the lines produced in the spectra of the stars. The distances to the stars can be estimated by the intensity of the lines. Sometimes, several gas clouds are found moving at different velocities in the line of sight, dividing the spectral lines into several components. Interstellar lines identify the elements contained in the cosmic gas, including neutral and ionized calcium, sodium, titanium, potassium, and iron, as well as compounds such as cyanogen and hydrides.

interstellar magnetic field Magnetic fields in interstellar space believed to exist because of *interstellar polarization* and the peculiar filamentary structure of many galactic nebulae.

interstellar matter Substance found in space between the stars primarily in the direction of the plane of the Milky Way. Predominantly hydrogen, the gas appears in the neutral (H-I region) and ionized (H-II region) states. The neutral hydrogen can be studied by means of radio astronomy, which has revealed that hydrogen clouds follow the Milky Way's spiral structure. The ionized hydrogen can be studied by optical methods. See: *galactic nebulae*. In addition to hydrogen clouds, cosmic dust can be observed as *dark nebulae*. Interstellar matter has been observed in other star systems (spiral galaxies) concentrated in the spiral arms as in the Milky Way. The spectra of distant stars reveal *interstellar lines* which are produced by tenuous gas clouds located between us and the stars. Among the substances identified are calcium, sodium, potassium, hydrocarbon compounds, and cyanogen.

interstellar polarization Starlight polarized in passing through clouds of cosmic dust. Discovered in 1949 by Hall and Hiltner of the United States, this phenomenon is caused by elongated particles that may be magnetic. As a result of interstellar magnetic fields, gravitation, or radiation pressure, the particles are oriented in one direction, causing polarization to take place.

interstellar space Space between the stars.

intra-Mercurial planets Hypothetical planets once believed to occupy orbits between the planet Mercury and the sun. In spite of intensive observations, including those made during total eclipses of the sun, no intra-Mercurial planets have been found.

intrinsic variables Stars that are variable in light because of internal physical conditions.

invar An iron-nickel alloy with a negligible coefficient of expansion. Invar parts are used in pendulums and astronomical instruments such as the Schmidt telescope in order to make the distance of the photographic plate from the mirror independent of temperature variations.

Io The innermost Galilean moon of Jupiter. Its mean distance from the planet is about 262,000 miles and its period of revolution is 1.77 days.

ionization The formation of ions. Atoms exposed to short-wave radiation will become ionized. When electrons are freed, the atom becomes positively charged. Generally, matter within the stars and nebulae is strongly ionized. A singly ionized atom has lost one of its electrons, a doubly ionized atom has lost two, etc.

ionization potential The energy, expressed in electron volts, that is required to free an electron from a neutral atom.

ionosphere The region of the earth's atmosphere between 45 miles and 350 miles altitude where ionized atoms occur. The ionized layers of the ionosphere (Heaviside, Appleton) reflect radio waves longer than about 15 meters.

IQSY The International Years of the Quiet Sun (1964 and 1965) when the sun was in minimum activity. Through international co-operation by several observatories all over the world, solar and geophysical phenomena were studied intensively.

iris diaphragm photometer A photometer containing an iris diaphragm to regulate the amount of light entering the instrument. The size of the diaphragm is varied by a series of thin, movable metal plates controlled by a ring. Several types are in use. Special instruments have been constructed for careful measurement of photographic images in determining stellar magnitudes.

irradiation An optical illusion which causes a bright object to appear larger than it should. For example, the bright, thin crescent appears to overlap the dark edge of the moon at new moon phase.

irregular galaxy An asymmetrical galaxy that lacks a specific structure.

irregular nebulae Bright nebulae lacking symmetry. See: *galactic nebulae* and *nebulae*.

irregular variables Variable stars with uneven light variations.

island universe A poetic term for the Milky Way and other galaxies when characterized as islands of stars in immeasurable space.

isophotes Lines connecting points of equal intensity. Isophotes are used in the study of light distribution in nebulae, or the intensity of cosmic radio frequency radiation.

isotopes Basic elements with atoms of the same atomic number (same number of protons) but of different mass (different number of neutrons). Almost all substances consist of a mixture of isotopes.

J

Jacob's Staff   Golden Yardarm. **1.** An early name for the three stars in the *belt of Orion*. **2.** A primitive instrument for measuring angles, consisting of a graduated rod with a shorter crossbar. Used as an early navigational instrument. (Fig. J1.)

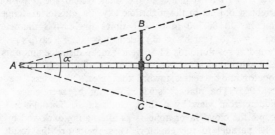

J1. Jacob's Staff.

Jeans, Sir James   (1877–1946) English mathematician, physicist, and astronomer who studied theoretical problems in astrophysics and the origin of the solar system. He was the author of many popular books on astronomy.

jiggle-camera technique   See: *Schraffiercassette method.*

Jodrell Bank   A radio astronomy observatory with one of the largest steerable parabolic antennae, 250 feet in diameter. The observatory is located in Cheshire not far from Manchester, England.

Jovian planets   (From the Latin name of Jupiter.) See: **giant planets.*

Julian calendar   The calendar established by Julius Caesar in the year 46 B.C. Since the tropical year contains about 365¼ days, a cycle of 4 years was established with 3 years of 365 days and a fourth, a *leap year,* of 366 days. The year began on January 1. The Julian calendar lacked complications and remained unchanged for 1600 years. However, the year is actually 365.2422 days and an error of almost 8 days will accumulate in 1000 years. To correct the error and to avoid the problem in the future, the *Gregorian calendar* was established in 1582 upon the recommendation of Pope Gregory XIII.

Julian day A dating system that is independent of months and years. Proposed by Joseph Scaliger in 1582 and named for his father Julius, the Julian day is the number of days that have elapsed since 12:00 noon, January 1, 4713 B.C. Basically, the Julian day is used to determine the epoch, the time of maximum or minimum of a variable star. January 1, 1960 = JD 2,436,935.

Juno An asteroid discovered in 1804. Its diameter is about 150 miles.

Jupiter The largest planet in the solar system and one of the brightest objects in the nighttime sky. Its equatorial diameter amounts to 88,700 miles (11 times the earth's diameter); mass = 318 (earth's = 1); density = 0.24 (earth's = 1). Period of revolution is 11.86 years; mean distance amounts to 5.20 astronomical units. Period of rotation is 9h 50m at the equator and increases toward the poles. Oblateness is equal to 0.065. The planet's surface cannot be seen since it is hidden from view by a thick cloud layer. Through a telescope, the cloud layer appears as alternating dark and bright belts parallel to the equator. These belts are the result of swirling eddies in the atmosphere caused by Jupiter's rapid rotation. Besides the equatorial belts, the so-called *red spot* can be observed in the southern hemisphere periodically changing in intensity and size. The nature of this atmospheric phenomenon is unknown. In addition to hydrogen and helium, Jupiter's atmosphere contains largely ammonia and methane. The cloud layer probably consists of ammonia crystals. The temperature amounts to about −130° C. Opinions are divided regarding the interior constitution of Jupiter. According to one theory, a thick atmosphere of hydrogen, nitrogen, and methane, with clouds of ammonia, covers a layer of ice of a thickness equal to 40% of Jupiter's radius. Below this ice layer lies a solid core of metals and rock. According to another theory, Jupiter consists almost entirely of hydrogen (80%) and helium that is gaseous in the outer regions but changes to the liquid and solid state toward the center as a result of increased pressure. Consequently, the planet would lack an iron-nickel core. Through radio astronomy techniques, Van Allen type belts have been detected. Jupiter has 12 satellites, of which the four brightest are the Galilean moons, discovered by Galileo in 1610.

Jupiter, moons of The planet Jupiter has 12 satellites. The four brightest, Io, Europa, Ganymede, and Callisto, make up the *Galilean moons* which were discovered by Galileo in 1610. These satellites have diameters ranging from 1750 to 3220 miles. The other eight satellites have diameters between 15 and 35 miles (except Satellites V and VI with diameters greater than 100 miles) and are therefore exceedingly faint. The periods of revolution for the Galilean satellites range from 1d 18h (Io) to 16d 16h (Callisto). Jupiter V, the closest satellite to Jupiter, has a period of revolution of almost 12 hours. The periods for Satellites VI to XII range from 250 to 760 days. The mean distances from the planet are: Jupiter V, 113,000 miles; Io (I), 262,000 miles; Europa (II), 417,000 miles; Ganymede (III), 666,000 miles; Callisto (IV), 1,170,000 miles. The distances for the remaining satellites range from 7,120,000 to 14,700,000 miles.

Jupiter's family of comets A number of comets "captured" by the planet Jupiter so that their present orbits conform to the orbit of Jupiter. At the present time, Jupiter's known family of comets contains about 40 members.

K

Kant's hypothesis *Nebular hypothesis.* The hypothesis of the origin of the solar system proposed by I. Kant in 1755. According to this theory, the solar system began as a nebula of tenuous gas and cosmic dust. Particles collided and gradually, under the influence of gravitation, the condensing gas took the form of a disc. Larger bodies formed, moving in circular orbits around a central condensation (the sun). Gradually the nebula dissolved into smaller nebulae that formed the planets. In recent years, there has been a revival of Kant's hypothesis, though in greatly modified form. See: *cosmogony.*

Kapteyn, Jacobus Cornelis (1851–1922) Dutch astronomer. He was a pioneer in the investigation of the motions and distribution of the stars.

Kapteyn's method A numerical method proposed by J. C. Kapteyn to derive the distribution of the stars in space. In this method, space is considered to be divided into concentric shells centered at the sun. The thickness of each shell was selected so that stars with the same absolute magnitude appear one magnitude fainter in each successive shell away from the sun.

Kapteyn's selected areas Two hundred six small areas evenly divided across the sky within which the size, color, spectral type, motion, etc., of the stars down to the faintest possible magnitude is to be determined photographically. To these, a number of areas of special interest were added. A statistical investigation of these areas has revealed data regarding the structure of the Milky Way. The plan was proposed by J. C. Kapteyn in 1906 and is on its way toward completion through the joint efforts of many observatories.

Kapteyn's star streams Through a comprehensive study of stellar motion, J. C. Kapteyn discovered a tendency of the stars to move with respect to the solar neighborhood in two streams toward and away from the center of the Milky Way Galaxy.

K corona One of the components of the solar corona composed of a cloud of free electrons which surrounds the sun as an extensive atmospheric shroud. Temperatures are on the order of one million degrees. The sun's light is scattered by the electrons and is polarized. See: *solar corona.*

Keel Part of the constellation *Argo* in the southern hemisphere. See: *Carina.*

Kellner ocular A positive ocular consisting of a convex lens and a plano-convex lens. The convex surfaces are turned toward one another.

Kelvin contraction The stage in the development of a star where the star is formed through the contraction of a diffuse nebula. Radiation takes place at the expense of the potential energy lost during contraction. At the same time, temperatures within the star increase and the star moves from the low temperature region in the *Hertzsprung-Russell diagram* to the main sequence.

Kelvin scale (°K.) Temperature measured from absolute zero (−273° C., or −460° F.). See: *absolute temperature.*

Kennelly-Heaviside layer Electrically charged layer in the earth's atmosphere at an altitude of 65 miles from the surface which reflects radio waves (*E layer*).

Kepler, Johannes (1571=1630) German astronomer and pupil of Tycho Brahe. As a result of the many careful observations of the planet Mars by Tycho Brahe at Hren, Kepler derived his three famous laws of planetary motion. Kepler also made important contributions to optics.

Kepler's equation An equation that expresses the relationship between the eccentric *anomaly* and the mean anomaly in an elliptical orbit. Kepler's equation serves an important function in determining orbits.

Kepler's laws **1.** Each planetary orbit is an ellipse with the sun situated at one of the focal points. **2.** The straight line joining the sun and a planet (radius vector) will sweep equal areas in the same time interval (the *law of equal areas*). These two laws were published in 1609. **3.** The squares of the periods of any two planets are proportional to the cubes of their distances from the sun (1619). These laws preceded **Newton's law of gravitation.* They have played an important role in the determination of planetary orbits and the derivation of the relative distance of the planets from the sun (third law). (Fig. K1.)

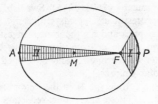

K1. Kepler's second law, law of equal areas: Area I = Area II.

Kepler's Nova A so-called new star that burst forth in Ophiuchus in October 1604 and was observed with the unaided eye for 18 months until March 1606. Studied by Kepler, it was probably a *supernova*. See: *exploding stars.*

Kepler's telescope The **astronomical telescope.* A telescope constructed by J. Kepler containing two positive lenses, an objective and ocular.

kiloparsec A distance of 1000 parsecs, or 3260 light-years.

Kimura effect An apparent change in latitude by $0\overset{''}{.}1$ in a period of one year not caused by "variations in latitude." The phenomenon, discovered by H. Kimura of Japan, is attributed to periodic changes in atmospheric refraction.

kinetic energy Energy of motion. The kinetic energy of a body is equal to one half the product of its mass and the square of its velocity.

kinetic theory of gases According to this theory, the molecules of a gas are in continuous motion obeying the law of kinetic energy.

Kirchhoff's law According to this law, at a given temperature all substances are able to absorb the same radiations that they emit.

Kirkwood gaps Gaps in the asteroid belt where periods of revolution would be equal to a fraction of Jupiter's period (½, ⅓, ⅖). The gaps are the result of perturbations by Jupiter of the asteroid orbits.

Kitt Peak National Observatory The American National Observatory in Arizona on a mountain peak 6800 feet above sea level. The observatory has a 36-inch photoelectric telescope and an 80-inch stellar telescope has recently been installed. A solar telescope has been constructed with an 80-inch heliostat which reflects sunlight down a 500-foot shaft to a 60-inch-long focus mirror. The solar image formed is about 34 inches in diameter.

Klingenstierna, Samuel (1698–1765) Swedish mathematician and physicist, professor at Uppsala University. Klingenstierna was devoted to optics and his theoretical investigations led to the construction of the *achromatic objective* by J. Dollond. He was a writer on astronomy and developed a method for determining solar eclipses.

K stars Stars of spectral type K in the *Harvard classification* of stellar spectra. These are yellow-red stars (temperatures about 5000° C.), with intense metallic lines and the beginning of molecular absorption bands in the spectra.

K term An effect in the radial velocities of O and B stars detected by Kapteyn and Frost in 1910 and more thoroughly studied by Campbell (1911) and later by many others. When corrected for the sun's motion, the average value for the radial velocities of these stars is not reduced to zero but is +4 to +5 km/sec. Unsuccessful attempts have been made to explain the effect as a systematic error in the measurement of the wave lengths of the spectral lines used in determining radial velocity or as an *Einstein effect,* the displacement of spectral lines by the gravitational fields of massive stars.

L

Lacerta (Lizard) A small constellation in the northern hemisphere at 22h 20m right ascension (α = 22h 20m), 45° north declination (δ = +45°).

Lagrange, Joseph Louis (1736–1813) Italian-born French mathematician and astronomer. Lagrange made original contributions to mechanics. In celestial mechanics, he studied the three-body problem.

Lagrangian point In a special example of the *problem of three bodies* theoretically treated by *Lagrange,* a minor planet will form an equilateral triangle (see: *Trojan group*) with the planet Jupiter and the sun. As a result of Jupiter's perturbations, such asteroids often oscillate around one vertex of the triangle, which is called a Lagrangian point. In the general case, there are three more solutions to the problem with points that lie on a line joining the two major bodies.

Laika The name of the dog that was placed in orbit aboard the Russian Sputnik II on November 3, 1957.

Laplace, nebular hypothesis of Laplace assumes that the sun was surrounded by an extensive tenuous nebula stretching far beyond the boundaries of the solar system prior to the birth of the planets. By a cooling process the gas sphere contracted, increasing the speed of rotation. Gradually, a critical speed was reached when the centrifugal effect became equal to gravitational attraction and a ring formed around the equator of the sun. The ring separated from the contracting nebula. After the first ring was formed, the process was repeated, producing smaller rings. The rings were not permanent but condensed to form the planets and satellites.—Later investigations have shown that the process is not theoretically possible. See: *Roche's model.* Today, the hypothesis has only historical value.

Laplace, Pierre Simon de (1749–1827) French mathematician and astronomer. Laplace pioneered in celestial mechanics and, in 1796, formulated his famous nebular hypothesis for the origin of the solar system. See: *Laplace, nebular hypothesis of.*

Large Magellanic Cloud The larger of the two *Magellanic Clouds* located in the southern hemisphere.

laser A type of *maser* producing coherent light.

lateral motion The component of a star's motion at right angles to the line of sight. See: *proper motion; tangential velocity.*

lateral refraction A component of *atmospheric refraction* which is perpendicular to vertical refraction. As a rule, only vertical refraction is considered. If the earth were a sphere surrounded by concentric layers of air of decreasing density, only vertical refraction would take place. Since these conditions do not exist, a very slight horizontal bending, called lateral refraction, occurs.

latitude The co-ordinate that defines the angular distance of a
celestial body from a fundamental plane. **1.** CELESTIAL LATI-
TUDE. The angular distance β between a celestial body and
the ecliptic. **2.** GALACTIC LATITUDE. The angular distance b
from the plane of the Milky Way. **3.** GEOGRAPHIC LATITUDE.
The angular distance φ between the plane of the equator and
the observer's zenith. (See Fig. L1.) **4.** GEOCENTRIC LATI-

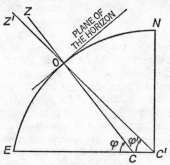

L1. Latitude.
φ = *geographic*
φ' = *geocentric*

TUDE. The angle φ' at the center of the earth between the
observer's position and the plane of the equator. Since the
earth is not a perfect sphere, φ and φ' do not coincide. **5.**
HELIOCENTRIC LATITUDE. The celestial latitude of a planet or
comet measured from the center of the sun. **6.** HELIOGRAPHIC
LATITUDE. Angular distance on the sun north and south of the
sun's equator.

law of equal areas Kepler's second law, which states that the
radius vector joining a planet and the sun will describe equal
areas in equal times. See: *Kepler's laws.*

leap day A day added to the year. See: *leap year.*

leap month An extra month added to the lunar calendar every
third year to make the lunar year and the seasons coincide.
A leap month is used in the Hebrew calendar.

leap year A year of 366 days. Since the tropical year contains
almost 365¼ days, in his calendar reform in 46 B.C., Julius
Caesar decreed that every fourth year shall be a leap year
and contain 366 days. See: *Julian calendar.* However, the
year is 11m 14s shorter than 365¼ days, making the Julian

calendar too long. The error was corrected through the Papal
Bull of Gregory XIII (1582) whereby the century years di-
visible by 400 shall be leap years and contain 366 days. See:
Gregorian calendar.

Leavitt, Henrietta S. (1868–1921) American astronomer at
the Harvard Observatory. She discovered the *period-luminosity* relationship of cepheid variable stars.

lenses Spherically curved pieces of glass or quartz with refractive properties, utilized in the construction of optical instruments. Lenses are divided into two main types: positive, or
converging, lenses and negative, or *diverging,* lenses. Converging lenses include *double convex, plano-convex,* and
concave-convex. Diverging lenses are called *double concave,
plano-concave,* and *convex-concave.* Various kinds of objectives and oculars have been constructed by combining the
different types of lenses. (Fig. L2.)

$$A \quad B \quad C \quad D \quad E \quad F$$

L2. *Various types of lenses:*
   Positive lenses:
      A. Double convex
      B. Plano-convex
      C. Concave-convex
   Negative lenses:
      D. Double concave
      E. Plano-concave
      F. Convex-concave

Leo (Lion) One of the most conspicuous constellations in the
northern hemisphere, at 10h 30m right ascension (α = 10h
30m), 15° north declination (δ = +15°). Leo is a constellation of the Zodiac. The star Alpha (α) Leonis, or Regulus,
is of the first magnitude.

Leo Minor (Lesser Lion) A faint constellation in the northern
hemisphere at 10h 20m right ascension (α = 10h 20m), 35°
north declination (δ = +35°).

Leonids A meteor shower occurring between November 12
and 17 with its radiant located in the constellation of *Leo.*
The Leonids consist of the remains of Comet 1866 I (Tempel's comet).

Lepus (Hare) A small constellation in the southern hemisphere at 5h 30m right ascension (α = 5h 30m), 20° south declination (δ = −20°).

Leverrier, Urbain Jean Joseph (1811–1877) French astronomer and mathematician. Most famous for his epoch-making investigations of the perturbations of the orbit of Uranus which led to the discovery of the planet Neptune (1846).

Lexell's comet A comet discovered by Messier in 1770. When Lexell determined its orbit and period of 5.5 years, he found that the short-period comet had been captured by the planet Jupiter in 1767. In 1779, the comet was to háve returned but could not be found. Lexell showed that Jupiter changed the orbit of the comet at its last approach to a period of at least 16 years. The comet was never seen again and has probably disintegrated.

Libra (Scales) A small constellation in the southern hemisphere at 15h 30m right ascension (α = 15h 30m), 15° south declination (δ = −15°); a sign of the Zodiac.

libration The apparent and real irregularities of the moon's motions revealing 4/7 of its surface although the same side of the moon always faces the earth. **1.** GEOMETRICAL LIBRATIONS. (a) *Libration in longitude.* Since the moon's rotation is uniform and its orbital velocity is variable, a small part of the eastern limb or western limb is revealed at different times. This libration amounts to a maximum value of about 8° in both directions. (b) *Libration in latitude.* Since the axis of the moon is not perpendicular to the moon's orbital plane but is tipped 6½°, the north and south poles will be alternately inclined toward the earth during a lunation. (c) *Diurnal libration.* As a result of the earth's rotation, an observer will see more of the western limb when the moon is rising than he will when the moon is setting. This libration equals the moon's parallax and amounts to about 1°. **2.** PHYSICAL LIBRATION. An irregularity in the rotation of the moon caused by the gravitational attraction of the earth on the equatorial bulge on the moon.

Lick Observatory One of the world's largest observatories, located on Mt. Hamilton (4200 feet above sea level) south of San Francisco, California. Donated by James Lick, of San Francisco, in 1874, the observatory was dedicated in 1888. It houses the world's second largest refractor, the Lick refractor, with a 36-inch objective, and the second largest reflector, with a diameter of 120 inches. Other instruments include the Crossley reflector (36-inch mirror) and a double astrograph.

light   Visible electromagnetic radiation; it travels at 186,300 miles/sec in a vacuum. The color of light is dependent upon wave length. For example, red light has a wave length of 0.0007 mm, and violet light 0.0004 mm. Wave length is expressed in Ångstrom units, Å = 0.0000001 mm. See: *electromagnetic spectrum*.

light curve   A graph of a variable star's change in brightness (expressed in magnitude) with respect to time. See: *variable stars*.

light-gathering power   The increase in the brightness of a star's image in proportion to the square of the diameter of the mirror or objective. The light-gathering power of the 200-inch Hale telescope at Mt. Palomar Observatory in the United States is about one million times greater than the human eye. With respect to surface brightness (moon, planets, nebulae, etc.) light-gathering power depends upon the square of the *magnifying power*.

light pressure   The pressure that light exerts on minute particles. See: *radiation pressure*.

light-time effect   The time required for light to reach the earth from a celestial body. Because the earth is in motion around the sun, the distance to a remote light source continuously varies so that light requires a greater or lesser time to reach the earth. Light requires 8.3 minutes to cover the distance between the earth and the sun. The amount of variation in time for a star depends upon the star's ecliptic co-ordinates, with ±8.3 minutes as maximum values. Corrections in time must always be made with short-period variable-star predictions. The corrected time is called "heliocentric" time.

light-year   An astronomical measurement of distance equal to the distance that light travels in one year; a distance of 5.86×10^{12} miles, or 0.307 parsecs.

limb   1. The edge of the apparent disc of a celestial body. 2. A graduated arc which is attached to instruments for measuring angles.

limb brightening   The increase in the intensity of radio frequency radiation toward the sun's limb. Investigations of the intensity distribution of radio radiation from the quiet sun in various frequencies and at different regions of the sun's surface show that a decrease in intensity occurs from the center for short waves (less than 5 cm) as well as long waves (over

1 meter). This decrease in intensity is similar to the *limb darkening* seen in optical telescopes. However, in the middle regions of the sun outward toward the limb, the intensity of radio radiation increases, causing a "limb brightening" since the radiation from the limb must pass through a greater thickness of the high-temperature corona than the radiation emitted from the center of the solar disc.

limb darkening The decrease in the intensity of light from the center to the edge of the sun. This darkening occurs more rapidly for blue than for red light. The phenomenon is due to the greater depth observed at the sun's center where the light originates from hotter layers than the light from the limb which is emitted from the higher and therefore cooler layers of the photosphere.

limiting magnitude The faintest magnitude observed through an astronomical telescope or on a photographic plate, which is dependent upon the diameter of the objective, the photographic emulsion, and the exposure as well as upon the atmospheric conditions.

line of equinoxes The line of intersection between the plane of the ecliptic and the plane of the celestial equator. The line of equinoxes meets the celestial sphere at the *vernal* and *autumnal equinoxes*.

line of nodes 1. The line joining the nodes of the moon's orbit, or the points of intersection between the moon's orbit and the ecliptic. 2. The intersection between the plane of the orbit of a planet or comet with the plane of the ecliptic.

line of sight A straight line from the eye of the observer to the celestial body.

line profile A graph showing how the intensity of light varies with wave length across the spectrum. A study of the line profile reveals the number of atoms required to produce a spectral line, a star's rotation and magnetism, and other physical conditions. See: *effective wave lengths.*

line spectrum The spectrum emitted by a luminous gas, consisting of a series of separate lines which are characteristic for each element (*emission spectrum*). If the radiation from a light source emitting a continuous spectrum passes through a gas of lower temperature, narrow dark lines are found in the continuous spectrum that correspond with the lines of the emission spectrum of the gas (*absorption spectrum*).

Linné A lunar crater located in the Mare Serenitatis. In the first half of the 19th century, Linné was observed as a very conspicuous object and was seen for the last time in 1843. A careful examination of the area was made in 1866, revealing a bright spot in place of the crater. Possibly a "moonquake" caused Linné to collapse sometime between 1843 and 1866.

Lion Constellation in the northern hemisphere. See: *Leo.*

lithosiderite A type of iron meteorite. See: *meteorites.*

Lizard Small constellation in the northern hemisphere. See: *Lacerta.*

local civil time See: *local time.*

local cluster A condensation of stars near the sun.

local constant A correction which must be made to the side-real time given in an ephemeris, such as Greenwich mean noon, to find the sidereal time for local mean noon. The local constant is easily calculated from the longitude of the position.

Local Group A group of galaxies, of which the Milky Way is a member, that forms a small cluster. The Local Group contains 17 members including the Andromeda Galaxy. The group extends about 2 million to 3 million light-years.

local time The measurement of mean solar time for a particular position.

longitude 1. CELESTIAL LONGITUDE. A co-ordinate in the *ecliptic system* measured from the vernal equinox along the ecliptic toward east from 0° to 360°. 2. HELIOCENTRIC LONGITUDE. Celestial longitude measured in a co-ordinate system with the origin located in the center of the sun. 3. GALACTIC LONGITUDE. A co-ordinate in the galactic system. See: *astronomical co-ordinates.* 4. GEOGRAPHIC LONGITUDE. A co-ordinate system on the surface of the earth. The angle between the meridian passing through a position and the prime meridian (Greenwich) measured east and west from 0° to 180°.

longitude of the perihelion See: *perihelion, argument of the.*

long-period cepheids See: *cepheids.*

long-period variable stars *Variable stars* (often *pulsating*), also known as *Mira* type stars after *Mira Ceti,* the first long-period star discovered. Periods are more than 100 days and are usually between 200 and 400 days in length. The light curve of a long-period variable is similar to that of a cepheid star but with a greater amplitude. With respect to spectral classification, the long-period variables are generally types M, R, and N. They are, therefore, extremely red in color with a deeper red color during minimum. Many complicated spectral phenomena occur in conjunction with the light variations. These stars belong to Population I as well as Population II, with the Population II stars having shorter periods. Among these variables there are also those having *irregular variations* in brightness. About 2000 long-period variables are known. (Fig. L3.)

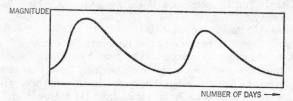

L3. Light curve of a long-period variable (Mira Ceti).

Lorentz-Fitzgerald contraction A hypothesis formulated by Fitzgerald in 1893 and applied to electromagnetic phenomena by Lorentz in 1895. According to the hypothesis, all bodies in motion will contract along the direction of travel.

Lowell, Percival (1855–1916) American astronomer who established the Lowell Observatory, Flagstaff, Arizona, where he made extensive observation of Mars. He strongly defended the existence on Mars of canals which he believed were created by intelligent beings.

luminosity A star's *absolute* brightness, usually expressed in magnitude. The absolute magnitude is the apparent magnitude a star would have if it were located at a distance of 10 parsecs (32.6 light-years).

luminosity classes Classification of stars according to absolute magnitude (luminosity) and spectral type (color) by Morgan, Keenan, and Kellman at Yerkes Observatory in the United States. Temperature classification closely follows the *Harvard classification while the luminosity values are indicated by Roman numerals as shown below:

Ia—supergiants of high luminosity
Ib—supergiants of low luminosity
II—luminous giant stars
III—normal giant stars
IV—subgiants with less luminosity than normal giants
V—main sequence stars in the Hertzsprung-Russell diagram

luminosity criteria The property of certain lines and bands in stellar spectra to be affected by the luminosity of the stars. The intensity of these lines indicates the luminosity of a star. The atmospheres of giant stars are significantly less dense than the atmospheres of dwarf stars of the same spectral class, causing elements to ionize more readily in the giant stars. Certain lines such as ionized strontium are more intense in the giant stars than in the dwarfs. The spectral lines of neutral substances approach maximum intensity in the dwarfs. The intensity of the lines is a measure of the star's absolute magnitude (luminosity). Spectral bands such as cyanogen are also used as luminosity criteria.

luminosity effects Physical conditions in the atmospheres of stars caused by their absolute magnitudes (luminosities) observed as differences in the intensity of certain spectral lines and bands. See: *luminosity criteria.*

luminosity function The distribution of stars according to absolute magnitude. Significant in statistical investigation such as sampling of the relative number of stars of a certain absolute magnitude in a given volume of space.

Luna The moon.

lunar craters See: *craters, lunar.*

lunar cycle See: *metonic cycle.*

lunar distance Angular distance between the moon's center and the sun, a planet, or bright star near the moon. These observations were used in navigation to determine longitude prior to accurate chronometers.

lunar eclipse The darkening of the moon which occurs when the moon enters the umbra of the earth's shadow at full moon phase. An eclipse can occur only when the moon is full and is near one of the orbit's nodes. The eclipse will be total if the entire moon enters the umbra. If only a part of the moon enters the umbra, the eclipse will be partial. During totality, the moon takes on a copper-colored hue, caused by sunlight pass-

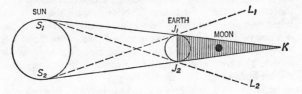

L4. Eclipse of the moon. J_1KJ_2 = umbra.

ing through the earth's atmosphere with short-wave, blue light absorbed more than the longer wave length red light. This red light is refracted into the earth's shadow by the atmosphere where it falls on the moon. A lunar eclipse can be seen from every point on the earth's surface where the moon is above the horizon. A similar eclipse will take place in the same series after a period of 18 years and 11 days (the *Saros*). (Fig. L4.)

lunarite   A substance of unknown composition that supposedly forms the bright areas of the moon's surface (mountain ranges, etc.).

lunar probes   Attempts have been made at various times by the United States and the Soviet Union to launch lunar probes. On January 2, 1959, the Russians launched a lunar probe, Lunik I, called Mechta, which passed the moon at a distance of about 2000 miles and thereafter went into orbit around the sun. Lunik II started from earth on September 12, 1959, and reached the moon after a journey of 35 hours, crashing in the vicinity of Mare Tranquilitatis. Lunik III was launched on October 4, 1959, photographed the far side of the moon and returned to the vicinity of earth where the photographs were telemetered back to the earth. The first American lunar probe to impact the moon, Ranger IV, crashed to the moon on April 26, 1962. Lunar probes represent a new method of studying the moon. Exploring the moon by probes makes a study of the moon's magnetic field and radiation possible, and on July 31, 1964, the American lunar probe (spacecraft) Ranger VII transmitted more than 4300 excellent pictures, by means of six TV cameras, of the surface of the moon near the lunar crater Guericke. The nearest close-up was taken from an elevation of a few hundred feet above the surface and objects with a diameter of a few feet were clearly distinguished. Even better results were obtained from Rangers VIII and IX, sent up in early 1965; the photographs transmitted by Ranger IX, which landed near the center of the great crater Alphonsus, were the most detailed ever taken, and show very minute features. Then, in the summer of 1965, the Russians launched their probe Zond III, which sent back further pictures of the moon's averted hemisphere. The Zond photographs were of far better quality than those obtained from Lunik III six years before.

lunar rays   A system of bright rays that emanate from several of the largest craters on the moon, e.g., Tycho and Copernicus. The nature of these rays is not known. They are most conspicuous at full moon phase.

lunar year A year containing 12 synodic months, used by the Hebrews, Babylonians, Greeks, and Arabs. Since 12 synodic months amounts to about 354 days and a solar year about 365, it becomes necessary to adopt a leap month every third year to have the two years coincide.

lunation The period required for the moon to complete all its phases, or the time between two successive new moons. One lunation averages about 29.53 days. See: *synodic month.*

Lunik (From *Luna,* moon, and *Sputnik,* satellite.) The name given to Soviet *lunar probes. Five were launched between 1959 and 1965. Lunik I was launched January 2, 1959, and passed within 2200 miles of the moon; Lunik II crashed on the moon on September 13, 1959; Lunik III passed the far side of the moon on October 6, 1959, and photographed the hidden side. Two later Luniks, V and VI, were apparently unsuccessful.

luni-solar precession The result of the combined attraction of the sun and the moon on the precessional motion of the earth. See: *precession.*

luni-solar year A lunar year corrected to coincide with a solar year.

Lupus (Wolf) A constellation in the southern hemisphere located at 15h 20m right ascension ($\alpha = $ 15h 20m), 40° south declination ($\delta = -40°$).

Lyman-alpha line ($L\alpha$) A spectral line emitted when an electron jumps from the second to the first orbit of a hydrogen atom and forms the resonance line at λ1216 Å. This line has been studied in the sun's spectrum by means of rocket observations.

Lyman series A series of lines in the spectrum of hydrogen which is emitted when electrons jump from outer orbits to the first orbit. The Lyman series lies entirely within the ultraviolet spectral region. The brightest lines are *$L\alpha$, $\lambda =$ 1216 Å; $L\alpha$, $\lambda =$ 1026 Å;* and *$L\gamma$, $\lambda =$ 972 Å.*

Lynx A faint constellation in the northern hemisphere at 8h right ascension ($\alpha = $ 8h), 45° north declination ($\delta = +45°$).

Lyot, Bernard (1897–1952) French astronomer who was a foremost solar observer. In 1930, he invented the *coronagraph,* an instrument that makes possible the study of the solar corona at times other than a total eclipse of the sun.

Lyra (Lyre) A constellation in the northern hemisphere at

18h 30m right ascension (α = 18h 30m), 36° north declination (δ = +36°). The brightest star, α Lyrae, Vega, has an apparent magnitude 0.1 and spectral type A0. β Lyre is an interesting eclipsing binary, while ε Lyrae is a multiple star. The famous *Ring Nebula* (Messier 57), a planetary nebula, lies midway between β Lyrae and γ Lyrae. Beta (β) Lyrae stars, named after the prototype β *Lyrae,* are eclipsing binary stars consisting of two stars revolving very near to one another around a common center of mass. Such stars are often deformed and are surrounded by an atmospheric mantle common to both. The prototype system consists of a large star of spectral type B8 and a smaller component of spectral type F. Both stars are ellipsoidal and the stream of gases exchanged between the stars forms an expanding ring around the system. The eclipse takes place when the type F star is in front of the type B8 star. The entire system is very complicated and difficult to interpret. Fig. L5

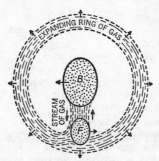

L5. Model of the star Beta (β) Lyrae.

is a model of β *Lyrae. Epsilon* (ε) *Lyrae* is a multiple star. In a small telescope, the star appears as a double. In a larger telescope, each component separates into two stars. Spectroscopic observations reveal a total of six stars in the system. *RR Lyrae,* a short-period cepheid variable, is the first **cluster type variable* discovered in the Milky Way system and the prototype for RR Lyrae stars. The average period for RR Lyrae stars is 0.57 days. These stars belong to Population II. *RR Lyrae variables, RR Lyrae stars* are short-period cepheid variables with a period less than one day (*cluster type variables*) classified as Population II stars.

Lyrids   A meteor shower that occurs between April 18 and 24. Its radiant is in the constellation of Lyra.

M

M   Symbol for objects in the Messier catalogue of nebulae and star clusters. See: *Messier*.

m, M   Symbol for visual (*m*) and absolute (*M*) **magnitude*.

Magellanic Clouds   Two galaxies in the southern hemisphere named after the Portuguese explorer Ferdinand Magellan. Visible to the unaided eye as faint patches of light, the Magellanic Clouds are located at a distance of about 150,000 light-years. The Large Cloud has a diameter of about 30,000 light-years while the diameter of the Small Cloud amounts to 20,000 light-years. These galaxies are sometimes considered to be satellites of the Milky Way system and are classified as irregular although there appear to be indications of a spiral structure. The Magellanic Clouds are easily resolved into stars and contain a great number of objects found in the Milky Way system such as different types of stars, clusters, and nebulae. The clouds are rich in variables, including cepheid variable stars. Radio astronomy investigations have shown that the galaxies are enshrouded in extensive clouds of hydrogen. The total mass of the Large Cloud has been determined from its rotation to be about 1500 million solar masses, while the Small Cloud is estimated to have a mass equal to about 1000 million suns. Both clouds are among the most interesting objects in the sky.

magnetic fields   **1.** The motion of ionized matter in the solar system is explained by the presence of an *interplanetary magnetic field*. **2.** The discovery of interstellar polarization shows the existence of an *interstellar magnetic field* with lines of force following the spiral arms of the Milky Way. The strength of the field has not as yet been determined although estimated to be about 10^{-5} gauss. **3.** The *magnetic fields* of the *sun* and *stars* have been studied by their effect on spectral lines (**Zeeman effect*). The sun's general field has a strength of a few gauss. Sunspots, on the other hand, have shown field strengths of several thousand gauss. Many stars are found to have strong magnetic fields. See: *magnetic variables*. **4.** *Earth's magnetic field* has a field strength of 0.63 gauss at the magnetic poles and about one half as much at the equator. It is probable that some other planets have magnetic fields, though space probes have given negative results for the moon, Venus, and Mars.

magnetic storms Sudden and energetic disturbances of the earth's magnetic field which often occur in conjunction with the eruption of *solar *flares*.

magnetic variables In their study of the magnetic fields of stars, H. D. Babcock and H. W. Babcock at Mt. Wilson Observatory have discovered stars with variable magnetic fields. For example, the magnetic field of the star α^2 *Canum Venaticorum* varies between +5000 and —4000 gauss in a period of 5.5 days. In addition, the intensity of certain spectral lines varies within the same period. Attempts have been made to interpret the phenomenon as a result of the rotation of the star alternately turning its north and south magnetic poles toward the direction of the earth. Several other magnetic variables are known.

magnetogram A graphic representation of the intensity of the magnetic field and its polarity as distributed over the surface of the sun. At the poles, the field strength is comparatively weak, of opposite polarity, while in the sunspots the magnetic fields are found to be very strong.

magnetohydrodynamics The change in motion of an electrified gas or liquid moving in a magnetic field as the result of interaction between the electric current and the magnetic field. This coupling between magnetic and hydrodynamic forces, called magnetohydrodynamics, was demonstrated for the first time by Hannes Alfvén, of Sweden. The phenomenon has astrophysical applications. For example, sunspots can be partly explained by assuming that reactions at the sun's center result in magnetohydrodynamic waves (*Alfvén waves*), which travel to the surface where the sunspots are produced.

magnification The ratio between the focal lengths of the objective and ocular in a telescope.

magnitude A measure of a star's brightness. Since antiquity the naked-eye stars have been divided into six magnitudes according to estimates of brightness. Today, magnitude has become precise and permanent. The lower the numerical value of the magnitude, the brighter the star. On this scale, a star of the first magnitude is 2.512 times brighter than a star of the second, etc. A difference of five magnitudes represents a ratio of apparent brightness of 100. The apparent magnitude is the observed brightness of a star. The brightest star in the sky, Sirius, has an apparent magnitude of —1.6.

The 200-inch Hale telescope at Mt. Palomar Observatory can resolve stars of apparent magnitude of 22. The apparent magnitude of the sun is -26.7 which is 10^{20} times brighter than the faintest star seen through the Hale telescope. Various other magnitudes are determined using various colored filters. See: *astrophotometry*. The magnitude determined with the eye is called *visual magnitude*. By using a suitable photometer in agreement with the visual scale, photovisual magnitude can be determined. The magnitude measured from blue-sensitive photographic plates is called *photographic magnitude*. Various other magnitudes can be derived by using suitable emulsions and color filters sensitive to ultraviolet, blue, yellow, red, infrared. *Monochromatic magnitude* is the magnitude derived in a very narrow spectral region. The measure of the total radiation of a star is called *bolometric magnitude*. *Absolute magnitude* is the apparent magnitude a star would have if it were situated at a distance of 10 parsecs, or 32.6 light-years, from the earth. The absolute magnitude of the sun is $+4.8$.

magnitude at opposition The apparent brightness of a planet when reaching opposition. Since a planet's distance from the earth is continuously changing, the apparent magnitude of the planet will vary, hence magnitude is given at opposition.

main sequence The principal series of stars in the *Hertzsprung-Russell diagram*. The main sequence stretches from the upper left portion of the diagram (white and blue-white stars of spectral type O and B) to the lower right corner (red dwarf stars of spectral type M).

major axis The large diameter of an ellipse.

major planets The nine largest planets in the solar system in contrast to the *minor planets*. As measured from the sun, the major planets are: Mercury, Venus, Earth, Mars, Jupiter, Saturn, Uranus, Neptune, and Pluto. Physically, the major planets are divided into two groups: *terrestrial planets* (Mercury, Venus, Earth, Mars, and apparently Pluto) that are comparatively small bodies of high density and solid surfaces, slow axial rotation, and none or few satellites; and *giant planets,* or the *Jovian planets* (Jupiter, Saturn, Uranus and Neptune), which are characterized by enormous dimensions, low density, rapid axial rotation, extensive atmospheres, and often a great number of satellites.

Maksutov telescope (Meniscus-mirror system) An optical system of A. Bouwers, of the Netherlands (1940), and D. D.

Maksutov, of the Soviet Union (1944). The Maksutov telescope has a spherical mirror whose aberration is reduced by
a negative concave meniscus. The meniscus is mounted in
several ways and the telescope may include a secondary mirror similar to a *Cassegrainian telescope.* Usually, the concave and convex surfaces have the same center of curvature
as the mirror. A diaphragm is placed midway between the
meniscus and the mirror and a curved photographic plate
at the focal point. The system is illustrated in Fig. M1.

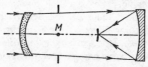

M1. Maksutov telescope.

mare (Lat., seas) A term used for the dark markings on the
moon since early times. The name is entirely misleading since
water is lacking on the moon and the maria are probably
huge plains. The most important lunar seas are: *Mare Cri-
sium* (Sea of Crisis); *Mare Fecunditatis* (Sea of Fertility);
Mare Frigoris (Sea of Cold); *Mare Humorum* (Sea of Hu-
mors); *Mare Imbrium* (Sea of Showers); *Mare Nectaris* (Sea
of Nectar); *Mare Nubium* (Sea of Clouds); *Mare Serenitatis*
(Sea of Serenity); *Mare Tranquilitatis* (Sea of Tranquillity);
Mare Vaporum (Sea of Vapors).

Mariner's Compass Constellation in the southern hemisphere.
See: *Pyxis.*

Mariner II An American space probe launched from Cape
Kennedy (Cape Canaveral) on August 27, 1962, which
passed across the surface of the planet Venus on December
14 at a distance of about 20,000 miles. During the flight this
probe sent valuable data concerning the physical conditions
on Venus.

Mariner IV An American space probe which passed within
6000 miles of the planet Mars on July 15, 1965, and sent
back close-range photographs of the surface, showing that
Mars is covered with craters which seem to be similar to
those of the moon.

Mars The fourth major planet measured from the sun. Mean
distance from the sun = 1.52 A.U., or 142 million miles;
equatorial diameter = 4200 miles; mass = 0.11 earth
masses; average density = 3.85; period of rotation = 24.62

hours; period of revolution = 1.88 years. The planet's equator is inclined 25°2 to the plane of the orbit. During favorable *oppositions*, Mars is well situated for observations, with an apparent diameter of 25″ of arc (at a distance of 35 million miles). White polar caps that surround the poles of the planet very likely consist of a thin layer of snow or frost. On the surface, dark hues are seen on a red-orange disc. These dark regions have been called seas and the lighter areas have been called continents or deserts since the time of their discovery. The dark markings are unquestionably permanent and are subject to seasonal changes in color as the polar caps advance and retreat. As a result of the inclination of the axis, a year on Mars is like a year on earth except that on Mars it is almost twice as long. Mars evidently lacks mountain ranges. Investigations using polarized light seem to indicate that the lighter surface markings may be covered with volcanic ash or a fine-grained volcanic rock. The red color is evidently caused by iron oxides. The infrared spectrum of the dark regions is similar to the spectra obtained from primitive vegetation such as algae and mosses. Organic molecular bands have also been detected in the planet's spectrum. Occasionally, clouds appear in the Martian atmosphere that are white, blue, and yellow in color. The yellow clouds are believed to be dust, swirled aloft from the planet's surface. The atmosphere of Mars is very tenuous, with a pressure of only 10% of the earth's atmosphere at the surface. Mars's atmosphere contains a substantial amount of carbon dioxide and slight traces of water vapor, but no oxygen has been detected. Temperature measurements show that the noon temperature in the tropics can reach 20° to 30° C., while the nighttime and polar temperatures are very low (about −70° to −100° C.). Of all Martian phenomena, the canals have aroused the greatest interest. Some observers have reported seeing fine dark lines crossing the surface of Mars forming a geometric network (Schiaparelli, Lowell, and others). These striations have received the unfortunate name *canals*. Other observers have been unable to detect canals but instead find that the surface of Mars is covered with small details seen at the threshold of vision (Antoniadi, Barnard, Dollfus, Kuiper, and others). Some dark markings have been photographed, which indicates that some of the prominent canals are probably real (surface faults). The geometric canal network is now believed to be an optical illusion caused by the eye striving to give geometric structure to faint details. It is possible that some form of primitive vegetation, similar to the kind found in the tundra, may exist on Mars but any higher form of life on the planet is probably out of the question. Mars has two very small moons, *Phobos* and *Deimos*.

Mars, oppositions of   The occasions when Mars is at a celestial longitude 180° from the sun and is suitably located for observation. Because of the eccentricity of Mars's orbit, the distance between the earth and Mars during opposition will vary from 35 million miles to over 60 million miles. *Favorable oppositions* occur in intervals of 15 or 17 years when Mars has an apparent diameter of 25″ of arc. The last favorable opposition occurred in September 1956. The next favorable oppositions will take place on August 10, 1971, and September 28, 1988. (Fig. M2.)

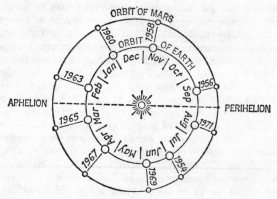

M2. Oppositions of Mars.

maser   An acronym for *M*icrowave *A*mplification by *S*timulated *E*mission of *R*adiation. A low-noise amplifier used in radio astronomy. The maser is based upon the principle of wave generation by means of natural resonators within the atoms of matter.

mass   The material content of a body. Since, according to Newton's law, the attraction of one celestial body for another is a result of their masses, this value can be determined by the amount of gravitational attraction. For example, the mass of a planet can be found from its disturbing influence on the motion of another planet. If a planet possesses satellites, the mass of the planet can be found from the period of revolution and distance of one of the satellites. The most reliable method of determining the mass of stars is based upon the motions of the stars in a binary system. The total mass of the binary system can be determined from the period of revolution and the size of the orbit on one star. To find the mass of each star, the motions of both components around their common center of gravity must be known.

mass-energy relation The equivalence of energy, E, and mass, m. According to Einstein's formula, $E = mc^2$, where $c =$ speed of light in a vacuum.

mass-luminosity relation The curve which describes the relationship between the masses and luminosities of stars. The curve is almost a straight line in a diagram whose abscissa is the logarithm of the mass and the ordinate is the absolute magnitude (luminosity). This relationship was derived theoretically by Eddington and only applies to main-sequence stars. The white dwarf stars show the greatest digression from the mass-luminosity relation. The relation is a means by which the mass of a star can be derived if the absolute magnitude is known. (Fig. M3.)

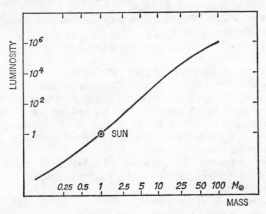

M3. Mass-luminosity relation.

matter, bridges of Faint wisps of matter that are seen to bridge galaxies located near one another. These bridges are probably the result of a tidal effect caused by a close approach of the two systems. There is evidence that similar bridges have been traced between the two Magellanic Clouds and the Large Cloud with the Milky Way.

McDonald Observatory   At Fort Davis, Texas, operated by the University of Texas together with Yerkes Observatory of the University of Chicago. The observatory was dedicated in 1939. The main instrument is a reflecting telescope with an 82-inch primary mirror.

mean anomaly   See: *anomaly.*

mean equinox   The mean vernal equinox. As a result of *nutation*, the vernal equinox is subjected to small periodic displacements about a mean position.

mean noon   The moment when the *mean sun* crosses the meridian.

mean parallax   The parallax derived for a large number of stars when the parallax for individual stars is not possible to find. A statistical study of the motions and brightness of the stars is made in determining the mean value of the parallax. Mean parallaxes are significant in investigations of stellar distribution in space, etc.

mean position   The position of a star after corrections have been made for refraction (bending of light in the atmosphere) and *nutation*. Consequently, mean position is referred to the *mean equinox.*

mean solar day   The period of time between two successive culminations of the sun.

mean solar time   The time measurement based on the motion of the *mean sun.*

mean sun   A fictitious sun used as a timekeeper rather than the actual sun whose apparent motion is not uniform. It is assumed that the mean sun moves along the equator at a constant speed in the same time that the real sun moves along the ecliptic at varying speeds. The mean sun will complete its annual course with respect to the vernal equinox in precisely the same time as the real sun.

median magnitude   In astronomy, the value of the magnitude halfway between maximum and minimum brightness of a variable star.

megaparsec   A million parsecs.

meniscus telescope   See: *Maksutov telescope.*

Mensa   (Table) A faint constellation near the south celestial pole at 5h right ascension ($\alpha = 5h$), 80° south declination ($\delta = -80°$).

Mercury   The nearest planet to the sun is the smallest of the major planets. Its equatorial diameter is 3100 miles; mass = 0.05 (the earth's = 1); density is 5.3; orbital eccentricity is 0.206, second only to Pluto among the major planets. Mercury's mean distance from the sun is 36 million miles; its period of revolution, 0.24 years, or 88 days. The planet rotates in the same time interval as its period of revolution, thereby keeping the same face toward the sun. Because Mercury is close to the sun, surface details are observed with difficulty.

Mercury transits When the planet Mercury is observed to pass across the disc of the sun, which can only occur at the time the earth is near the line of nodes of Mercury's orbit. Mercury transits occur about 13 times each century. The next two transits will take place May 8, 1970, and November 9, 1973.

meridian *Celestial meridian,* the great circle on the celestial sphere which passes through both poles, the zenith and the nadir. The meridian intersects the horizon at the north and south points. On the earth, meridians are great circles through the poles which are perpendicular to the equator.

meridian circle An instrument used to determine with precision the position of a celestial object. It consists of an accurately divided circle attached to a telescope mounted to pivot on an east–west axis. As the telescope turns, the line of sight generates a plane which coincides with the plane of the meridian. During observations, the telescope is pointed at the celestial object shortly before meridian passage (culmination). The graduated circle reading will give the altitude at the instant of culmination. Right ascension is found by timing the meridian passage with a sidereal clock. Declination is calculated from the altitude of the star and the altitude of the pole of the observer. Modern meridian circles are very complicated instruments with automated registering of meridian passage and altitude (or zenith distance) reading on the graduated circle.

meridian error The error that results in a transit reading if the axis of rotation is at an angle to the horizontal plane.

meridian instruments Astronomical instruments mounted to swing along the meridian. They are used to determine the positions of celestial bodies with great accuracy. The most important are the *meridian circle and the *transit instrument.

meridian photometer A visual photometer constructed by E. C. Pickering at the Harvard Observatory. A telescope is mounted horizontally toward the meridian. Mirrors reflect the image of a star near the meridian into the telescope simultaneously with Polaris, the Pole Star, so that the observer can see both stars at the same time. The brightness of these images can be varied so that they are equalized. Polaris is used as a comparison star for all observations. Extensive photometric observations have been made with the meridian photometer, but this instrument is no longer in common use.

meridian transit instrument   A telescope mounted on an east-west axis, used to time the passage of a star across the meridian. The instrument contains a reticle with a series of vertical transit wires. The star is timed with a sidereal clock the moment it crosses a wire. The instrument can be pivoted 180° so that the star passes over the same lines a second time. Reversing the instrument makes the correction of *collimation error* possible. Often, a *transit micrometer* is used to reduce the personal equation. The micrometer contains a movable wire in the reticle which is electrically controlled by the observer. The star is followed in the field of view with the movable wire by turning a micrometer screw. When a star crosses the wire, an electric circuit is made to a *chronograph* so that the mark is registered on a chronograph record. Modern transits register meridian passage by photoelectric methods. A photoelectric cell produces a current that activates the chronograph.

Merope   One of the stars in the *Pleiades* (Seven Sisters). Nearby Merope is a nebula that shines by reflected light.

Messier, Charles   (1730–1817) French astronomer who compiled the first catalogue of nebulae and clusters, containing 103 objects (1784). Nebulae and clusters are often identified by the numbers in Messier's catalogue. As an example, M13, Messier 13, is number 13 in his catalogue (the globular cluster in Hercules).

Me stars   Red stars with emission lines in their spectra belonging to spectral type M in the *Harvard classification*. As a rule, they are *long-period variables* (Mira stars).

metagalactic space   Space beyond the Milky Way.

metagalaxy   All galaxies observed beyond the Milky Way.

metallic-line stars   A type of A stars with unusually strong lines of the metals. The majority of these stars have variable spectra.

meteor   A *falling star*. A bright streak of light which occurs when a *meteoroid* enters the atmosphere of the earth at velocities approaching 45 miles/sec. Plunging through the atmosphere at high speed, the particle is heated to incandes-

cence. Atoms escape and collide with molecules of air to form
a bright streak in the atmosphere along the path of the meteor. On the average, about six meteors can be observed each
hour. See: *meteor swarm*. Generally, meteors become incandescent at altitudes between 50 and 70 miles above the earth.
Today, radar is used in meteor investigations.

Meteor Crater in Arizona (The Barringer Crater) A crater
near Canyon Diablo in northeast Arizona formed by the impact of a meteorite. This circular depression has a diameter of
4200 feet and is 570 feet deep. About 30 tons of meteoric
iron have been found around the crater. The size of the meteorite that caused the crater is estimated to have had a diameter of about 200 feet and a weight of approximately one
million tons.

meteor craters Craters on the earth caused by the fall of meteorites. Several meteor craters have been discovered in different parts of the world. The most famous is the Barringer
Crater in Arizona with a diameter of 4200 feet and a depth
of 570 feet. Tons of iron and nickel meteorites have been
gathered in the surrounding area but the main body of the
meteorite has not been found. Other meteor craters have been
discovered in Canada, Argentina, Australia, and South Africa.
Two severe meteorite falls have occurred in Siberia; on June
30, 1908, at Podkamennaia Tunguska, where 50 square kilo-
meters of forest was destroyed, and on February 12, 1948,
near Lake Baikal.

meteorite A metallic or stony body from space that passes
through the atmosphere as a bright meteor (*fireball*, or
bolide), and falls to the surface of the earth. A meteorite
may vary in weight from a few ounces to several tons. (The
largest known meteorite, found at Grootfontein, South Africa,
has a weight of about 64 tons.) Chemically, meteorites are
classified in two main groups: *iron meteorites* (siderites)
composed of iron and nickel alloys, and *stony meteorites*
(aerolites) of a granular structure containing various silicates and oxides. (An intermediate type, *siderolites*, contains
both minerals and metals.) When the cut surfaces of siderites
are polished and etched, the crystaling structure of the iron-
nickel alloys forms banded patterns called *Widmanstätten figures*. Radioactive methods indicate an age between 60
million and 7600 million years. Chemically, a meteorite is
composed of the same elements in similar proportions as the
earth and stars.

meteorite, stony See: *stony meteorite.*

meteoroid A small cosmic body which, upon entering the atmosphere of the earth, causes a **meteor.*

meteor shower When the earth encounters the remains of a comet, the number of meteors observed each hour increases and gives the appearance of a rain of stars. The Leonids produced rich meteor showers in the years 1799, 1833, and 1866. The richest annual shower occurs in early August (the Perseids).

meteor swarm A *meteor shower.* The appearance of a large number of meteors as a result of the passage of the earth through a cloud of meteoroids, the debris of disintegrated comets. These particles move in parallel paths through space but because of perspective they appear to come from one point in the sky called the *radiant.* Generally, meteor swarms are named after the constellation in which the radiant is located, such as the Lyrids (April 18 to 24), Perseids (August 12), Leonids (about November 15), etc. The Leonids produced rich showers in 1799, 1833, and 1866, when several hundred thousand meteors were observed each hour. A relationship has been established between meteor swarms and comets. The Perseids move in the same orbit as Comet 1862 III and the Leonids in the orbit of Comet 1866 I (Tempel's comet).

meteors, sporadic Meteors that are independent of each other and occur during the entire year. Their number varies during the course of a day (diurnal variation) as well as with the season (annual variation). About twice as many sporadic meteors are seen after midnight as during the early evening. The greatest number are observed in the autumn, while the least number are seen in the spring.

methane A hydrocarbon compound called marsh gas, with the formula CH_4. It is found in the atmosphere of the giant planets and in comets.

method of least squares A mathematical method that makes possible the calculation of the most probable value of the unknown quantities found in observations. The number of observations must be greater than the values calculated from the unknowns.

Metonic cycle A cycle of 19 years, discovered by Meton (Fifth Century). It is equal to 235 synodic months, after which time the phases of the moon are repeated on the same days of the month.

micrometeorites Microscopic particles of iron of cosmic origin with diameters of 10 to 40μ. Micrometeorites are found in rain water and in samplings of the ocean floor. Most artificial satellites are equipped with instruments to study micrometeorites.

micrometer A measuring device used with a telescope to measure accurately small distances on the celestial sphere. In its simplest form, it consists of a fixed and movable wire whose displacement is read off on a graduated scale. Often, micrometers can be rotated around the optical axis, making position angle measurements possible (*position micrometer*). The micrometer is used to measure the relative positions of visual double stars, their distances apart, and the angle formed by the line joining the primary star and the component with the hour circle through the primary star (position angle).

micron Measurement of length $= 10^{-3}$ mm, indicated by μ.

microphotometer An instrument used to measure the density of star images on photographic plates. The construction of modern microphotometers is based upon thermoelectric and photoelectric principles.

Microscope Constellation in the southern hemisphere. See: *Microscopium.*

Microscopium (Microscope) A faint constellation in the southern hemisphere at 21h right ascension ($\alpha = 21$h), $37°$ south declination ($\delta = -37°$).

Middle European time The standard time one hour before Greenwich time. Sweden, Norway, Denmark, and central Europe are in this time zone.

midnight The time when the sun reaches its lowest position.

midnight sun The sun visible above the horizon at midnight. The midnight sun can be seen at positions north of the Arctic Circle and south of the Antarctic Circle when the sun is circumpolar.

Milky Way The diffuse, glowing band of light seen on dark nights spanning the sky as a great circle. Its central line is the galactic equator, inclined $62°$ to the celestial equator. Its width varies between $5°$ and $50°$. From Cygnus to Scorpius, the Milky Way is divided by a dark rift. Light intensity varies with different regions; sometimes very dark or very bright portions are found, dark nebulae or star clouds. Galileo discovered that the Milky Way consists of an enormous number of faint stars. Actually, the Milky Way outlines the plane of our stellar system, the central plane, or plane of symmetry, of the *Milky Way system.

Milky Way system *The Galaxy,* or *galactic system.* The huge
star system of which the sun is a member, containing a mass
equivalent to about 100,000 million suns forming a spherical
condensation of stars at its center with a flat disc surrounding
the nucleus. The Galaxy has a diameter of 100,000 light-years
and an average thickness of 10,000 light-years. The sun is
located at a distance of about 30,000 light-years from the
center, which lies in the direction of the constellation of Sagittarius. The halo and nucleus contain old stars of Population
II while the disc contains young stars of Population I and
enormous clouds of gas and dust. The pronounced spiral
structure in the disc has been traced by the distribution of
neutral hydrogen radiating at 21 cm wave length. Several
spiral arms have been observed to wind around the center
of the system. The Galaxy is rotating around an axis through
the center of the system, at velocities that vary according to
distance from the center. At the sun's distance, the speed is
about 250 km/sec in a period of 220 million years. Globular
clusters surround the central portions of the Galaxy. In addition, there are two satellite galaxies, the *Magellanic Clouds,*
which are external star systems.

Data for the Galactic System

Diameter	100,000 light-years
Thickness at right angles to the plane of:	
nucleus	16,000 light-years
disc	3,000 light-years
Halo's diameter	160,000 light-years
Sun's distance from center	30,000 light-years
Sun's distance from the plane of the Galaxy	45 light-years north
Rotation near the sun:	
velocity	250 km/sec
period	220 million years
Total mass	200,000 million solar masses
Mean density	0.1 solar masses per cubic parsec
Total magnitude (visual)	−20.5
Estimated number of globular clusters	300
Estimated number of galactic clusters	15,000
Estimated number of associations	700

millimicron Measurement of length $= 10^{-3}$ microns $= 10^{-6}$ mm, indicated by $m\mu$.

Mills cross antenna A high-resolution antenna system devised by B. Y. Mills, of Australia, which is used in radio astronomy. Based on the principle of wave interference, the antenna consists of two lengths of wire mesh about 500 yards long that intersect at right angles to each other. Suspended several yards above the ground and supporting over a thousand dipoles, the network acts as a reflector. When the system is tuned, resolving power is increased by interference of the radio waves.

Mimas The planet Saturn's inner satellite, discovered by W. Herschel in 1789. The mean distance to the planet is 113,000 miles, and the period of revolution, 22h 37m.

minor axis The shorter axis of an ellipse.

minor planets The *asteroids,* or *planetoids.* A multitude of small celestial bodies that are members of the solar system in orbits primarily between Mars and Jupiter. The largest and first one discovered, Ceres (1801), has a diameter of 480 miles. Only 2% of the known minor planets have diameters greater than 60 miles. The larger asteroids are nearly spherical, while the vast majority show light fluctuations indicating the rotation of irregular bodies. Some asteroids have appreciable orbital eccentricity, such as Eros which can pass very close to the earth, or Adonis and Icarus which almost approach the orbit of Mercury. At present, over 1600 minor planets are known but a large number are discovered each year and the total population probably approaches 100,000 members. Their combined mass is estimated to be no more than $\frac{1}{1000}$ of the earth's mass. Asteroids invite many interesting problems in celestial mechanics. Thus, clusters of asteroids, such as the *Trojans,* have been "captured" by the planet Jupiter. The minor planets may have originated through the disintegration of a large planet although it is conceivable that the gravitational influence of Jupiter made the formation of a planet in this region of the protonebula impossible and, instead, the existing matter congealed into a large number of smaller bodies. See: *Kirkwood gaps.*

Mira Ceti o Ceti (Omicron Ceti), the *Wonderful,* in *Cetus,* the Whale. A long-period variable discovered by D. Fabricius, August 13, 1596. The star's brightness varies from a minimum of 8th to 10th magnitudes to a maximum that lies between 2nd and 5th magnitudes. The average period is about

330 days. The star's spectrum is of late M type and its color is red (temperature, at maximum, 2900° C.; at minimum, 1900° C.). Mira is a binary with a fainter component of spectral type B. The primary star is a supergiant with a diameter 300 times the diameter of the sun. Mira is a long-period variable star whose changes in brightness are caused by pulsations. Mira is the prototype for the *Mira stars,* called *Me stars,* since their spectra contain emission lines. See: *long-period variables.*

Miranda One of the planet Uranus's satellites, discovered by Kuiper in 1948. Its mean distance from the planet is about 76,000 miles; period of revolution, 1.41 days.

Mira stars A type of long-period variables named after **Mira Ceti.*

mire A marker placed at a distance of several miles from a transit or meridian circle to indicate the direction of the meridian.

Mirfak The star Alpha (α) Pegasi, with an apparent visual magnitude 1.9 and spectral type F5.

Mizar The star Zeta (ζ) Ursae Majoris, of apparent magnitude 2.4 and spectral type A2. Mizar was the first star discovered to be a visual binary as well as the first to be identified as a spectroscopic binary. In 1650, Riccioli discovered that Mizar is a visual binary with a period of revolution of 300 years. The brightest component was found to be a spectroscopic binary with a period of 20.5 days by E. C. Pickering at Harvard Observatory in 1889. Since then it has been found that even the *B* component is a spectroscopic binary. Therefore, Mizar is a double double star.

MKK system A classification system of stars according to luminosity developed at Yerkes Observatory by Morgan, Keenan, and Kellman. See: *luminosity classes.*

modulus of distance (distance modulus) The same as $m - M$, where m is apparent and M absolute magnitude. The distance in parsecs r is then obtained from $\log r = \dfrac{m - M}{5} + 1$.

Mohammedan calendar A calendar consisting of a lunar year of 354 days (12 months with 29 and 30 days alternately) beginning in the year A.D. 622, the year of the Hagiera.

molecular hydrogen H_2, with characteristic spectral lines at 8270 Å, has been identified within the atmospheres of the giant planets.

monistic theories Theories for the origin of the solar system according to which the planets were formed through internal forces. Examples include Kant's nebular hypothesis, von Weizsäcker's turbulence theory, etc. See: *cosmogony*.

Monoceros (Unicorn) An extensive but faint constellation across the celestial equator at 7h right ascension ($\alpha = 7$h), 4° south declination ($\delta = -4°$).

monochromatic photographs Photograph made with light of a selected wave length. Monochromatic photographs are used to study the bright masses of hydrogen gas in space (H-II regions) which are photographed through a filter allowing the light from the Hα line to pass through. In solar observations, an interference filter is very often used to transmit light of a selected wave length such as a hydrogen or calcium line. A *spectroheliograph* is used to obtain monochromatic photographs of the sun by isolating a selected spectral line in the solar spectrum, thereby showing the sun in the light of the wave length in question.

monochromator An instrument used to photograph the sun in the light received from one spectral line. A monochromatic polarizing or interference filter with a transmission band less than 1 Å wide is employed. If a suitable filter is placed between the objective and ocular in a telescope, the sun can be observed in the light of the Hα line and prominences, filaments, flares, and other phenomena may be studied.

month The period of time required by the moon to complete one revolution around the earth. The length of the month is measured in various ways depending upon the point of origin. **1.** ANOMALISTIC MONTH. The moon's period in two successive passages of perigee (the point in the moon's orbit nearest the earth), equal to 27.5546 days. **2.** DRACONITIC MONTH. The *nodical month*. The moon's period with respect to one of its nodes, equal to 27.2122 days. **3.** SIDEREAL MONTH. The moon's period with respect to the stars, equal to 27.3217 days. **4.** SYNODIC MONTH. The time between two successive similar phases (new moon to new moon), equal to 29.5306 days. **5.** TROPICAL MONTH. The time it takes the moon to return to the same longitude, equal to 27.3216 (only 7 seconds less than a sidereal month). **6.** CALENDAR MONTH. One of the 12 divisions of the Gregorian year, varying in length between 28 and 31 days.

moon Satellite of the earth. The moon's mean distance from the earth is 238,857 miles (60¼ times the earth's radius). Its mass is ⅟₈₁ that of earth and its density is ⅗ that of earth.

The moon's true period of revolution (the sidereal month) is equal to its period of rotation, or 27⅓ days, and the period of revolution with respect to the sun (synodic month) is 29½ days. Since the period of revolution is equal to the period of rotation, the moon keeps the same side toward the earth. The moon's phases are caused by its changing position with respect to the sun, allowing more or less of the lighted portion to be seen. At new moon phase, the moon stands between the earth and the sun and is invisible. At full phase, the moon is in opposition, or opposite the sun with the fully lighted side of the moon facing the earth. Since the moon does not possess an appreciable atmosphere, the surface details can be clearly seen. With a large telescope, details of about 2000 feet diameter are observed. Even the maria, or *seas,* the enormous plains that cover half of the surface of the moon, are visible as dark patches to the unaided eye. The maria may possibly be covered with a layer of dust. Some maria are bordered by mountain ranges and low, long ridges are seen on the surface. The most common lunar feature is the craters. There are over 100,000 craters of various sizes from a few hundred feet to over 100 miles in diameter. The largest craters are called *ring mountains,* or *walled plains,* with diameters from 50 to more than 100 miles. The smallest seen from the earth are *crater pits,* or *craterlets,* amounting to several hundred feet in diameter. The floor of a crater lies below the level of the surrounding lunar surface and quite often a mountain peak is found in the center of the crater (*central peak*). On July 31, 1964, before crashing on the surface of the moon, the American space probe Ranger VII took more than 4300 pictures of the moon by means of six TV cameras. The final pictures taken prior to the crash showed small craterlike objects with diameters as small as a few feet. Similar pictures were taken with Rangers VIII and IX in 1965. Very often small craters are found on the crater floor or on the central peak. Photographs of the far side of the moon were taken by the Russian lunar rocket Lunik III, launched on October 4, 1959, and by another vehicle, Zond III, in 1965. Analysis of these photographs reveals about 700 details including craters and mountains. The surface of the moon contains many features. There are majestic *mountain ranges;* single peaks reach altitudes of 30,000 feet above the surrounding plain. The mountains are often crossed by deep clefts and valleys. The most familiar is the *Alpine Valley.* Other unique phenomena include the bright *rays* that streak out from some of the larger craters such as Tycho and Copernicus. These rays are most pronounced during the full moon phase. Extending independent of the terrain, the rays can reach lengths approaching 1500 miles, and are presumably surface deposits. Apparently, weak volcanic activity may have been observed from time to time. On the night of November 2 to 3, 1958, the Russian astronomer Kozyrev discovered a phenomenon near the center of the crater Alphonsus that appeared to be a volcanic eruption on the moon. Similar phenomena have been reported near Aristarchus by American astronomers at Lowell Observatory, in Arizona. Several theories for the origin of the craters have been proposed. According to one, the craters are volcanic. However, they do not coincide in shape or size with volcanoes on the earth. A more common theory suggests that the lunar craters were formed by the bombardment of meteorites. Temperatures on the moon vary from a maximum of 220° F. with the sun in the zenith to a minimum of −240° F. Radio frequency radiation at 1.25 cm wave length indicates a decidedly smaller range in temperature variation (86° to −160° F.) from a layer just below the surface. Longer wave lengths show even smaller amplitudes at greater depths. According to investigations, including the study of polarized light, the surface of the moon seems to bear a resemblance to volcanic ash, pumice, and similar substances on the earth. Meanwhile, opinions are divided regarding the surface material. In recent years, investigations seem to indicate that the floors of the craters and the seas have a porous, glassy surface structure.

moonquakes A phenomenon analogous to earthquakes on earth. Certain observed changes on the surface of the moon have been explained by assuming the existence of moonquakes.

Morning Star (Gr. *Phosphorus.*) The name of the planet Venus when it is west of the sun and appears in the east prior to sunrise.

mounting The different ways in which a telescope may be supported. Small telescopes employ an *altazimuth mounting* where the telescope is moved in the horizontal and vertical planes (for example, a *theodolite). A meridian circle has a telescope that only turns in the plane of the meridian. The most common telescope support, the *equatorial mounting*, consists of two axes perpendicular to each other. One, the polar axis, points toward the celestial pole while the other, the declination axis, carries the telescope. See: *equatorial mounting*.

Mt. Palomar Observatory One of the world's largest observatories, located on a mountain plateau about 125 miles from Pasadena, California, 5600 feet above sea level. The *Hale telescope*, the largest optical telescope in the world, with a mirror diameter of 200 inches, is located at Mt. Palomar. In addition, the observatory has two Schmidt photographic telescopes, the largest of which has a mirror diameter of 72 inches and a correcting plate of 48 inches diameter.

Mt. Palomar Sky Atlas See: *Palomar Sky Atlas*.

Mt. Stromlo The national observatory of Australia, at Canberra. The observatory is equipped with superior instruments to observe the sky in the southern hemisphere.

Mt. Wilson Observatory One of the world's largest observatories, located on a mountain 5600 feet above sea level near Pasadena, California. Built in 1905 as a solar observatory, Mt. Wilson was developed into an observatory for stellar investigations. The solar instruments include two *tower telescopes* with mirrors to reflect the sun's image vertically to an underground room where spectrographs and other auxiliary instruments are installed. Mt. Wilson Observatory has two famous reflectors, one of 60 inches diameter and the other, the 100-inch-diameter Hooker telescope.

moving cluster A star cluster in motion. The brightest and nearest galactic clusters of stars with large proper motions that can be measured. These stars are united gravitationally and move in parallel paths through space. Because of the effect of perspective, the stars appear to be moving toward a point called the convergent point. The distance to a cluster can be found when the positions of the convergent point and the velocities of the stars are known. Among the various moving clusters, the most familiar is the Hyades in the constellation of Taurus. See: *galactic star clusters*.

M regions Areas of the solar surface that are responsible for magnetic disturbances on the earth.

M stars Red stars of spectral type M in the *Harvard classification* of stellar spectra. Titanium oxide bands dominate the spectra of these stars. Surface temperature reaches about 3000° C.

multiple galaxy A group of three or more galaxies forming a physical system.

multiple star A system of stars containing three or more components linked together by gravitation.

multi-stage rocket A rocket consisting of several rockets attached in tandem, each with its own rocket engine. When the first rocket has burned out, it is separated and falls to earth as the next stage begins to function. By means of a multistage rocket, usually a three-stage rocket, artificial satellites or space vehicles are placed into orbit.

mural quadrant An instrument used to determine stellar positions prior to the invention of the telescope. The quadrant consisted of a wall supporting a 90° graduated arc carefully oriented to the meridian. By means of a movable arm equipped with a sight, the altitude of a star could be determined at meridian passage. Tycho Brahe used mural quadrants in his observations at Hven. Readings were made to an accuracy approaching $\pm 10''$ of arc.

Musca (Fly) A small constellation in the southern hemisphere at 13h right ascension ($\alpha = 13$h), 70° south declination ($\delta = -70°$).

N

nadir The point where a vertical line extended underfoot meets the celestial sphere on the other side of the earth. The *zenith* is the opposite point where a vertical line meets the celestial sphere overhead.

NASA Abbreviation for National Aeronautics and Space Administration, highest organization in the United States for civilian space research, established 1958. NASA is directly responsible to the Vice President of the United States.

natural broadening The width of a spectral line dependent upon the time spent by an atom in an energy level during a downward transition.

nautical astronomy The branch of practical astronomy concerned with the determination of position on the sea and in the air by means of astronomical observations.

n-body problem The complete solution of the motions of any number of bodies, *n*, that mutually attract one another according to Newton's laws. Generally, the problem is unsolvable. See: *three-body problem* and *perturbations*.

neap tide The rise of the water in the oceans during the quarter moon phase when the gravitational attraction of the moon and sun will oppose each other. The tide is modified and the rise will be less than normal. See: *tides*.

nearest stars   There are about 40 stars within a distance of 5 parsecs (16.3 light-years) of the sun. The nearest star is *Alpha* (α) *Centauri* (4.3 light-years), a star of approximately the same absolute magnitude and spectral type as the sun. Only two of the nearest stars are more luminous than the sun, namely, the primary component of *Sirius* (8.7 light-years, spectral type A0, absolute magnitude +1.3) and *Procyon* (11.3 light-years, F5, +2.6). No giant stars are found and over 70% of the stars are faint dwarfs of spectral type M0 and later. One of the faintest stars is *Wolf 359* with an absolute magnitude +16.6 (M6e). About 37% of the nearest stars are binary or multiple stars. There are five *white dwarfs* and several stars with invisible companions.

nebulae   Clouds of particles and gases in interstellar space (see: *interstellar matter*). Nebulae found in the Milky Way are called *galactic nebulae*. These are classified in different ways: *bright nebulae,* among which are found *emission nebulae,* gas nebulae that emit light; *reflection nebulae* that consist of particles that reflect light from nearby stars. In addition, there are *dark nebulae,* extensive dust aggregations that absorb the light from stars that lie beyond them. Because of their nebulous appearance, the extragalactic star systems, the galaxies, were called nebulae, a name that persists in publications today (*extragalactic nebulae*). The name *diffuse nebulae* describes irregular galactic nebulae. Special types of nebulae include the *planetary nebulae.*

nebular hypotheses   The theories for the origin of the solar system based upon the assumption that the material of the solar system was once a nebula. The oldest is derived from I. Kant (1755) and P. S. Laplace (1796). Modern nebular hypotheses are derived from C. F. von Weizsäcker, G. P. Kuiper, D. ter Haar, and others. See: *cosmogony.*

nebular variable   Variable stars with irregular periods which are found within galactic nebulae (for example, the Great Nebula in Orion) and whose light variation is associated with the nebulosity.

nebulium   A hypothetical element that was once believed to be responsible for the spectral lines in gaseous nebulae ($\lambda 3726$, 3729, 4959, 5007 Å). Today, these lines have been identified as "forbidden lines" of ionized nitrogen and oxygen; hence, the element nebulium does not exist.

negative hydrogen ion   (H$-$) A negative ion is formed when a neutral hydrogen atom captures a free electron. The negative ion is responsible for the continuous absorption of light within stellar atmospheres.

negative ocular An ocular consisting of two lenses with the image located between the lenses. A frequently used negative ocular, the Huygenian eyepiece, consists of two plano-convex lenses with the flat surfaces facing the eye.

Neptune The eighth major planet measured from the sun was discovered by Galle in 1846 at the Berlin Observatory near the place in the sky predicted by the Frenchman, Leverrier, and the Englishman, Adams. The location of the planet was determined by theoretical calculations based upon the observed deviations of the orbital motions of the planet Uranus. Neptune's mean distance from the sun is 30 times greater than the earth's distance from the sun, or 2793 million miles. Its period of revolution is equal to 164.79 years. Its diameter is about 27,700 miles; mass is 17.3 earth masses; density is 0.29 of the earth's density; period of rotation is about 14 hours. Because of the great distance between the earth and Neptune, hardly any details of the planet's disc have been observed. Neptune is surrounded by an atmosphere that contains methane, ammonia, hydrogen, and other gases. The temperature is estimated to be $-220°$ C. The physical conditions of Neptune are similar to those found on the other giant planets, Jupiter, Saturn, and Uranus. Two hypotheses describing the interior of the planet have been suggested: that Neptune is composed of a rocky central core surrounded by a thick shell of ice under an atmosphere of methane and hydrogen (with clouds of ammonia); or that the planet is almost entirely composed of hydrogen highly concentrated toward the center where it is found in the liquid or solid state. Neptune has two satellites, Triton and Nereid, with periods of revolution of 5.88 days and 359.4 days, respectively.

Nereid Neptune's second moon was discovered photographically by Kuiper in 1949. Its period of revolution is 359.4 days and its mean distance from Neptune is about 3.5 million miles.

Net Constellation in the southern hemisphere. See: *Reticulum*.

neutrino An elementary particle without mass which carries no electrical charge. The neutrino plays an important role in modern theories of the internal constitution of giant stars.

neutron A neutral elementary atomic particle that together with protons constitutes the nucleus of the atom.

neutron star   A theoretical stellar body composed mainly of neutrons. Recently discovered X ray sources may be examples of neutron stars.

New General Catalogue of Nebulae and Clusters of Stars (NGC)   The general catalogue of J. L. E. Dreyer (1888) of star clusters and nebulae (galaxies) including about 8000 objects.

new moon   The phase when the moon is in conjunction. The dark side is toward the earth and the moon is invisible.

new style   The Gregorian dating method. See: *Gregorian calendar*. The difference between the new style and *old style* dating (*Julian calendar*) amounts to 13 days at the present time.

Newton, Isaac   (1642–1727) English physicist, astronomer, and one of the foremost scientists of all time. His greatest discovery was the universal law of gravitation set forth in the *Philosophiae Naturalis Principia Mathematica* (*Principia*, 1687). Newton made extensive experiments in optics and constructed the reflecting telescope named after him (1671).

Newtonian focus   The focus obtained by diverting the converging light beam of a reflecting telescope with a prism or diagonal plane mirror to the side of the tube where the ocular, photographic plate, photocell, or other accessory apparatus can be placed. See: *Newtonian telescope*.

Newtonian telescope   A reflecting telescope designed by Newton in 1671. The light from the primary mirror is reflected by a diagonal secondary plane mirror or prism to the side of the telescope tube where ocular or photographic equipment is attached. (Fig. N1.)

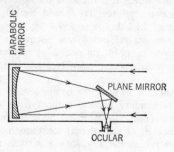

N1. Newtonian telescope.

Newton's law of gravitation Isaac Newton's universal law formulated in 1687 that forms the basis for celestial mechanics. In accordance with this law, every particle in the universe attracts other particles with a force that varies directly as the product of their masses and inversely as the square of their distance. In 1905 and 1915, Albert Einstein showed that the law is valid only when the masses are relatively small, moving at speeds that are slow compared with the speed of light.

Newton's laws The three laws of motion that form the basis of classical mechanics, set forth by Isaac Newton in his *Principia* (1687). **1.** LAW OF INERTIA. Every body remains in a state of rest or uniform motion unless acted upon by an outside force. **2.** LAW OF ACCELERATION. Acceleration is directly proportional to the force in the direction of the straight line in which the force acts. **3.** LAW OF ACTION AND REACTION. For every action, there is an equal and opposite reaction so that the mutual actions of two bodies are always equal and opposite. See: *Newton's law of gravitation.*

NGC Abbreviation for J. L. E. Dreyer's *New General Catalogue of Nebulae and Clusters of Stars* used with a number system for listing star clusters, galaxies, and nebulae. For example, NGC 6205 is the designation for the globular cluster in Hercules, listed as Messier 13 (M13) in the **Messier catalogue.*

Nicol prism A prism used in astrophotometry to dim the light from a comparison star and measure the change in intensity. The Nicol prism utilizes the double refractive characteristics of calcite crystal. The prism consists of two calcite crystals cemented together, cut, and oriented so that only the extraordinary ray passes through the prism. Two prisms are used with the photometer; one prism acts as the polarizer and the other as the analyzer. The analyzer is rotated and the angle measured. Since the light variations in the analyzer are controlled by its rotation, the Nicol prism is suitable for use in visual photometers.

night The time interval when the sun is below the horizon for a given position on the earth. The length of nighttime is determined by the time of year and latitude of the position. At the equator, day and night are almost equally long (12 hours). For all other positions on the earth, day and night are equal at the time of the vernal and autumnal equinoxes, March 21 and September 23. At the poles, day and night are each six months long.

noctilucent clouds Clouds of dust particles, possibly of inter-planetary origin, that hover at an altitude of approximately 50 miles and can therefore be observed long after sunset.

nodes The points of intersection between the orbit of a celestial body and the ecliptic. The moon's orbit is inclined 5° to and intersects the ecliptic at two diametrically opposite points, called the nodes of the moon's orbit. The *ascending node* is the node the moon, planet, or comet passes from the south to the north side of the ecliptic, and the *descending node* is where passage occurs from the north to the south side of the ecliptic.

nodical month A *draconitic* month, or the moon's period of revolution with respect to the same node.

noon The time of day when the sun passes the meridian and is at its highest point above the horizon.

noon correction A correction that must be made in determining the time of the sun's passage across the meridian using *corresponding altitudes*. It depends upon the change of the sun's declination during the series of observations.

Norma (Square) A constellation in the southern hemisphere located in the Milky Way at 16h right ascension ($\alpha = 16h$), 50° south declination ($\delta = -50°$).

normal spiral galaxy A type of spiral galaxy possessing a more or less pronounced nucleus from which spiral arms extend. Divided into subgroups Sa, Sb, and Sc according to the size of the nucleus. See: *galaxies* (Hubble's classification).

North America Nebula A bright gas nebula (NGC 7000) located near the star α Cygni (Deneb). The nebula was so named because of its resemblance to the North American continent.

Northern Cross An asterism in the form of a cross in the constellation of Cygnus, the Swan.

Northern Crown Constellation in the northern hemisphere. See: *Corona Borealis*.

north pole 1. TERRESTRIAL. The northern terminal point of the earth's axis. 2. CELESTIAL. The point where the extension of the earth's axis will intersect the celestial sphere. The celestial north pole is located about 1°3 from Polaris (α Ursae Minoris) in the direction of the star β Ursae Minoris.

novae (Lat., new stars) Exploding or erupting stars. See: *exploding stars*. Sometimes called *temporary stars*.

November swarm The *Leonids*. A meteor shower visible in mid-November with a radial point located in the constellation of Leo, the Lion. It has produced brilliant showers in the past, but since 1866 has been relatively feeble.

N stars Very red stars of low temperature belonging to spectral type N in the *Harvard classification* of stellar spectra. Absorption bands of carbon and cyanogen are contained in the spectra.

Nubecula Major The Latin name for the *Large Magellanic Cloud*. See: *Magellanic Clouds*.

Nubecula Minor The Latin name for the *Small Magellanic Cloud*. See: *Magellanic Clouds*.

nuclear reactions The transformation of one element to another by the fusion of atomic nuclei. The source of the radiant energy of the sun and other stars is nuclear reaction. The most important reactions include the *proton-proton reaction* and the *carbon-nitrogen cycle*. See: *energy production* in the stars.

nutation Periodic variations in *precession* discovered by J. Bradley, of England, in 1747. The largest is caused by the 5° inclination of the moon's orbit to the ecliptic. Nutation has a period of 18.6 years, the same as the regression of the node of the moon. Stellar co-ordinates are also subject to small periodic change as a result of nutation.

nutations ellipse The curve formed by the axis of the earth as a result of *nutation*. The pole oscillates about a mean pole which advances with *precession* around the pole of the ecliptic. The major axis of the ellipse amounts to 9".22 of arc, the *constant of nutation*.

O

OAO (Orbiting Astronomical Observatory) American project to launch a satellite equipped with a telescope in an orbit around the earth.

O association A stellar association consisting mainly of O and B stars. See: *association*.

Oberon The remotest satellite of the planet Uranus, with a period of revolution of 13.46 days. Mean distance to the planet is 364,000 miles. Oberon was discovered by W. Herschel in 1787.

objective The lens or lens system that forms the image in a refracting telescope. The light-gathering power of an objective increases as the square of its diameter. The resolving power of the objective is the smallest angular distance observed between the components of a binary system. The following table gives approximate values for the limiting magnitude and the distance between the components of a binary system that can be separated by objectives of various sizes (diameters are expressed in centimeters):

Diameter	5	10	20	30
Limiting Magnitude	10.5	12.0	13.5	14.4
Angular Distance	2″3	1″14	0″57	0″38

The largest objective, Yerkes refractor, has a diameter of 40 inches. For photographic purposes, complicated objectives are used to obtain a large field.

objective grating A coarse diffraction grating consisting of equally-spaced wires or rods placed in front of the objective of a telescope. Star images take the form of a central image with short spectra that are points of light if the grating is sufficiently coarse. Used in photographic photometry. See: *effective wave length, photographic photometry,* and *stellar photometry.*

objective prism A prism placed in front of the objective of a telescope. Star images are produced as small spectra rather than as points of light. An objective prism is suitable in statistical investigations, since the spectra of all the stars in an area can be photographed in one exposure. Such plates permit rapid spectral or luminosity classification of stars. (Fig. O1.)

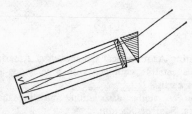

O1. Objective prism.

oblateness The measure of the amount of deviation from a spherical form of a planet or a star, usually as a result of rotation. This polar flattening can be calculated by the formula: $c = \dfrac{(a-b)}{a}$; where a = equatorial radius, and b =

polar radius. The earth's oblateness is $\frac{1}{297}$; Mars's, $\frac{1}{200}$; Jupiter's, $\frac{1}{15}$; Saturn's, $\frac{1}{10}$; Uranus', $\frac{1}{14}$; Neptune's, $\frac{1}{15}$. The sun, Mercury, and Venus have no appreciable oblateness. The oblateness of Pluto is unknown.

obliquity (obliquity of the ecliptic) The angle between the celestial equator and the ecliptic. The obliquity of the ecliptic amounts to 23° 26′ 54″ at the present time but is diminishing about 0″.5 each year. After 1500 years the angle will increase. Maximum deviation amounts to about 1°.5.

observational astronomy The branch of astronomy that employs astronomical instruments and observational methods.

observatory A center for astronomical research with different types of permanently mounted astronomical instruments. See: *astronomical observatory*.

occultation An eclipse of a star or planet by the moon. Since the moon has an easterly motion, a star or planet will disappear at the moon's eastern limb (immersion) and reappear at the western limb (emersion). Occultations are valuable in determining accurately the position of the moon.

Ocean of Storms *Oceanus Procellarum*, a lunar "sea."

Oceanus Procellarum (Sea of Storms) One of the larger seas, located in the northeast portion of the moon.

O cluster A star cluster usually found in the center of an O association. In general, the cluster contains O type stars.

Octans (Octant) A faint constellation near the south celestial pole at 21h right ascension ($\alpha = 21h$), 80° south declination ($\delta = -80°$).

octant An instrument similar to a sextant, used to measure angular distances. The graduated arc of the octant is $\frac{1}{8}$ of a circle (45°).

Octant A faint constellation in the southern hemisphere. See: *Octans*.

ocular The lens system of a telescope by which the image formed by an objective (or mirror) can be observed. As a rule, the ocular contains two lenses, the field lens (toward the objective) and the eyepiece (nearest the eye). There are two main types: a *positive ocular*, with the image in front of the lenses (such as a Ramsden ocular); and a *negative ocular*, where the image is situated between the lenses (such as a Huygenian ocular). A Ramsden ocular consists of two plano-convex lenses with the convex sides turned toward each other. A Huygenian ocular has two plano-convex with the plane surfaces turned toward the eye. Other oculars include the Kellner, an improved type of Ramsden ocular, containing a field lens made of two achromatic lenses. Several other types of oculars are in use.

ocular spectroscope A small spectroscope placed at the focus of a telescope in place of an ocular. The objective acts as a collimator. To spread the spectrum into a band, a cylindrical lens is placed in the light path at right angles to the length of the spectrum.

Olbers, Heinrich Wilhelm (1758–1840) German astronomer who developed simplified methods for calculating comet orbits, and paid great attention to the asteroids.

Olbers' paradox According to H. W. Olbers (1826) at night the sky should glow with a brightness of daytime if there are an infinite number of stars uniformly distributed in space. Many attempts have been made to arrive at a solution to this paradox and explain why the sky is dark at night without assuming that the number of stars is finite. Today, the sky is believed to be dark at night because of the *red shift* of the receding galaxies which causes the brightness of the distant stars to diminish more rapidly than the square of the distance. Accordingly, the night sky is dark because the universe is expanding.

old style The *Julian calendar*. In contrast to this calendar there is the *Gregorian calendar,* or *new style.* At present, the difference between the calendars amounts to 13 days. January 1 in the Julian calendar is comparable to January 14 in the Gregorian calendar. (Julian calendar = Gregorian calendar − 13 days.)

Omega (ω) The last letter in the Greek alphabet. Omega Centauri; see: *Centaurus.*

Oort's constants The constants for galactic rotation that appear in *Oort's formulas for galactic rotation.*

Oort's formulas for galactic rotation Formulas derived by the Dutch astronomer Oort (1927) which express the differential effect of galactic rotation on proper motions (μ) and radial velocities (ρ) of stars. (l^{I} = galactic longitude, r = distance in parsecs):

$$\rho = rA \sin 2(l^{\mathrm{I}} - lo^{\mathrm{I}}) = rA \sin 2l^{\mathrm{II}}$$
$$\mu = rA \cos 2(l^{\mathrm{I}} - l^{\mathrm{II}}) + Br = rA \cos 2l^{\mathrm{II}} + Br$$
$$lo^{\mathrm{I}} = 325° \text{ (direction toward the center of the galaxy)}$$
$$A = 0.0195 \text{ km/sec per parsec}$$
$$B = -0.024 \text{ km/sec per parsec}$$

A and B are referred to as *Oort's constants.*

opacity Lack of *transparency*. In the atmospheres of the sun and other stars, the negative hydrogen ion is the primary cause of opacity.

open star clusters A type of *galactic star cluster*.

opera glass The optical system developed by Galileo in the beginning of the 17th century, consisting of convex objective lens and a concave ocular. This form of telescope is used today as an opera glass because of its compact construction.

Ophiuchus (Serpent Bearer) An extensive constellation most of which is located in the southern hemisphere at 17h 20m right ascension ($\alpha = 17h\ 20m$), 5° south declination ($\delta = -5°$). The constellation contains extensive dark nebulosity. See: *Ophiuchus Nebula*.

Ophiuchus Nebula A very extensive dark nebula located in the constellation of *Ophiuchus* (Serpent Bearer) in the southern hemisphere. Its distance is about 800 light-years and absorption amounts to between 2 and 4 magnitudes.

opposition The position of an outer planet situated in a plane containing the sun and the earth, at celestial longitude 180° from the sun and crossing the meridian at midnight. When a planet is at opposition, it is nearest the earth and in a favorable position for observation. The moon is in opposition at the full moon phase.

optical axis The line connecting the midpoints of the lenses and mirrors in an optical system.

optical depth A measure of the transparency of a substance.

optical double stars Stars that appear close together but are actually at great distances from one another in the same line of sight. Physical double stars are true binaries revolving about a common center of gravity.

optical temperature The temperature obtained from an investigation of the optical radiation of a celestial body.

optical window Gaps in the earth's atmospheric absorption through which visible radiation and radiation from adjoining wave length regions pass down to the surface. The optical window includes the spectral region between 3000 Å and 20,000 Å (radio frequency radiation reaches the surface by means of another absorption gap). See: *radio window and* Fig. A14.

optics Originally, the science of light. Today, optics includes the theory of the formation of images in optical instruments.

orbit The curve in which a celestial body moves under the influence of gravitation. The majority of orbits are elliptical.

The orbits of the planets are almost circular, while the orbits of comets are usually elongated ellipses. In rare instances, an orbit may be parabolic or hyperbolic.

orbital velocity The velocity required by a satellite to enter an orbit around the earth (or any other celestial body). Theoretically, the minimum period of revolution for an earth satellite is 84.5 minutes and an orbital velocity of about 6.2 miles/sec (when the altitude of the orbit above the earth's surface is 0 miles). At an altitude of 180 miles and a period of revolution of 90 minutes, orbital velocity will be about 4.8 miles/sec. A 24-hour period can be achieved at an altitude of 22,000 miles with an orbital velocity of 2 miles/sec. *Escape velocity,* the velocity required by a satellite to leave the vicinity of the earth, is equal to about 7 miles/sec.

orbit determination The problem of deriving by means of Newton's laws the orbit of a celestial body from several observations. Several methods have been worked out to determine orbits. A preliminary orbit is found from a minimum number of observations (usually three). Later, a more precise calculation can be made from additional observations, with allowances for perturbations by the planets or other nearby bodies. Various methods have been developed to determine the orbits of double stars (visual, spectroscopic, and photometric binaries).

ordinate Y co-ordinate (the vertical co-ordinate) in a Cartesian co-ordinate system.

origin The 0 point in a co-ordinate system.

Orion One of the largest and most impressive constellations, located at the celestial equator at 5h 30m right ascension ($\alpha = $ 5h 30m), 0° declination ($\delta = 0°$). The second brightest star is Alpha (α) Orionis, Betelgeuse (a variable with apparent visual magnitude between 0.2 and 1.0, spectral type M0). The brightest star is Beta (β) Orionis, or Rigel, (apparent visual magnitude 0.2, spectral type B8p). Orion contains the Great Nebula (M42 and M43) which is visible to the unaided eye.

Orion arm The spiral arm of the Milky Way on whose inner edge the sun is located. In addition, there is the Great Nebula in Orion and related stellar associations. The arm has been studied by means of 21 cm radio frequency emission of neutral hydrogen.

Orion association A stellar association located in the constellation of Orion which is related to the Great Nebula. In the center, a cluster of four bright stars form a trapezium (*Trapezium in Orion*). The stars are primarily O type stars, but there are also T Tauri stars forming a T association.

Orionids A meteor swarm occurring between October 18 and 20 with its radiant in the constellation of Orion.

Orion Nebula (M42 and M43) *The Great Nebula in Orion.* A gaseous nebula located south of Orion's Belt which is visible to the unaided eye as a dim patch of light. Its distance is about 1300 light-years. A star cluster in the center of the nebula forms the famous *Trapezium in Orion.* Embedded in the nebula are other high-luminosity stars of spectral type O radiating intense short-wave lengths (ultraviolet), causing the nebula to glow. These stars, which include many variables of the T Tauri type, form the *Orion association.* The nebula is extremely tenuous, only $\frac{1}{1,000,000}$ as dense as the best vacuum produced on earth. The Trapezium group consists of very young stars with ages no more than a few hundred thousand years.

orthochromatic plates Photographic plates with emulsions sensitive to yellow light which are used with yellow filters to determine *photovisual magnitude.* See: *astrophotography.*

osculating element See: *osculating orbit.*

osculating orbit The orbit that a planet or comet would follow if, in a given instant, all perturbations were removed and its motion was dictated only by the sun's attraction. The starting point is called the *osculation epoch* and the undisturbed orbital elements are called *osculating elements.*

osculation epoch See: *osculating orbit.*

OSO (Orbiting Solar Observatory) An American satellite launched on March 7, 1962, with very complicated instruments to study solar radiation. The satellite circles the earth in an orbit between 340 and 370 miles above the surface.

O stars Stars of spectral type O in the *Harvard classification* of stellar spectra. These are blue-white stars of very high surface temperature (50,000° C.), whose spectra contain absorption lines from ionized helium, oxygen, and nitrogen. Sometimes emission bands are observed.

outburst Strong disturbances that occur during a *radio storm;* the sudden increase in radio frequency radiation from the sun in conjunction with flares.

outer planets The planets that lie beyond the asteroid belt, namely, Jupiter, Saturn, Uranus, Neptune, and Pluto.

OZMA An American program of investigation with a large radio telescope to study radio noises from nearby stars in an attempt to detect a difference in reception which might indicate the presence of intelligent life. It has now been discontinued.

ozone (O_3) An allotrope of oxygen formed in the upper atmosphere by the action of ultraviolet radiation from the sun.

ozone layer The layer of ozone found in the earth's atmosphere at an altitude between 10 and 20 miles that absorbs the short-wave ultraviolet radiation from space with wave lengths less than 2900 Å.

P

Painter Constellation in the southern hemisphere. See: *Pictor*.

Pallas The second largest asteroid, discovered by Olbers in 1802. Its diameter is about 280 miles and its period of revolution is 4.62 years.

Palomar Observatory See: *Mt. Palomar Observatory*.

Palomar Sky Atlas A photographic atlas of the northern hemisphere and a portion of the southern hemisphere to −33° declination, produced in two colors (blue and red) using the 48-inch Schmidt telescope on Mt. Palomar in southern California. The atlas includes stars to 19th and 20th magnitudes on 1872 photographic prints.

panspermia hypothesis A hypothesis proposed by *S. *Arrhenius* of Sweden (1906) whereby life in the form of spores could exist in space and be transplanted from one celestial body to another by means of radiation pressure.

parabola A *conic section* formed by cutting a cone with a plane parallel to one of the sides of the cone. A parabola is an open curve with only one focal point. Its eccentricity is equal to 1 and the curve can be considered to be an ellipse with an infinite major axis. Comet orbits are often nearly parabolic with eccentricities approaching 1. (Fig. P1.)

parabolic mirror A mirror whose surface has the form of a paraboloid of revolution. A cross-section through the surface generates a parabola rather than an arc of a circle as with spherical mirrors. Parabolic mirrors are used in reflecting telescopes in place of spherical mirrors to avoid **spherical*

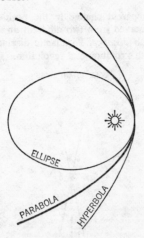

P1. A parabola compared with an ellipse and a hyperbola.

aberration. Since comatic images appear a short distance off the optical axis, parabolic mirrors have a limited field of view. To obtain a wide usable field, a spherical mirror is used together with a thin lens to correct for spherical aberration. See: *Schmidt telescope.*

parabolic velocity *Escape velocity.* Theoretically, if the velocity of a body moving in a circular orbit is multiplied by $\sqrt{2}$, the orbit will become parabolic. The earth is moving in an almost circular orbit at a mean velocity of 18.5 miles/sec and will therefore have a parabolic velocity of 26 miles/sec. If the earth's orbital velocity should reach this value, the planet would leave the sun's vicinity.

parallactic angle The angle formed at the star in an astronomical triangle with vertices at the celestial pole, the zenith, and the star under observation. Often used in calculations in spherical astronomy.

parallactic inequality An irregularity in the moon's motion caused by the sun's disturbing influence which sets the moon ahead or back of its normal position. This periodic effect occurs every lunation. The amount of irregularity is inversely proportional to the distance to the sun.

parallactic motion The apparent motion of a star from the apex toward the antapex of the sun's way which reflects the motion of the solar system through space.

parallax The apparent change in the position of a celestial body when observed from two different directions. Used synonymously with *distance*. Parallactic displacement is the result of the earth's rotation and revolution. (Fig. P2.) **1.** STEL-

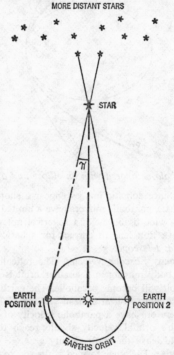

P2. Parallax = the angle π in the diagram.

LAR PARALLAX. (a) *Trigonometric.* Annual parallax. The angle formed by the radius of the earth's orbit observed at the distance of a given star. Only the distances to nearby stars are measured by this method. The nearest bright star beyond the sun, Alpha (α) Centauri, in the southern hemisphere, has a parallax of 0″.76. As a result of the earth's orbital motion, the nearby stars seem to follow elliptical paths in the sky in a period of one year (parallactic ellipse). The semi-major axis of the ellipse is equal to the star's parallax. Stars at the poles of the ecliptic scribe a circular path while stars at the ecliptic will oscillate back and forth along a straight line. Parallax decreases with distance, i.e., a remote star will have a smaller parallax than a nearer star. Since small angles become increasingly more difficult to measure, accurate determinations cannot be made for distances greater than a few hundred light-years. (b) For *moving cluster* stars in parallel paths, distance can be measured from the stars' proper motion, radial velocity, and location of the convergent point. (c) *Dynamic.* The determination of distance to binary stars of known mass and orbital motion by means of the relationship between the period of revolution, semi-major axis of the orbit, and mass as stated in Kepler's third law. (d) *Spectroscopic.* Distances derived from the star's absolute and apparent magnitudes. See: *luminosity criteria.* (e) *Cepheid.* The absolute magnitude of cepheid variable stars is derived from the *period-luminosity relation.* Parallax is found by the relationship between the absolute and apparent magnitudes. (Cepheid and spectroscopic parallaxes are also called *photometric.*) (f) *Statistical.* Generally, faint stars with small proper motions are more distant than bright stars with large proper motions. The *mean parallax* for groups of stars with different apparent magnitudes and proper motions is found by statistical methods. With a large selection of stars, mean values for proper motion and apparent magnitude are obtained. Reference is also made to *secular parallax,* the parallactic displacement reflecting the sun's motion through space. (g) *Galactic rotation.* Derived from the rotation of the Milky Way by means of *Oort's rotation formulas.* See: *distance finding.* 2. PARALLAX WITHIN THE SOLAR SYSTEM. (a) *Diurnal.* Geocentric parallax. The difference in direction of an object viewed from the surface and the center of the earth. The maximum value for this parallax occurs when the object is viewed on the horizon (*horizontal parallax*). The moon's horizontal parallax averages 57'. (b) *Solar.* The mean equatorial horizontal parallax of the sun found by first determining the distance to a nearby asteroid (such as Eros) and applying Kepler's third law. Recently, a much more accurate value for the solar parallax has been derived by radar observations of the planet Venus.

parallel of altitude Circles of equal altitude. See: *almucantar.*

parallels of declination Circles parallel to the celestial equator. See: *diurnal circle.*

parsec Astronomical unit of length equal to the distance at which the radius of earth's orbit subtends an angle of 1″ (parallax = 1″). (The name is a contraction of *par*allax and *sec*ond.) One parsec is equal to 3.259 light-years, or 19.16 × 10¹² miles. (Fig. P3.)

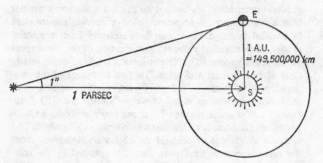

P3. Parsec.

path of totality The narrow region on the earth's surface in which a solar eclipse is total and, consequently, the sun is entirely covered by the moon.

Pavo (Peacock) A constellation in the southern hemisphere at 19h 30m right ascension (α = 19h 30m), 65° south declination (δ = −65°).

P Cygni stars See: *Cygnus.*

Peacock A constellation in the southern hemisphere. See: *Pavo.*

peculiar motion The real or true motion of a star in space which is determined when the star's proper motion and radial velocity are corrected for the sun's motion. Peculiar motion also describes a star's motion relative to the system to which it belongs.

peculiar stars Stars with unusual spectra that cannot be fitted into the usual spectral classification. Such stars are designated with a *p* after the spectral type. For example, A2p.

peculiar variables Variable stars with irregular light variations. These include novae, novalike stars (T Pyxides, η Carinae, P Cygni), R Coronae stars, RR Tauri stars, T Tauri stars, and others. See: *variable stars.*

Pegasus A large constellation in the northern hemisphere at 22h 50m right ascension (α = 22h 50m), 20° north declination (δ = +20°). The stars Alpha (α) Pegasi (Markab), Beta (β) Pegasi (Scheat), Gamma (γ) Pegasi (Algenib),

together with Alpha (α) Andromedae (Alpheratz), form the
famous *Great Square of Pegasus.*

pendulum clock A clock whose time regulator consists of a
pendulum. Prior to the use of *quartz crystal* and *atomic
clocks,* the pendulum clock was standard for astronomical
observatories and continues to have wide use as a precise
timekeeper. In modern pendulum clocks, the pendulum
swings in a vacuum at constant temperature with friction reduced to a minimum. By means of electric impulses, the
pendulum controls a slave clock from which readings are
made. See: *clocks.*

penumbra **1.** The partial shadow cast on the night side by
planets or satellites when illuminated by the sun. A partial
eclipse of the sun will occur where the moon's penumbra
falls on the surface of the earth. (Fig. P4.) **2.** The lighter

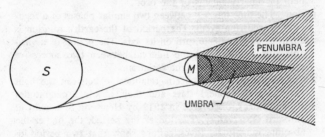

P4. Umbra and penumbra.

zone surrounding the dark center (umbra) of a sunspot.

periastron The point in the orbit of a component star in a
binary system nearest the primary star.

perigee The point in the orbit of a satellite located nearest the
earth.

perihelion The point in the orbit of a planet or comet nearest
the sun. The opposite point, farthest from the sun, is called
aphelion.

perihelion, argument of the The angular distance from the
perihelion of a comet's or planet's orbit to the *ascending
node.* The argument of the perihelion is one of the *elements
of the orbit.*

perihelion, time of passing The instant that a planet or comet
passes *perihelion* in its orbit.

perihelion distance The distance from the focal point to the vertex of the parabola in a parabolic orbit. Perihelion distance is one of the *orbital elements* of a parabolic orbit.

perihelion of Mercury, advance of the The slow, direct motion of the major axis (line of apsides) of the orbit of Mercury. This advance amounts to 9′ 34″ per century. The motion cannot be completely explained by Newton's law of gravitation since the perihelion advances 43″ more than predicted by the old theory. A complete explanation of the advance of the perihelion was made in Einstein's General Theory of Relativity. An advance of the perihelion occurs with the orbit of other planets near the sun but only by an insignificant amount. See: *Einstein effects.*

perihelion passage The time of perihelion passage, *T*, is one of the *elements of the orbit.* If *T* is known, the position of a celestial body for a given date can be calculated with the help of other elements of the orbit.

period The time interval between two similar phases of a regularly reoccurring event. The period of the earth's rotation is equal to one complete turn on its axis. The period of a variable star is defined as the interval between two successive maxima or minima of light variation.

period-luminosity relation The relationship between the light variations of cepheid stars and their absolute magnitudes (luminosities), discovered in 1912 by Henrietta S. Leavitt at Harvard Observatory. The longer the period, the higher the absolute magnitude. Investigations show that two period-luminosity relations exist; one for Population I stars (classical cepheids), and another for Population II. Distance measurements to the variable stars are possible using the *period-*

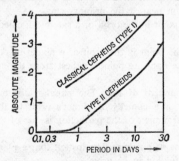

P5. Period-luminosity relation.

luminosity relation. The absolute magnitude of a star is found from its period. A comparison between the absolute magnitude and the apparent magnitude will give the distance, assuming that space is free from absorption. The period-luminosity relation permits the cepheid stars to be the most important yardstick used to measure distances to the galaxies. See: *cepheids.* (Fig. P5.)

period-spectrum relation A statistical relation between the periods of cepheid stars and their spectra (color, temperature) whereby the stars with longer periods have later type spectra (redder color, lower temperature).

perioeci People who live on the same latitude but at a difference of 180° in longitude. Seasons are identical but night and day are opposite.

Perseids A meteor swarm with maximum frequency occurring about August 11 with a radiant in the constellation of Perseus. The Perseids follow the same orbit as Tuttle's comet of 1862, with the main body of the shower reaching perihelion about four years after the comet.

Perseus A star-rich constellation in the northern hemisphere between *Auriga* and *Cassiopeia* at 3h 20m right ascension (α = 3h 20m), 45° north declination (δ = +45°). Beta (β) Persei (*Algol*) is a famous eclipsing binary star. The constellation also contains the familiar Double Cluster *h* and χ Persei.

Perseus arm One of the spiral arms of the Milky Way located in the direction of Perseus at a distance of about 7000 light-years.

personal equation Subjective error which occurs in any measurement such as the timing of the passage of a star across the wires of a reticle in a transit instrument. An observer has difficulty with perception and will time the passage a little early or late. The error is diminished by using transit micrometers, photographic or photoelectric methods for registering the position of the star independent of visual observation.

perturbations Changes or deviations in orbital motion. Among the forces that affect a planet's motion, the gravitational attraction of the sun is far superior to all others. As a result, the planets follow an orbit according to *Kepler's laws. Perturbations* are minor deviations in this motion caused by the attraction of the planets on one another. Perturbations modify the orbits in inclination and eccentricity but the changes are

very slight or take place so slowly that only careful measurements can verify their existence. Small periodic oscillations are called *periodic perturbations*. Long-period changes
in the orbits are called *secular perturbations*. The motion of
the moon is subject to rather significant perturbations because
of the moon's proximity to the earth. Thus, the mathematical
description of the moon's motion is very complicated. Comet
orbits are subject to strong perturbations whenever a comet
passes near a major planet. Comets have been "captured" by
Jupiter, changing the comet's orbit from a very elongated
ellipse to one of less eccentricity and shorter period (families
of comets). A comet's orbit may also be changed from elliptical to hyperbolic, causing the comet to disappear from the
solar system altogether.

phase The shape of the portion of the moon or a planet
lighted by the sun as seen from earth. There are four main
phases of the moon: *new, first quarter, full,* and *last quarter*.
At new moon phase, the moon is between the earth and the
sun with its dark side toward the earth; at full moon phase,
the moon is opposite the sun with its entire lighted surface
toward the earth. At quarter moon, half of the lighted surface
is turned toward earth. Venus and Mercury also reveal phases
when observed in a telescope.

phase angle The angle formed by the earth and the sun as
seen from the moon or another planet. (Fig. P6.)

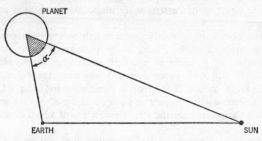

P6. Phase angle.

Phobos The inner satellite of Mars, discovered by Hall in
1877. Its mean distance from the center of Mars is 5815
miles, period of revolution 7h 39m, and diameter about 10
miles. Phobos revolves in the same direction as Mars rotates.
Since Mars's period of rotation is about 24 hours, an observer

on Mars would see Phobos rising in the west and setting in the east.

Phoebe The remotest satellite of Saturn, at a mean distance of 8,044,000 miles and a period of 550 days. Phoebe has *retrograde motion*.

Phoenix An extensive but faint constellation in the southern hemisphere at 0h 30m right ascension (α = 0h 30m), 50° south declination (δ = −50°).

Phosphorus The Greek name for the planet Venus when it appears as a morning star.

photoelectric cell An apparatus for converting light to electrical impulses. In astronomy, the most common photoelectric cell consists of a cathode of an alkaline metal (or a combination of several metals) that will emit an electric current when light falls upon it. Today, the simple photoelectric cell has been replaced by the *electron multiplier tube* containing many anodes that amplify the electron stream a million times through secondary emission. See: *photoelectric photometry*.

photoelectric photometry The measurement of the intensity of light from the electrical effects produced by the light on contact with a suitable light-sensitive substance. At present, there are several types of *photo-tubes* in which light energy is converted to electrical energy and measured with sensitive galvanometers. The light from faint stars may be amplified as much as a million times before measurements can be made. This is made possible by means of a series of anodes or dynodes which amplify to successively higher voltages, increasing the strength of the original current. Several types of tubes called *photo-multipliers* are presently used in astronomy. Today, photoelectric methods are highly developed, making possible measurements of stellar magnitudes of the faintest stars. *Star colors* may be found by measuring the intensity of light with various filters inserted into the light beam. Photometric measurements are at least ten times more accurate than those obtained by photographic methods. See: *stellar photometry*.

photographic photometry The measurement of the brightness of celestial bodies by photographic methods. The fundamental problem of photographic photometry is to find the relationship between the images produced on the photographic plate and the actual intensity of the light. To accomplish this, a comparison scale is made with *standard sequence* stars of known brightness measured with photoelectric techniques. By employing filters in various combinations with appropriate photographic emulsions, brightness is measured photographically in different colors. The color of a star is derived by comparing magnitude measurements made with blue and red sensitive plates. Photographic images are measured with a *microphotometer*. See: *stellar photometry*.

photographic star atlas See: *Carte du Ciel*.

photometer An instrument for determining the intensity of light from a light source. In astronomy, photometers are constructed for use in visual and photoelectric investigations.

photometer, wedge A visual photometer in which the brightness of an artificial star is varied by means of an optical wedge of tinted glass. The wedge is placed into the light beam until the brightness of the artificial star and a real star are the same. The magnitude of the star can be measured by the light absorption of the wedge and the amount of its displacement. It is used in double star photometry.

photometry Light measurement. Methods of determining the brightness of stars or the intensity of their radiant energy. See: *stellar photometry*.

photon A particle of light or a quantum of radiation. In many ways, light can be likened to a stream of elementary particles called photons.

photon counter An instrument used to measure the faintest photon emission in *photoelectric photometry*.

photosphere The apparent visible surface of the sun. See: *sun*.

photovisual magnitude The magnitude of a star measured photographically using a photographic plate sensitive to yellow light and exposed with an appropriate yellow filter. The color composition of photovisual magnitude is the same as visual magnitude, the magnitude of a star as seen by the unaided eye.

physical double stars Two stars that describe orbits around a common center of gravity united by their mutual gravitation. In contrast, *optical double stars* appear to be in the same direction in space purely by chance. These stars are at different distances and are independent of one another.

physical libration A very minute irregularity of the moon's rotation which occurs because the moon's diameter is elongated in the direction of the earth. See: *libration*.

Pic du Midi A French observatory favorably located for astronomical observations in the Pyrenees at an altitude of 9300 feet above sea level. The observatory is famous for its planetary, lunar, and solar photographs.

Pickering, Edward Charles (1846–1919) American astronomer who carried out extensive photometric investigations and spectral analysis of stars. He devised a number of stellar photometers. Pickering was director of *Harvard Observatory* from 1877 to 1917.

Pictor (Painter) A faint constellation in the southern hemisphere at 5h 30m right ascension (α = 5h 30m), 50° south declination (δ = −50°).

Pioneer V A satellite launched by the United States on March 11, 1960, with solar batteries contained on two projecting arms. Placed in an orbit between Venus and the earth, Pioneer V experiments included investigations of corpuscular radiation and micrometeoroids.

Pisces (Fish) An extensive but faint constellation of the Zodiac located in the northern hemisphere at 1h right ascension (α = 1h), 15° north declination (δ = +15°).

Piscis Auratus (Swordfish) Constellation in the southern hemisphere. See: *Dorado*.

Piscis Austrinus (Southern Fish) A fairly small constellation in the southern hemisphere at 22h 30m right ascension (α = 22h 30m), 30° south declination (δ = −30°). The brightest star, Alpha (α) Piscis Austrini, or Fomalhaut, has an apparent visual magnitude 1.3, spectral type A3.

Piscis Volans (Flying Fish) Constellation in the southern hemisphere. See: *Volans*.

plages See: *flocculi*.

Planck's law An important radiation law which describes the relationship between temperature, wave length, and rate of radiation. By means of this law the star's surface temperature or its effective temperature can be determined. (Fig. P7.)

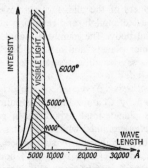

P7. Planck's law.

planetarium A projection instrument used to demonstrate the positions and motions of celestial bodies. The most famous planetarium is constructed by the German firm Carl Zeiss. Installed in the center of a room, the instrument projects images of the stars and planets on a domed ceiling, creating the illusion of seeing the sky of the past, present, and future.

planetary aberration The difference between the true position of a planet and its apparent position due to the time required for light to travel the distance from the planet to earth. Correction for planetary aberration is necessary in determining orbits.

planetary nebula A small ring or circular nebula with a central star of high temperature (50,000° to 100,000° C.). The nebulae consist of gas shells which appear as planetary discs in a small telescope, hence the name. At present, about 400 planetary nebulae are known. A typical planetary has a diameter of about 50,000 astronomical units and a mass of $\frac{1}{100}$ solar masses. Consisting of ionized gases, mainly hydrogen, the nebulae glow because of the intense short-wave radiation of the central star. The planetary nebulae emit a fluorescent glow similar to bright nebulae. Their spectra contain emission lines of doubly ionized nitrogen and oxygen. The rate of expansion of the shell averages about 20 km/sec. The planetary nebulae are remindful of *novae* with their central stars and expanding envelopes. A relationship is suggested between planetary nebulae and novae. Sometimes they are referred to as ex-novae. One of the most familiar planetary nebulae is the Ring Nebula in the constellation of Lyra, the Lyre.

planetary system The system of celestial bodies which revolve around the sun as the center and, with it, form the solar system. The members of the planetary system are dark bodies shining by reflected sunlight and revolving at great distances from the central body. The members include the nine major planets, the minor planets, and meteoroids. Some of the major planets possess a satellite system. See: *solar system, cosmogony,* and *Bode's law.*

planetesimal hypothesis A version of the origin of the solar system proposed by Chamberlin and Moulton in 1901. According to the planetesimal hypothesis, a great number of small bodies, *planetesimals,* whirled about a central concentration which became the sun. A star passed close to the sun causing matter to be ejected from both bodies. Local condensations occurred which eventually increased in size to form the planets. Today, the hypothesis is of historical interest only.

planetoids   Another name for the *minor planets* (*asteroids*).

planets   (Gr., wandering stars.) Dark celestial bodies like the earth that revolve around the sun. In the solar system there are nine *major planets* measured from the sun: *Mercury, *Venus, *Earth, *Mars, *Jupiter, *Saturn, *Uranus, *Neptune, and *Pluto. In addition, there are a large number of smaller bodies, the so-called minor planets, often of irregular form, most of which revolve around the sun in orbits generally located between Jupiter and Mars. Dark bodies have been detected revolving about other stars.

plasma   A gas consisting of ionized atoms, subject to electrohydrodynamic laws. Plasma physics is a young science which has become increasingly significant in problems in astrophysics.

plasma clouds   Clouds of ionized gases with diameters between 10,000 and 100,000 km (protons and electrons) emitted by the sun at speeds greater than 1000 km/sec during intense solar activity. When such a cloud envelops the earth, violent disturbances occur in the earth's magnetic field.

plasma oscillation   The oscillation in ionized gas or plasma when interstellar gas clouds collide emitting radio frequency radiation. The origin of the oscillation is unknown, but is believed to have been caused by compression waves.

Platonic year   The time required for the celestial pole to scribe a circle around the pole of the ecliptic as a result of precession. A Platonic year is equal to 25,800 years.

Pleiades (The Seven Sisters)   An open cluster located in the constellation of *Taurus*, the Bull. To the unaided eye, six or seven stars are visible but the cluster contains several hundred. The twenty brightest stars are blue-white spectral type B while the remainder are A, F, and later types. The distance to the cluster is about 400 light-years. The brightest star, *Alcyone*, is 1400 times brighter than the sun. The entire cluster is shrouded in nebulosity consisting of dust clouds that reflect the light of the embedded stars (reflection nebulae).

Pluto   The most distant major planet, discovered by C. W. Tombaugh in 1930. It is very faint and can only be observed with difficulty even in the largest instruments. The planet's diameter amounts to approximately 3600 miles (Kuiper, 1950) and its mass is about that of the earth, but this measurement is very uncertain. Its period of rotation amounts to 6.4 days, sidereal period of revolution is 248.43 years, and mean distance to the sun is 39.52 astronomical units. The eccentricity of the orbit is large (0.25) which is sufficient to bring part of Pluto's orbit within the orbit of Neptune.

Pogson's ratio The constant 2.512 which is the 5th root of 100 ($[2.512]^5 = 100$). The ratio between the brightness of two successive stellar magnitudes, proposed by Pogson in 1856. (Log of 2.512 is 0.4.) $= 100^{1/5}$.

point source The same as a *radio source* (radio star); a small area of the sky emitting intense radio frequency radiation.

point source model A model of a star based on the principle that the source of energy does not occur throughout the entire star but is concentrated in a small region of the core.

polar axis 1. The axis of an equatorial mounting that is parallel to the earth's axis and consequently points to the celestial pole. The instrument turns about the polar axis in the opposite direction of the earth's rotation by means of a clock-drive, keeping the celestial object in the field of view. In following a star in its diurnal motion, the telescope rotates around the polar axis. 2. The imaginary straight line that connects the two poles of a sphere.

polar caps Ice, snow, or frost surrounding the poles of the earth and Mars. Observations indicate that polar caps may occur on Venus although the nature of the effect may be atmospheric.

polar circle A parallel circle on the celestial sphere or on the earth at a distance of 23°5 from the pole (the tilt of the equator to the ecliptic). In the northern hemisphere at the time of the summer solstice, all positions on the *polar circle* will see the sun on the northern horizon at midnight. At the winter solstice, the sun barely reaches the southern horizon at noon. The conditions are reversed in the southern hemisphere.

polar day and polar night The time when the sun is either above or below the horizon for 24 hours. Polar day and night occur for positions located north of the Arctic Circle (66°5 N. latitude) or south of the Antarctic Circle (66°5 S. latitude). At the poles, polar day and night are each six months long.

polar distance The complement of *declination* or the angular distance of a celestial body to the celestial pole measured along the hour circle.

Polaris *Pole Star,* the star Alpha (α) Ursae Minoris. Polaris' apparent visual magnitude varies between 2.08 and 2.17, spectral type F8. The star is a cepheid with a period of four days and is presently located at a distance of slightly less than one degree from the north celestial pole.

polarization curve The relationship between the angle of reflection and polarization. The degree of polarization of a given substance depends upon the angle of reflection of the light. (In reference to the surface of a planet, the term *phase angle* is used rather than polarizing angle.) The nature of the surface of the moon and two planets (Mercury and Mars) has been interpreted by means of polarization curves. (Fig. P8.)

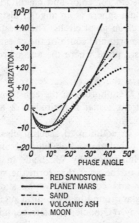

P8. Polarization curves.

polarization instrument An instrument constructed to study polarization of light.

polarization of light Vibrations of normal light waves are transversal (at right angles to the direction of propagation) and in all planes. Polarized light vibrates in one plane only. Investigations of polarized light give clues to the nature and the source of radiation and are used together with spectral and photometric techniques. The study of polarized light is of major importance in modern astrophysics, with the construction of several instruments based upon the principle of polarization. Polarization occurs when light is reflected from a surface or refracted in certain crystals. The light from distant stars is polarized in passing through clouds of interstellar dust in the Milky Way because of the orientation of the dust particles in the presence of a magnetic field. The light of certain nebulae (Crab Nebula) comets, solar corona, and the zodiacal light is found to be polarized. The surfaces of the moon and planets are studied in polarized light.

polar sequence   A standard sequence of stars located near the north celestial pole whose exact magnitudes and colors are known. The determination of the magnitudes of these stars was a joint undertaking by many observatories (*International Polar Sequence*). By comparing other photometric measurements with the polar sequence, these stars provide a uniform international system for color and magnitude determinations.

pole   The point on a sphere at an angular distance of 90° from all points on a given great circle. The celestial poles are at a distance of 90° north and south of the celestial equator. On a planet, a pole is a point where the axis of rotation meets the surface.

Pole Star   *Polaris,* the North Star.

Pollux   Beta (β) Geminorum in the constellation Gemini, the Twins, of apparent visual magnitude 1.2 and spectral type K0.

population types   In addition to spectral classes, stars are divided into two populations, Population I and Population II, a classification introduced by W. Baade in 1944. Population I includes most of the stars that form the spiral structure of the Milky Way and consists of young stars. Population II consists of old stars found in the central regions and the halo of the Milky Way. (Globular clusters contain stars of Population II, while galactic clusters contain stars of Population I.) Population I stars are richer in metals than Population II.

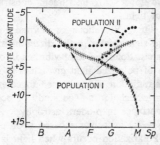

P9. Schematic Hertzsprung-Russell diagram for both population types.

The differences between the two populations is evident in the Hertzsprung-Russell diagram. Population I includes O and B type stars, supergiants, classical cepheids, while Population II includes subdwarfs, RR Lyra stars. Some stars appear to be transition types between the two populations, while other stars are more extreme. Both Population I and Population II stars are found in spiral galaxies. (Fig. P9.)

pore The smallest visible sunspot.

position The location of a body on the celestial sphere, or the point where a line between the observer and the body intersects the celestial sphere. **1.** APPARENT POSITION. The true position of a star corrected for aberration and annual parallax. **2.** TRUE POSITION. The mean position of a star corrected for mutation. **3.** MEAN POSITION. The position of a star on the celestial sphere with the sun at the center and referred to the mean equator and equinox. As a rule, the stars' positions are referred to the equinox for a given year, such as 1960. A star's *instantaneous position* is its mean position with respect to the equinox at the instant of observation. In the solar system, *geocentric position* and *heliocentric position* are used when measurements are made with respect to the center of the earth or sun.

positional astronomy The branch of astronomy that is primarily concerned with the determination of the position of celestial bodies.

position angle The angle formed by a great circle through two double stars and the hour angle of the primary star. The position angle is measured from north in an easterly direction from 0° to 360°.

position micrometer An instrument attached to a telescope, used to measure the relative distance between two celestial bodies. The instrument contains a stationary and a movable wire whose setting is read by means of a screw-head graduation. The wires can be moved around the optical axis making position-angle readings possible. The position micrometer (also called *filar micrometer*) is primarily used to measure the relative distance between visual double stars. See: *micrometer.*

positive ocular An ocular consisting of two plano-convex lenses with the convex sides turned toward each other (e.g., a Ramsden ocular). The image is formed beyond the lenses. Generally, only a positive ocular can be used when a micrometer and cross-wires are mounted in the focal plane.

positron A positive electron; a positively charged elementary
particle with a mass equal to that of an electron.

post-nova stage The physical condition of a nova after the explosion when the star has returned to its original brightness.

potassium-argon method A method for determining the age of
minerals (over 10 million years). See: *age determination*.

potassium-calcium method A method for determining the age
of minerals (about 1000 million years). See: *age*.

Poynting-Robertson effect The spiraling into the sun of small
dust particles found between the planets. The particles inter-
act with solar radiation in such a way as to make them lose
momentum and gradually fall into the sun.

practical astronomy The branch of astronomy that is concerned with the determination of the apparent positions and
motions of the celestial bodies in the sky. Practical astronomy deals with the study of the various instruments and
methods of observation. Applications of practical astronomy
include nautical astronomy (navigation) and geodesy.

Praesepe An open star cluster visible to the unaided eye as a
hazy patch of light in the constellation of Cancer, the Crab.
It contains several hundreds of stars and is located at a distance of about 500 light-years.

precession A slow, gradual turning of the earth's axis around
the pole of the ecliptic. The earth's equatorial plane always
remains at 23°5 to the plane of the ecliptic, while the points
of intersection of these two planes continually change. Consequently, the celestial pole scribes a circle 47° diameter around
the sky in a period of 25,800 years and the vernal equinox
advances westward 50″ per year. Precession was discovered
by Hipparchus in the middle of the second century B.C. The
phenomenon is caused by the earth's deviation from a true
sphere. The earth is flattened at the poles, and can be considered to be a sphere whose equator is surrounded by an
equatorial bulge. The attraction of the sun and the moon on
this equatorial bulge attempts to bring the equatorial plane
to coincide with the plane of the ecliptic and the orbital plane
of the moon. This action of the sun and the moon is opposed
by the rotation of the earth, resulting in an oscillation of the
earth's axis around the pole of the ecliptic. The combined
effect of the gravitational attraction of the sun and the moon
is called *luni-solar precession*. The disturbing influence of
the planets on the earth's orbit causes a precessional effect
in an eastward motion of the equinoxes. This phenomenon
is called *planetary precession*. The combined effect of the

luni-solar and planetary precession is called *general precession*. As a result, the positions of the stars in right ascension and declination are continuously changing. Star catalogues, therefore, list the positions of the stars for a given epoch, such as 1900, 1950, or 2000.

precession, constant of Numerical expression for the annual general precession equal to $50''2564 + 0''000222$ t per year (t = number of years after 1900).

pre-nova stage The physical condition of an exploding star prior to its outburst as a nova. Very little is known about this stage. A pre-nova is apparently a subdwarf of spectral type A.

pressure broadening A widening of spectral lines caused by the pressure in a star's atmosphere.

prime focus The focus of an objective lens or primary mirror. The point to which parallel rays refract or reflect.

prime meridian The meridian through Greenwich which serves as the basis for measurement of longitude on the earth.

prime movement According to ancient concepts, the outermost crystal sphere on which the stars were fastened and turned once in 24 hours from east to west.

primeval atom According to some cosmologists (for example, G. Lemaître), the original state of the universe at the beginning of time, when all matter was concentrated within a small volume of space. An explosion of enormous density within this primeval atom caused its substance to scatter into space. See: *universe*.

primeval nebula The nebula consisting of gas and dust particles out of which the sun and planets are believed to have been formed.

prime vertical The great circle through the zenith at right angles to the meridian. The prime vertical intersects the horizon at the east and west points.

Principia Common name of *Philosophia Naturalis Principia Mathematica*, Sir Isaac Newton's famous work of 1687 in which the law of gravitation was formulated.

prism A wedge-shaped glass solid with three or more plane faces. One edge formed by the faces is called the refracting edge, and the angle between the faces, the refracting angle. Prisms are used to form a spectrum in a spectrograph or as *objective prisms* when a large number of stellar spectra are desired in one photographic exposure.

prismatic astrolabe (Astrolabe à prisme) An instrument invented by A. Claude and L. Driencourt for the precise timing of a star's passage across a vertical circle. It consists of an artificial horizon and a 60° prism placed in front of the objective of a telescope mounted horizontally. Parallel rays of light from a star fall on the artificial horizon and prism and are reflected by the prism into the telescope. When the zenith distance of the star is 30°, these separate images will coincide. The instant when the star reaches this altitude is carefully recorded. Recently, advanced work has been performed by A. Danjon using automatic timing devices. The prismatic astrolabe is considered to be one of the most accurate astrometrical instruments. (Fig. P10.)

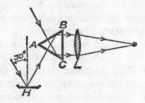

P10. *Prismatic astrolabe.* ABC = *triangular prism,* L = *lens,* H = *artificial horizon.*

prism circle An angle-measuring instrument related to the *sextant* with a complete circle rather than a 60° graduated arc. The instrument is equipped with two opposing verniers, allowing greater accuracy in reading angles.

prism ocular An ocular equipped with a prism that forms an upright image in an astronomical telescope (*erecting prism*).

Procyon The star Alpha (α) Canis Minoris, of apparent visual magnitude 0.5 and spectral type F5 in *Canis Minor,* the Lesser Dog. The distance to the star is about 11 light-years. Procyon is a double star with a white dwarf companion 12.5 magnitudes fainter than the primary.

Project Mercury The initial man-in-space program of the United States. On May 5, 1961, Alan Shepard became the first American in space in the "Freedom 7" capsule. Virgil Grissom soared into suborbital flight on July 21, 1961. On February 20, 1962, John Glenn became the first American in orbit in the "Friendship 7" capsule. Scott Carpenter made three orbits in the "Aurora 7" capsule on May 24, 1962. Six orbits were made by Walter Schirra in "Sigma 7" on October 3, 1962. On May 15, 1963, the final Mercury capsule, "Faith 7," was launched with Gordon Cooper who completed 22 orbits around the earth.

prominences Huge gaseous eruptions on the sun that reach altitudes of several hundred thousand miles above the solar surface. Sometimes, prominences appear as twisted columns of gas held high above the sun (by the sun's magnetic field) before plunging back to the surface. Monochromatic photographs in the light of calcium and hydrogen lines show prominences as bright formations at the limb of the sun. Projected against the solar surface, prominences appear as narrow, dark *filaments*. Prominences are also subject to the 11-year sunspot cycle. They were discovered by B. Vassenius of Sweden, during the total eclipse in Göteborg, 1733.

proper motion The continuous change in a star's direction on the celestial sphere which amounts to the projection of the star's motion relative to the solar system. Proper motion is determined by measuring the star's position on two occasions as widely separated as possible. Proper motion is very small; only about 200 stars have a larger proper motion than 1″ per year. For the great majority of stars, proper motion is negligible. (Fig. P11.)

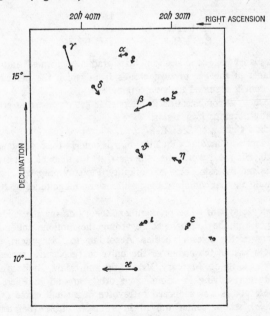

P11. A chart of the constellation Delphinus with arrows indicating proper motion in 10,000 years.

proper motion parallax Average distance for groups of stars derived from their proper motions. See: *distance finding.*

proton A positively charged elementary particle which is part of the nucleus of the atom. The mass of a proton is 1837 times greater than that of an electron.

proton-proton reaction A nuclear process that occurs in the interior of the sun and stars releasing great amounts of energy. In this reaction, at temperatures of millions of degrees, hydrogen is transformed into helium. Two protons (hydrogen nuclei) combine to form a heavy hydrogen (deuterium) nucleus, releasing a positron. The deuterium nucleus collides with a proton to form an isotope of helium with the release of gamma (γ) rays. Finally, two isotopes of helium form a normal helium nucleus and two protons. As a result, a helium nucleus is formed from four hydrogen nuclei, liberating a considerable amount of energy. The reaction, similar to the process occurring in the hydrogen bomb, is outlined below:

$$H^1 + H^1 \qquad\qquad H^2 + e^+$$
$$H^2 + H^1 \qquad\qquad H^3 + \gamma$$
$$He^3 + He^3 \qquad\qquad He^4 + 2H^1$$

protoplanet A condensation that gradually formed into a planet in the gas or dust clouds from which the planetary system is assumed to have originated.

protostar A condensation in interstellar gas or dust that gradually develops into a star.

Proxima Centauri See: *Centaurus.*

Ptolemaeus, Claudius Ptolemy of Alexandria lived about A.D. 140. His great work, the *Almagest*, was a manual that summarized the astronomy of antiquity. Ptolemy prepared a star catalogue that contained the positions and magnitudes of 1028 stars.

Ptolemaic system The predominant theory during the Middle Ages and the Renaissance regarding the motions and positions of the celestial bodies. According to this system, the earth was in the center of the universe (geocentric system) with the moon, Mercury, Venus, the sun, Mars, Jupiter, and Saturn revolving in complicated orbits around it. Each of these bodies was supposed to revolve in a small circle (*epicycle*) whose center moved in a larger circle (deferent) around the earth. The motions of the sun, moon, and planets

were resolved by this *epicycle theory*. More accurate results were derived using eccentric circles. Beyond the seven
deferents was the sphere of the fixed stars. The entire system
was believed to rotate daily around the earth.

Ptolemy's rules The *triquetrum*. An instrument of antiquity
used in measuring the altitude of a celestial body. The instrument consisted of a vertical post, the upper portion of which
could be turned horizontally. Fastened to the vertical post
were two arms, one with a sight at both ends and the other
with a graduated scale forming an isosceles triangle. An object was sighted along one arm and its zenith distance was
read on the graduated scale. (Fig. P12.)

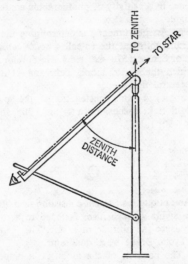

P12. Ptolemy's rules, or triquetrum.

Pulkova Observatory Astronomical observatory located at
Leningrad, USSR. Originally constructed in 1839, Pulkova
was completely destroyed during World War II. The observatory was reconstructed and rededicated in 1954 as one of the
largest well-equipped observatories in the Soviet Union.

pulsating stars A type of variable star showing light variation
due to the expansion and contraction of the star. This category includes *cepheid stars,* *Mira stars,* etc. See: *variable
stars.*

Puppis (Stern) A part of the constellation *Argo* located in the southern hemisphere at 7h 30m right ascension ($\alpha = 7h$ 30m), 40° south declination ($\delta = -40°$).

Purkinje effect Originally the name of a physiological phenomenon relating to the sensitivity to light of the layer of rods and cones in the retina of the eye. The perception of color is the function of the cones while the rods are sensitive to light and darkness. If light is first received by the cones, then the rods, two stars of different colors but equal brightness (a blue and red star) will not appear to have the same brightness. The effect is eliminated with color filters. A similar condition found in photographic photometry is caused by the difference in sensitivity of photographic emulsions to blue and red light.

pyrheliometer An instrument for determining the intensity of the sun's radiation, i.e., the so-called *solar constant*.

Pythagoras of Samos (570–490 B.C.). He developed a cosmology in which the earth, moon, sun, and planets revolved around a central fire.

Pyxis (Compass) A faint constellation in the southern hemisphere at 9h right ascension ($\alpha = 9h$), 30° south declination ($\delta = -30°$).

Q

quadrant An antique instrument consisting of a 90° graduated arc with a sighting mechanism fastened to a movable arm; used to measure the altitude of a star. The principal instruments of Tycho Brahe were quadrants.

quadrature The position of the moon or a planet at 90° to the sun as measured from the earth. The moon's first and last quarters nearly correspond to eastern and western quadrature, respectively.

quartz crystal clock An astronomical precision clock regulated by the oscillation of a quartz crystal. Since the accuracy of the clock is impaired by the aging of the crystal, *atomic clocks* have begun to replace the quartz clock.

quasar or quasi-stellar radio sources Sources of radio frequency radiation which appear virtually as stars on ordinary photographs. Their optical spectrum indicates a *red shift* corresponding to a velocity of recession about half the speed

of light. Interpreted in terms of distance, these velocities indicate distances of several thousand million light-years to these
sources. Since they also appear rather bright, they must emit
energy a few hundred times as intense as from an ordinary
galaxy, in spite of their stellar appearance.

quasi-cepheids A type of semi-regular long-period variable
star with periods between the typical cepheids and the long-
period variables. One group represented includes the RV
Tauri stars.

quiet sun The condition of the sun when activity is at a minimum and the sun lacks spots, prominences, and flares. To
study the sun's radio emission, the radiation of the quiet sun
must be derived, a very difficult task since disturbances almost always occur on the sun. Through investigations of radio emission from the quiet sun at various wave lengths, the
temperature of the different layers of the solar atmosphere
can be derived. See: *sun.*

R

radar *Ra*dio *D*etection *a*nd *R*anging. Distance-findings by the
measurement of the time required for a radio signal to travel
from the transmitter to the target and back again. Radar has
become significant in astronomy in the study of meteor and
meteor swarms. Radar methods have been used to study the
surface of the moon and Venus as well as make precise measurements of distance to the sun and the nearer planets.

radial velocity The component of a star's velocity in the line
of sight is measured by the shift in the positions of the lines
in the star's spectrum as compared to the spectrum of a light
source at rest. According to the *Doppler principle* (**Doppler
effect*), the spectral lines shift to the blue if the star is approaching and toward the red if the star is receding. Radial
velocities are determined by the amount of displacement and
are measured in km/sec. If the star is receding, the displacement is positive (+), and negative (−) if the star is approaching.

radial velocity curve A smooth curve that graphically illustrates the changes in radial velocity of a *spectroscopic binary*
in one revolution. Through a study of the velocity curve, the

form and position of the star's orbit can be determined. (Fig. R1.)

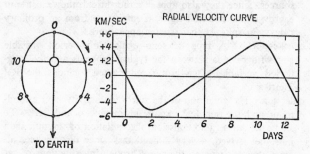

R1. Radial velocity curve. To the left, the orbit of a double star. To the right, the radial velocity curve developed from the orbital motion of the star.

radian The arc of a circle equal to the length of the radius. One radian is equal to 57°3; 3438'; 206265".

radiant The point in the sky from which a meteor swarm seems to emanate. The cosmic particles that cause a meteor swarm actually move in parallel paths through space. Because of perspective, they appear to come from the same point in the sky, called the radiant. Meteor swarms are identified by the constellation in which the radiant is located.

radiation belts Belts of charged particles around the earth. See: *Van Allen belts.*

radiation laws Radiation laws for black bodies. The most important are *Stefan-Boltzmann's, *Wien's,* and *Planck's radiation laws.* These laws are used in astronomy to determine temperatures.

radiation pressure The pressure exerted by radiation on all objects. Radiation pressure becomes a factor to be considered only when the bodies affected are very small (on the order of 10^{-3} to 10^{-4}mm or smaller) and can exceed the force of gravity many times over. The tails of comets are partially the result of radiation pressure.

radiation sources Point sources of radio frequency radiation. They are also called *radio sources* and sometimes *radio stars.*

radiation spectrum The same as *electromagnetic spectrum.*

radiative equilibrium The condition in a star where each volume of stellar gas absorbs as much energy per second as it emits.

radio activity Spontaneous fission of certain heavy atomic nuclei (radium, thorium, uranium) forming lighter elements with emission of radiation. The fission of uranium is used to determine the age of the earth and meteorites.

radio astronomy That branch of astronomy that studies radio frequency radiation from celestial bodies and the universe. In the early 1930s, the American radio technician K. G. Jansky, using a radio receiver tuned to a wave length of 15 meters, discovered radio noise of cosmic origin that coincided with the position of the Milky Way. After World War II, the study of cosmic radio waves was given a new impetus, resulting in entirely new areas of investigation. A special instrument, a *radio telescope,* is used to gather cosmic radio waves for analysis. Today, radio astronomical observatories are found throughout the entire world. The first giant radio telescope to be constructed has a diameter of 250 feet and is located at Jodrell Bank, in Cheshire, England. The radio frequency radiation is studied in a wave length region from a few millimeters to about 20 meters. Shorter wave lengths are absorbed by the atmosphere, while the longer wave lengths are reflected by the *ionosphere.* Among the most interesting radio astronomy discoveries are: **1.** Several thousand point sources of intense radiation called *radio sources* (sometimes called *radio stars*). Several sources have been identified optically as the remains of supernovae (Crab Nebula), peculiar filamentary emission nebulae (radio source Cassiopeia A), possible collisions between galaxies (radio source Cygnus A), as well as several "normal" galaxies (Andromeda Galaxy). **2.** In addition to radio sources, a general *continuous radiation* ("galactic noise") is concentrated in the plane of the Milky Way with a central condensation in the direction of the nucleus of the Galaxy. This radiation has been investigated in different wave lengths and isophotal charts have been constructed. Another radiation that is evenly distributed over the sky originates from the galactic halo surrounding the galactic system. **3.** An *emission* of 21 cm wave length originates from the neutral hydrogen in the Galaxy. From the form and intensity of this emission, the distribution of hydrogen and the structure of the spiral arms of the Galaxy can be studied. **4.** Investigations of radiation from various layers in the atmosphere of the sun have made it possible to determine the temperatures of these layers. Besides the sun, radio investigations of the temperatures of the moon and several planets have been made. Radio astronomy is developing rapidly and additional interesting discoveries are anticipated in the near future when large radio telescopes such as the 300-foot transit telescope at Green Bank, West Virginia, and the 1000-foot stationary disc at Arecibo, Puerto Rico, are used.

radio galaxy   A galaxy with abnormally high radio frequency radiation, such as the elliptical systems Messier 84 and 87 in the Virgo cluster. Attempts have been made to explain the intense radiation as supernovae explosions in the central regions whereby the entire nucleus of the galaxy should have exploded, but this theory is not generally accepted by astronomers, and the origin of intense radiation is still unknown.

radiometric magnitudes   Magnitudes determined by the total radiation of a body by means of sensitive *thermocouples.*

radio noise   Irregular variations in amplitude and oscillations of cosmic radio waves interpreted as an infinite number of frequencies in a broad band, a mixing of many tones, reproduced as noise in a speaker.

radio photometry   The determination of the intensity of radio frequency radiation.

radio source   *Point source; radio star;* a point source of radio frequency radiation. Several thousand radio sources have been discovered. Some have been identified optically as the remains of supernovae, strange emission nebulae, possible colliding galaxies and normal galaxies. See: *radio astronomy.*

radio stars   An earlier term used to describe radio frequency radiation sources. See: *radio sources.*

radio storm   Strong radio frequency radiation from the sun that occurs in conjunction with eruptions of *solar *flares* or other causes of solar activity.

radio sun   The "image" of the sun obtained from radio frequency radiation from the sun. The apparent size of the radio sun depends upon the wave length of the signal; centimeter waves produce a radio sun of about the same size as the optical sun since these waves radiate from the lower layers of the solar atmosphere, while meter waves produce a solar image that is many times larger than the optical sun and is flattened at the poles. These waves originate in the solar corona and the radio image produced coincides with the shape and size of the corona. (Radio investigations do not produce a real image. The size of the radio sun is derived from variations in radiation as the sun passes the radio telescope.)

radio telescope   An apparatus constructed to receive radio frequency radiation from celestial bodies and space. An antenna, often placed in the focus of a parabola of metal or metal grid, is tuned in to receive radio waves of a specific frequency. These waves are analyzed by a very sensitive radio receiver. Occasionally, a series of antennas is ganged to increase the resolving power of a radio telescope. Compared to an optical telescope, a radio telescope has low resolving power; a radio telescope with the same resolving power as the human eye must have a disc diameter of 5 km for waves of one meter. Real images are not seen with a radio telescope. Instead, radiation is detected and its intensity measured. Methods based upon wave interference are used to increase resolving power. See: *interferometer.*

radio waves Electromagnetic radiation with wave lengths located between 0.001 and 30,000 meters.

radio window The absorption gap in the atmosphere that admits radio waves of a few millimeters to about 20 meters in wave length. This radio frequency radiation is received by radio telescopes. (See Fig. A14.)

radius A straight line from the center to the surface of a sphere. In a few instances the radius of a star can be measured directly using methods based upon the interference of light (supergiant stars). In addition, it is possible to determine the radius of an eclipsing binary star as one component passes in front of the other. The radius of a star can be estimated from the total radiation of the star by means of radiation laws such as the *Stefan-Boltzmann law.

radius vector The straight line connecting the sun and a planet in an elliptical orbit.

Ram Constellation in the northern hemisphere. See: *Aries.*

Ramsden ocular A positive ocular frequently used in astronomy, consisting of two positive lenses (plano-convex) with the convex sides turned toward one another. Since the focal point is located beyond the lenses, the ocular can be used to great advantage with micrometer readings. (Fig. R2.)

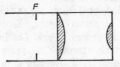

R2. Ramsden ocular.

Ranger vehicles American lunar probes. The last three, Ranger VII (1964) and Rangers VIII and IX (1965), obtained close-range photographs of the moon's surface, showing a tremendous amount of fine detail.

Ras Algethi The star Alpha (α) Herculis of apparent visual magnitude 3.5 and spectral type M3.

Rayleigh diffusion The diffusion of light by particles smaller than the wave length of light. Lord Rayleigh found that the diffusion by such particles is inversely proportional to the fourth power of the wave length of the light.

rays, lunar A phenomenon observed on the moon, especially at about the full moon. Bright rays are seen to emanate from larger craters (such as Tycho), and pass unhindered across the terrain, bisecting craters and mountain ranges.

reading microscope A microscope sighted on the graduated circle of a meridian circle to facilitate precise readings.

receiver noise Disturbances emitted by the electrical resistance and the vacuum tubes in a radio receiver.

recombination The capture of a free electron by a proton. Radiation is emitted when the kinetic energy of the electron is released.

recurrent nova A type of exploding star where several nova eruptions have been seen to occur, i.e., stars such as RS Ophiuchi, U Scorpie, T Pyxidis, and others.

red shift A phenomenon in the spectra of galaxies observed as a shift of the spectral lines toward the red. Interpreted as a *Doppler effect,* the red shift indicates that the galaxies are receding. In 1929, the American astronomer Hubble found that the amount of red shift increased according to the distance of the galaxy at the rate of 180 km/sec per one million light-years. Recent measurements of radial velocities of galaxies with speeds approaching 61,000 km/sec and an improved distance scale have lowered the rate of increase (*Hubble constant*) to only about $\frac{1}{10}$ of the original estimate. The value of the constant is still uncertain and is believed to be about 20 km/sec per million light-years. Distances are determined by the amount of red shift. See: *expansion of the universe* and *relativistic red shift.*

Red Spot A reddish oval spot, 30,000 miles long and 7000 miles wide, on the planet Jupiter, discovered in 1878 (but probably visible 50 years earlier). The intensity of the color of the spot has varied through the years. Although the spot is seen to drift slightly, it is assumed to be an atmospheric phenomenon; a more solid mass floating in an ocean of extremely dense gases. The nature of the spot is unknown.

reflecting telescope A telescope in which the image is produced by reflection of light by a concave mirror. Generally, the mirror is parabolic. By means of secondary mirrors, light is reflected to the side of the tube (*Newtonian telescope*), or back through a hole bored in the center of the primary mirror (*Cassegrainian telescope*), or directed to the ocular in some other way. One advantage of a reflecting telescope is the absence of chromatic aberration. Another advantage is size. Larger reflectors than refractors can be constructed since the mirror is supported across its back while a lens must be supported along its rim. A lens is therefore very easily deformed by its own weight. (The Hale telescope on Mt. Palomar Observatory has a primary mirror with a diameter of 200 inches.) The light-gathering power of reflecting telescopes is therefore greater than refracting telescopes. A *Schmidt telescope*, which has a spherical mirror and a correcting plate at the center of curvature to do away with spherical aberration, is used to photograph a wide area of the sky.

reflection To turn back a wave motion at the surface between two dissimilar media. The reflection of light is made use of in reflecting telescopes and radio waves in radio telescopes.

reflection grating A grating with fine parallel grooves on a mirrored surface used to produce a spectrum. Often a reflection grating will contain over 10,000 grooves per inch.

reflection instrument Angle-measuring instrument consisting of movable mirrors and prisms. The optical parts are turned so that two stars coincide in the field of view. The angular distance between the stars is derived from the amount that the mirrors are turned. The altitude of a celestial body can also be measured. The most common instruments of this type are the *sextant* and *prism circle*.

reflection nebulae Extensive clouds of small solid particles (cosmic dust) that reflect light from nearby stars and appear as bright nebulae when photographed.

refracting angle The angle formed by the faces of a prism.

refracting edge The edge of a prism.

refraction The bending of light in passing through optical media (glass, lenses, prisms) in astronomical instruments and through the atmosphere. Usually reference to refraction is made with respect to *atmospheric refraction*. As light penetrates the atmosphere, it encounters layers of air of increasing density, resulting in the continuous bending of light in accordance with the laws of refraction. The amount of change in direction is dependent upon the composition of the atmosphere and the zenith distance of the celestial body. Refraction causes the star to appear higher in the sky and this increase in altitude varies with respect to zenith distance. At the zenith, refraction is $0'0''$; at $45°$ zenith distance, refraction will be about $1'$; at the horizon, refraction amounts to about $35'$. Usually, a correction for refraction is necessary to obtain the true position of a star after its apparent position has been measured. (See Fig. A15.) A light beam that passes from one medium to a denser medium bends toward the vertical so that the angle formed by the entering beam (α_1) (angle of incidence) and the angle of the refracted beam (α_2) (angle of refraction) may be expressed in the following relationship:

$$\frac{\sin\alpha_1}{\sin\alpha_2} = \frac{n_2}{n_1}$$

where n = index of refraction, which is a constant for each substance. The index of refraction varies with the wave length of light. (In yellow light, for water, $n = 1.3$, and for glass, between 1.5 and 1.7.) Refraction has its application in astronomy through the use of lenses and prisms.

refraction, angle of   The difference between a star's true and apparent zenith distance.

refraction, constant of   A constant related to the index of refraction of the atmosphere. The amount of refraction is found by multiplying the constant by the tangent of the zenith distance. The value of the constant reaches $58''2$.

refractor   Astronomical telescope in which an image is formed by the refraction of light through a lens or lens system (*objective*). See: *astronomical instruments*.

Regulus   The star Alpha (α) Leonis of apparent visual magnitude 1.3 and spectral type B8.

relativistic red shift   A phenomenon that is predicted by Einstein's general theory of relativity. According to the theory, energy and mass are equivalent. Light emitted by a star is influenced by the gravitational field of the star and will suffer a slight loss in energy with spectral lines displaced toward the red. The red shift is very small in normal stars, but reaches measurable amounts among the dense white dwarfs of small radii. The displacement for the white dwarf companion of Sirius was observed for the first time by W. S. Adams, at Mt. Wilson Observatory in 1925. See: *Einstein effects*.

relativity, theories of   The theories developed by Albert Einstein regarding time and space. According to the special theory of relativity (1905), time and distance are not absolute values but are dependent upon the relative motion of the observer and the body under investigation. The general theory of relativity (1916) treats the structure of space and gravitation. See: *Einstein's theories of relativity.*

Relay   American satellites for transmitting radio and TV programs between distant places on earth.

resolving power   The ability of an astronomical instrument to separate close stars or details on the surface of the moon and planets. Resolving power depends upon the diffraction of light in the telescope. A point source of light will form into a small disc (spurious disc) whose diameter is proportional to the wave length and the focal length of the objective and inversely proportional to the diameter of the aperture. The resolving power of a telescope is a measure of the distance between the centers of the spurious discs when the edge of one disc coincides with the center of the other. A refracting telescope with an aperture of 4.5 inches can resolve a double star with an angular separation of 1″. The resolving power of the Yerkes refractor, the largest in the world, is 0″.14. The resolving power of radio telescopes is very low.

reticle   A cross of fine wire placed in the focal plane of a telescope so that the optical axis coincides with the straight line between the centers of the objective and the cross-wire. Sometimes, a reticle will contain a series of parallel lines on both sides of the central cross-wire used during the installation of the telescope.

Reticulum   (Net) A faint constellation in the southern hemisphere at 4h right ascension ($\alpha = 4h$), 62° south declination ($\delta = -62°$).

retrograde motion   Any motion contrary to the usual, or direct, sense. **1.** Apparent retrograde motion is the westward motion among the stars of a body in the solar system. This is caused by the overtaking and passing of one planet with respect to the earth, resulting in apparent "backward" motion of the other planet. **2.** A comet may have a real retrograde motion in the sense that it revolves around the sun in a clockwise direction as seen from the north side of the solar system. Similarly, several natural satellites around planets in the solar system possess retrograde revolutions. **3.** Uranus and Venus appear to rotate in a clockwise manner as viewed from the north side of the solar system.

Rhea   One of the planet Saturn's satellites, discovered by Cassini in 1672. Its period of revolution is 4.52 days and its mean distance from Saturn is 328,000 miles.

Rigel   The star Beta (β) Orionis of apparent visual magnitude 0.3 and spectral type B8p.

right ascension   (α) A co-ordinate in the equator system measured from the vernal equinox eastward to the point where the hour circle of a star intersects the celestial equator. Right ascension is expressed in hours, minutes, and seconds and is independent of diurnal motion. Right ascension is one of the co-ordinates more frequently used in stellar catalogues. See: *astronomical co-ordinates.*

ring mountains   The most characteristic formation on the moon. The craters consist of a high circular wall that slopes gently outward and steeply inward toward the crater floor which is usually depressed below the surrounding lunar surface. A central mountain peak is found in many craters. The diameters of the craters vary from the largest, over 100 miles across, to the smallest which are barely visible. The origin of the craters is controversial, with meteor bombardment receiving the greatest support.

ring nebula   A kind of *planetary nebula* that has the appearance of a ring when viewed in the telescope or on a photographic plate. The best known is the *Ring Nebula* in Lyra, M 57 or NGC 6720.

ring plains   The moon's largest crater formations, *walled plains* with diameters from 30 to 185 miles.

Roche's limit   A limiting value for a satellite's distance from the planet, discovered by E. Roche. A satellite will disintegrate unless it revolves in an orbit at a distance greater than 2.4 times the radius of the planet (assuming that both bodies have the same density). Inside Roche's limit, the disturbing effect of the planet is great enough to disintegrate the satellite and have its substance scattered along the orbit. See: *Saturn's rings.*

Roche's model   A lenticular body with a sharp edge along the equator, formed through rapid rotation. Increased rotation introduces instability, with particles of matter released along the edge. The concept has been applied in theories of the origin of binary stars and the solar system.

rocket observations   Rockets are principally used to study the short-wave radiation from the sun. Instrumented rockets have been launched above the absorption layers in the earth's atmosphere to several hundred miles altitude.

Rockoon   A rocket fired from a balloon in the stratosphere, used by American geophysicists to study the conditions in the earth's upper atmosphere as well as solar radiation.

Rømer, Ole   (1644–1710) Danish astronomer who invented the meridian circle and determined the speed of light by observing the satellites of Jupiter being eclipsed by the planet.

rotation   The spinning motion of a celestial body about an axis within the body. **1.** ROTATION OF THE PLANETS. See topic for each planet. **2.** STELLAR ROTATION. The rotation of the stars can be determined with spectroscopic techniques. One edge of the star will approach while the other edge will recede unless the axis of rotation lies in the line of sight. The contours of the lines in its spectrum will be deformed. This method is used with stars of rapid rotation, and in certain circumstances, applied to eclipsing binary stars. **3.** GALACTIC ROTATION. Theoretical investigations of B. Lindblad (1925) and the study of stellar motion in selected areas of the Milky Way by J. Oort (1926) led to the discovery of galactic rotation centered in the direction of the constellation of Sagittarius. The speed of rotation varies with the distance from the center. In the vicinity of the sun, the period of revolution is 225 million years at a velocity of 250 km/sec. The distance to the center of rotation amounts to 30,000 light-years. **4.** ROTATION OF EXTERIOR SYSTEMS. Rotation analogous to the Milky Way has been detected in several galaxies including the Great Galaxy in Andromeda. (Fig. R3.)

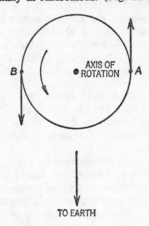

R3. Rotation of a star.

rotation parallax The mean distance to star clusters determined from their galactic rotation.

RR Lyrae (variable stars) See: *Lyra*.

R series A branch of the *Harvard classification* of stellar spectra that includes spectral types R and N and is joined to the main sequence at the position of the G stars. N stars are exceedingly red. These stars are now classified as carbon stars.

rubidium-strontium method A radioactive method to determine age. See: *age*.

Russell diagram See: *Hertzsprung-Russell diagram*.

Russell, Henry Norris (1879–1957) American astronomer. Russell was director of Princeton Observatory, 1912–47, and made many significant contributions in astrophysics. He determined the relative distribution of the basic elements in the universe, developed the theory for eclipsing binaries, and was one of the originators of the *Hertzsprung-Russell diagram*.

RV Tauri stars See: *Taurus*.

S

Sagitta (Arrow) A small constellation in the northern hemisphere located in the Milky Way at 19h 40m right ascension (α = 19h 40m), 18° north declination (δ = +18°).

Sagittarius (Archer) A large constellation belonging to the Zodiac located in the southern hemisphere at approximately 19h right ascension (α = 19h), 25° south declination (δ = −25°). The constellation, part of which lies in the Milky Way, contains star clouds, many globular clusters, and gaseous nebulae. The center of the Galaxy lies in the direction of Sagittarius.

Saha, Meghnad (1893–1956) Indian physicist and astrophysicist. He developed a formula named after him which gives the proportion of ionized to neutral atoms that made it possible to deduce exact temperatures of the stars of different spectral types.

Sails Constellation in the southern hemisphere. See: *Vela*.

Salpeter process A nuclear process, named after E. E. Salpeter, in which helium is transmuted to the heavier elements such as carbon, requiring temperatures to 2×10^8 degrees C. See: *energy production* in the stars.

Saros A period of 18 years 11 days used by ancient astronomers to predict eclipses. After each Saros, eclipses of the sun and moon will occur in the same order in the same time. The Saros was known to the Babylonians. Because of perturbations in the moon's motion, the nodes regress a complete revolution around the ecliptic in a Saros with the sun and the moon returning to the same node, repeating the eclipse cycle.

satellite A moon, a small celestial body moving in an orbit about a planet. See: *artificial satellites*.

satellite galaxy A smaller galaxy that is physically united with a larger. The Milky Way system has two satellite galaxies, the *Magellanic Clouds*. The Andromeda Galaxy also has two satellite galaxies (elliptical galaxies).

Saturn The sixth major planet measured from the sun. The planet has been known since antiquity. Its mean distance to the sun amounts to 9.54 astronomical units and its period of revolution is 29.46 years. The planet's mass is 95 earth masses; the equatorial diameter is 75,000 miles, the polar diameter 67,000 miles. Density = 0.7 (water = 1). The planet has a rapid rotation, amounting to 10.2 hours. Through a telescope, the planet's disc appears similar to Jupiter's, with cloud belts seen parallel to the equator, although on Saturn they are more diffuse. Saturn, like Jupiter, does not reveal a solid surface but, instead, we see the outer layers of a dense cloud cover in an extensive atmosphere. Spectroscopic investigations have revealed that the atmosphere contains methane and ammonia. Saturn is one of the giant planets and is presumed to have the same structure as Jupiter and the other giants. Regarding the internal composition, two hypotheses have been postulated: 1. The planet has a deep atmosphere of hydrogen and methane with drifting clouds of ammonia. A thick layer of ice lies beneath the atmosphere and, at the center, a rocky metallic core. 2. In addition to methane and ammonia in outer layers of the atmosphere, the entire planet consists of hydrogen and helium which are highly compressed in the core and found in the liquid or solid state. Saturn is surrounded by a ring system, *Saturn's rings,* first observed by Galileo in 1610 but identified as rings by C. Huygens in 1655. The outer diameter of the ring system amounts to about 171,000 miles, while the inner diameter is 93,000 miles. The thickness of the ring is estimated to be between 7 and 15 miles. Three concentric rings are distinctly seen lying in the planet's equatorial plane: the outer ring (Ring A), the middle ring (Ring B), and the crêpe ring (Ring C). The two outer rings are separated by a dark gap, *Cassini's division*. The crêpe ring is substantially fainter and more difficult to observe than the two outer rings. The rings consist of a huge swarm of small solid particles (possibly of ice) that revolve around the planet in accordance with Kepler's laws. Since the rings lie within *Roche's limit*, this substance could not condense into a satellite but formed a ring instead. In addition to the ring system, Saturn has 9 satellites measured from the planet as follows: Mimas, Enceladus, Tethys, Dione, Rhea, Titan, Hyperion, Iapetus, and Phoebe. The largest, Titan, has a diameter of about 3000 miles and an atmosphere containing ammonia and methane. (In 1905, E. Pickering observed a tenth satellite that later could not be found.)

Saturn's rings The ring system surrounding the planet *Saturn.*

Scales Constellation in the southern hemisphere. See: *Libra.*

scattering of light 1. COLOR SEPARATION. See: *dispersion.* 2. DIFFUSE REFLECTION. A scattering of light rays when passing through a cloud of molecules or small solid particles whereby blue light is dispersed more than red. (Dispersion of light in the earth's atmosphere causes the sky to appear blue.) If the particles are small in comparison with the wave length (λ) of light, according to *Rayleigh's law,* dispersion is proportional to $1/\lambda^4$.

Schedar The star Alpha (α) Cassiopeiae. Its visual magnitude varies between 2.1 and 2.6 and its spectral type is K0.

Schiaparelli, Giovanni Virginio (1835–1910) Italian astronomer. In 1866, he discovered the relationship between comets and meteors and became famous for his comprehensive observations of the oppositions of Mars from 1877 to 1890. He observed the phenomenon that later came to be known as "Martian canals."

Schmidt, Bernhard (1879–1935) Swedish-Estonian optician active in Hamburg Observatory at Bergedorf, Germany. He became famous for his construction of the coma-free reflecting telescope named after him, the *Schmidt telescope.*

Schmidt telescope An optical system invented by B. Schmidt consisting of a spherical mirror and a correcting plate placed at the center of curvature of the mirror so that the images are freed from spherical aberration, coma, and astigmatism. The Schmidt telescope can have a very small focal ratio and can photograph wide angular fields with perfect images on plates and films bent to the curved focal surface. The world's three largest Schmidt telescopes are in Tautenburg, East Germany (1960), the diameter of the correcting plate being 53 inches, the diameter of the spherical mirror 72 inches and the focal length 157 inches (53 in./72 in./157 in.); Mt. Palomar Observatory, (1948) (48 in./72 in./121 in.); and the University of Uppsala Observatory, Kvistaberg Station, Sweden (1963) (40 in./53 in./119 in.). (Fig. S1.)

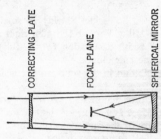

S1. Schmidt telescope.

Schönberg's limit   See: *Chandrasekhar limit* and *stellar evolution.*

Schraffiercassette method   A method of obtaining a square image of a point source of light, proposed by K. Schwarzschild of Germany. By means of a clock-drive, the plate holder is moved in a rectangle during exposure so that the image of a star is smeared to form a square of even brightness. The magnitude of a star can be accurately determined from the brightness of the square image. The camera used is called a *jiggle-camera.*

Schwarzschild, Karl   (1873–1916) German astronomer who made comprehensive photometric investigations, studied stellar motion, and devised new optical systems. He carried out fundamental work in theoretical astrophysics.

scintillation   The twinkling of the stars. As seen in a telescope, scintillation produces short, rapid changes in the position of the star. To the naked eye, scintillation appears as a change in the star's brightness and color. Scintillation is the result of uneven refraction of starlight during rapid changes of density in the earth's atmosphere.

Scorpion   A constellation in the southern hemisphere. See: *Scorpius.*

Scorpius (Scorpion) A large and impressive constellation belonging to the Zodiac. It is located in the southern hemisphere at approximately 16h 30m right ascension (α = 16h 30m), 30° south declination (δ = −30°). The brightest star is Alpha (α) Scorpii (Antares), a red star which is among the brightest stars in the sky. The constellation contains many star clusters.

Sculptor A faint constellation located in the southern hemisphere at 0h 30m right ascension (α = 0h 30m), 33° south declination (δ = −33°).

Scutum (Shield, or Sobieski's Shield) A small constellation in the southern Milky Way at 18h 40m right ascension (α = 18h 40m), 10° south declination (δ = −10°). Scutum contains an immense star cloud.

Sea Goat Constellation in the southern hemisphere. See: *Capricornus*.

Sea of Serenity (Mare Serenitatis) A lunar "sea."

Sea of Showers (Mare Imbrium) A lunar "sea" located in the northeastern part of the surface of the moon.

seasonal hours See: *temporary hours*.

seasons As a result of the obliquity of the ecliptic, the angular distance between the sun and the equator varies in the course of a year. This circumstance gives rise to the seasons. The four seasons are astronomically defined by the different positions of the sun with respect to the equator. In the northern hemisphere, *spring* is measured from the vernal equinox (March 21) to the summer solstice (June 22), *summer* from the summer solstice to the autumnal equinox (September 23), *autumn* from the autumnal equinox to the winter solstice (December 22), and *winter* from the winter solstice to the vernal equinox. The average lengths of the seasons are: spring, 92.8 days; summer, 93.6 days; autumn, 89.8 days; and winter, 89 days. (Lengths are subject to secular changes.)

Secchi, Angelo (1818–1878) Italian astronomer who made the first spectral classification of stars.

secondary spectrum A type of chromatic aberration in lenses. The secondary spectrum of an objective lens results in a colored ring of light around the image of the star or other celestial objects.

secular Continuing over a long period of time.

secular acceleration An increase in the mean angular velocity of the moon. By comparing recent and ancient eclipses, it is found that the moon's period is somewhat shorter today than

2000 years ago. The phenomenon can be explained by a change in the earth's rotational speed. However, the reasons for this irregular motion are controversial.

secular parallax The apparent displacement of a star in the sky as a result of the sun's motion through space, i.e., the component of the star's proper motion due to the sun's motion. The more distant a star is, the smaller its parallax. Assuming that the genuine motions of the stars are at random, the average value of the secular parallax for a group of stars may be found from their proper motions.

secular perturbations Perturbations in the motion of celestial bodies expressed as slow continuous changes in the positions of their orbits. See: *perturbations.*

secular variation The change in annual precession in 100 years.

seeing The condition of the atmosphere from an astronomical point of view. Good seeing indicates a calm, transparent atmosphere permitting well-defined images in the telescope. Bad seeing denotes turbulent air and blurred telescopic images.

selected areas Small areas of the sky evenly distributed over the celestial sphere which have been studied to obtain a sampling of the distribution of stars in the Milky Way system. Proposed by J. C. Kapteyn, the stars in the selected areas have their proper motions determined as accurately as possible. See: *Kapteyn's selected areas.*

selective absorption Absorption that is related to the wave length of light. *Interstellar absorption* is selective, as is the absorption of light in the atmosphere (*extinction*).

selenium photometer A photoelectric photometer which utilizes the properties of the substance selenium to change electric conductivity when illuminated. The selenium photometer has been replaced by instruments using alkali cells which are decidedly more sensitive and in many respects more effective.

selenography Topographic description and charting of the surface of the moon.

separation The apparent distance between the components of a binary system.

Serpens (Serpent) An inconspicuous irregular constellation situated on both sides of Ophiuchus (Serpent Bearer). The constellation is divided into two parts, *Serpens Caput* (Serpent's Head) at 15h 30m right ascension (α = 15h 30m),

15° north declination ($\delta = +15°$), and *Serpens Cauda* (Serpent's Tail) at 18h 30m right ascension ($\alpha =$ 18h 30m), 0° declination ($\delta = 0°$).

Serpent Constellation in the northern hemisphere. See: *Serpens.*

Serpentarius The Latin name for *Ophiuchus,* the Serpent Bearer, a constellation across the celestial sky.

Serpent Bearer Constellation that lies across the celestial equator. See: *Ophiuchus.*

Seven Sisters A star cluster in Taurus. See: *Pleiades.*

Sextans (Sextant) A faint constellation located at the celestial equator and 10h 20m ($\alpha =$ 10h 20m), 0° declination ($\delta = 0°$).

Sextant Constellation on the celestial equator. See: *Sextans.*

sextant An instrument used primarily in nautical astronomy to measure the angular distances of celestial bodies above the horizon. (See Fig. S2.) The sextant consists of a 60°

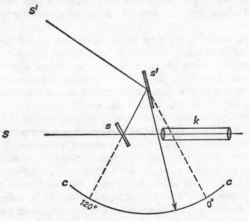

S2. Schematic diagram of a sextant.

graduated arc, or limb, *c,* a small telescope, *k,* and two mirrors, *s* and *s'.* Only half of one of the mirrors, the horizon glass, *s,* is silvered and, like the telescope, it is fastened to the frame supporting the limb. The other mirror, the index mirror, *s',* moves with an index arm pivoted at the center of the arc. The index arm, or **alidade,* is equipped with a vernier which moves along the limb. An object in direction *S* can be observed in the telescope through the unsilvered portion of the horizon glass, *s*. By moving the index arm, *S'* is made to coincide with *S* in the telescope. According to the law of reflection, the angle between *S* and *S'* is double the angle between the mirrors. The angular distance between the objects can be obtained from the vernier reading since the limb is numbered at half scale.

shadow bands An atmospheric phenomenon that occurs during a solar eclipse shortly before and after totality. A series of shadows, caused by differences in the optical density of the atmosphere, ripples across the terrain. This faint phenomenon was photographed for the first time by a Dutch expedition to Gotland at the 1954 eclipse.

Shapley's wing A winglike projection in the *Small Magellanic Cloud* in the direction of the *Large Magellanic Cloud,* discovered by H. Shapley.

shell model A model of the interior of a star where the radiation of energy occurs in a shell surrounding the core. The assumption is made that after the hydrogen in the central core has been converted to helium, energy continues to be produced in a shell surrounding the burned-out core. See: *energy production* in stars.

shell star A star surrounded by an extensive atmosphere or an expanding gas envelope. Many such stars are known including Wolf-Rayet and P Cygni stars characterized by emission lines in their spectra. Important conclusions regarding the physical conditions of these stars are made through the study of their complicated spectra.

Shepard, Alan (1923–) The first American astronaut. On May 5, 1961, Shepard undertook a suborbital flight in a Mercury capsule.

Ship Constellation in the southern hemisphere. See: *Argo.*

short-period cepheid A *cepheid variable* star with a period of less than one day. These are cluster type or RR Lyrae variables belonging to Population II classification (old stars).

sidereal Pertaining to the stars.

sidereal day The time required for two successive upper culminations of the same star. The sidereal day begins when the vernal equinox, the first point of Aries, crosses the observer's meridian at 0h 0m 0s, sidereal noon. A sidereal day is four minutes shorter than the mean solar day.

sidereal month The moon's true period of revolution around the earth, or the time required by the moon to complete one revolution with respect to the stars. The sidereal month = 27.3217 days.

sidereal period The time required by the moon or a planet to complete one revolution with respect to the stars.

sidereal time The time that is based upon the rotation of the earth with respect to the stars, with the sidereal day as the unit of measure (the time between two successive upper culminations of the vernal equinox). The instant the vernal equinox crosses the meridian in upper culmination, sidereal time is equal to 0h for that position. The hour angle of the vernal equinox is equal to sidereal time.

sidereal year The sun's period of revolution with respect to the stars which coincides with the earth's revolution in its orbit around the sun. The sidereal year = 365.2564 mean solar days.

siderite A *meteorite* containing 90% to 95% iron (with nickel and traces of other metals). Also called an *iron meteorite.*

siderostat A *heliostat.* A mirror arrangement with clock-drive that reflects light from a celestial body to a fixed position such as a horizontally-mounted camera. See: *coelostat.*

signs of the Zodiac Since antiquity, the Zodiac has been divided into 12 signs, each extending 30°. Beginning at the vernal equinox, the first 30° is assigned to Aries, followed by Taurus, etc. As a result of precession, the signs of the Zodiac no longer coincide with the constellations of the same name. During its annual motion, the sun is found in each sign for about one month.

Sirius The *Dog Star,* Alpha (α) Canis Majoris, the brightest star in the constellation *Canis Major,* the Greater Dog; the brightest star in the sky of apparent visual magnitude −1.6 and spectral type A0. Its distance is equal to 8.7 light-years, absolute magnitude +1.3, and surface temperature about 10,000° C. Sirius is a binary star with a component, *Sirius B,* 10 magnitudes fainter than the primary star. This component is a **white dwarf star* with a mass equal to the sun, but its diameter is only 0.034 solar diameters. The mean distance between the stars is about 20 astronomical units and a period of revolution of 50 years.

Sirius, Companion of The faint component of Sirius, *Sirius B,* an interesting **white dwarf star.* See: *Sirius.*

slit **1.** A narrow opening through which the light passes entering a spectrograph. **2.** The opening in an observatory dome from the lower edge to beyond the highest point. Shutters uncover the slit during observations.

slit spectrograph A spectrograph equipped with a narrow slit through which light is permitted to enter the spectrograph.

small circle The circle formed by the intersection of a sphere and a plane that does not pass through the center of the sphere.

Small Magellanic Cloud The smaller of the Magellanic Clouds, two nearby galaxies in the southern hemisphere. Its distance is about 200,000 light-years and diameter about 30,000 light-years. See: *Magellanic Clouds.*

solar activity Variable phenomena on the surface of the sun. Systematic observations from solar observatories around the world keep this activity under continuous surveillance. The most important examples include *sunspots, *faculae, *prominences,* and *flares.* Solar activity is reflected in the radio frequency radiation from the sun as *radio storms* or *bursts* or outbursts when unusually powerful. Solar activity follows an 11-year cycle. See: *sunspot cycle.*

solar battery A battery that converts solar energy to electrical current. Solar batteries are used as energy sources for artificial satellites. The basic element in a solar battery is a silicon semi-conductor that produces an electrical pressure of ⅓ volt. Solar batteries are wired in parallel or series to obtain the desired voltage and current.

solar constant The amount of energy that a surface of one square centimeter receives each minute when placed beyond the atmosphere at right angles to the sun's rays at the earth's mean distance from the sun. Its value is 1.94 calories per square centimeter per minute. The constant is subject to slight variations.

solar corona The sun's outer atmosphere. During a total eclipse, the corona surrounds the sun like a diffuse, pearly envelope. The corona is intensely bright near the sun but brightness diminishes rapidly outward. The corona has a continuous spectrum with bright lines of highly ionized iron, nickel, and calcium. The corona is divided into two components that blend to form the *white corona.* Differentiation is made between the actual corona, the *K corona,* formed by a cloud of free electrons with temperatures on the order of one million degrees, and the *F corona* produced in the outer regions. The F corona extends to a distance of 30 solar diameters and gradually merges with the small particles of dust which reflect the sun's light to produce the zodiacal light. The *E corona* originates from emission lines. The structure and form of the corona change with the sunspot cycle. At sunspot maximum, the corona is very symmetrical while at minimum, long streamers extend in the equatorial region.

solar day The sun's daily period. The time interval between two successive upper culminations of the sun is called an *apparent solar day*. Since the sun's annual motion along the ecliptic is not constant, apparent solar days are irregular in length. The average value of apparent solar days is called the *mean solar day*. See: *day* and *time*.

solar eclipse A solar eclipse occurs when the moon passes between the sun and the earth. Where the umbra of the moon's shadow strikes the earth, the eclipse will be *total* (*zone of totality*). The eclipse will be *partial* within the region covered by the penumbra. When the moon's distance is too great for the umbra to reach the earth, the eclipse will be *annular,* or ring-formed, at all points on the earth lying on the center line between the moon and sun. Total eclipses are events eagerly awaited by astronomers since several solar phenomena such as the *corona* can only be studied during totality. See: *flash spectrum.* (Fig. S3.)

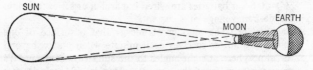

S3. Solar eclipse.

solar eruption An outburst of radiation on the sun; the same as solar flare, or **flare*.

solar flare The same as a **flare* (an eruption of radiation on the sun).

solar instruments Instruments of special construction for the investigation of solar phenomena. One of the earlier instruments used was the *spectroheliograph* constructed by G. E. Hale and H. Deslandres. Basically, this instrument is a spectrograph equipped with a secondary slit to isolate a particular spectral line and later photograph the sun in the light of this line. These photographs are called *spectroheliograms.* By using modern polarizing interference filters that isolate one wave length such as the Hα line, monochromatic photographs of the sun are obtained. These *monochromators* are used extensively in solar investigation. Other solar instruments include the **coronagraph*, which is used to study the corona in full daylight in the absence of a total eclipse.

solar parallax The angle subtended by the earth's equatorial radius as seen from the sun. The parallax amounts to 8".79, corresponding to a distance of 92,868,000 miles. Indirect methods must be used to measure the distance to the sun. The most common method of determination is the use of a third body. During favorable opposition of the asteroid Eros, a distance of about 13,900,000 miles and a parallax of 60", the sun's distance was calculated using **Kepler's third law*. Recent radar observations of Venus place the value of the solar parallax at 8".7943 ± 0".0003.

solar prominences Enormous eruptions in the sun's atmosphere (chromosphere) which appear as if they were giant tongues of flame when seen at the limb of the sun. See: *prominences*.

solar rotation The axial rotation of the sun. Solar rotation is determined from the motion of sunspots across the solar disc or by means of the Doppler principle (as a result of rotation, one edge of the sun approaches while the other recedes). The sun does not rotate as a solid body but turns faster at the equator than at the poles. The sidereal period of rotation (the true period) in the main region of the sunspots amounts to 25.4 days, while the synodic period (with respect to the earth's position) is 27.3 days. At ±70° heliographic latitude, the period is longer by 4 days. (At the equator the period of rotation is shorter than the above values by 0.4 days.)

solar spectrum A continuous spectrum with dark absorption lines (Fraunhofer lines) investigated for the first time by Newton in 1666. The lines were discovered by Wollaston in 1802 and Fraunhofer in 1814. The extreme brightness of the sun permits high dispersion, allowing both qualitative and quantitative analysis of the sun's atmosphere. A detailed atlas of the solar spectrum has been produced by M. Minnaert and his co-workers at Sonnenborgh Observatory, Utrecht, Netherlands. Through the study of spectral lines, it is possible to investigate different layers of the solar atmosphere, magnetic conditions, etc., of the enormously large number of absorption lines in the solar spectrum; over 20,000 have been measured. The sun's ultraviolet spectrum has been studied by means of rocket observations. The sun is a dwarf star of spectral type G2 in the *Harvard classification*.

solar system The sun and a large number of celestial bodies united as a physical unit by the gravitational attraction of the sun. The largest bodies are the nine *major planets,* Mercury, Venus, Earth, Mars, Jupiter, Saturn, Uranus, Neptune, and Pluto, which describe elliptical or nearly circular orbits in almost the same plane as the sun's equator with the sun at one focus. With the exception of Mercury, Venus, and Pluto, the planets are surrounded by smaller bodies, called moons or satellites. Besides the major planets, a large number of smaller bodies, the *minor planets,* are primarily located between the orbits of Mars and Jupiter. In addition, there is a group of celestial bodies called *comets* in elongated orbits that are almost parabolic in all possible inclinations to the plane of the ecliptic. Altogether, the comets form an immense cloud estimated to have a diameter of several light-years far beyond the limits of the solar system. Interplanetary space is filled with very tenuous matter including cosmic dust and charged particles as well as an occasional large mass of stone or iron alloy (meteorite). The small dust particles are observed as the *zodiacal light* and as outer *corona* during a total eclipse of the sun. The following table includes data for the solar system:

	Sidereal period*	Mean distance*	Mass*	Equatorial diameter*	Period of rotation
Sun	—	—	333,000	109.3	25 days
Mercury	0.24	0.39	0.04	0.39	88 days
Venus	0.62	0.72	0.82	0.97	250 days**
Earth	1.00	1.00	1.00	1.00	23^{h}9
Mars	1.88	1.52	0.11	0.53	24^{h}6
Asteroids	1.5–14.0	1.5–5.8	—	—	—
Jupiter	11.86	5.2	318.4	11.2	9^{h}8
Saturn	29.46	9.54	95.3	9.4	10^{h}2
Uranus	84.01	19.18	14.6	4.1	10^{h}7
Neptune	164.79	30.06	17.3	3.9	15^{h}8
Pluto	248.43	39.52	.9	0.5	6.4 days

* Expressed in terms of the values for the earth as unity.
** retrograde.

solar time Time based upon the daily motion of the sun which is generally used for civil purposes.

solar wind The steady stream of charged particles, protons or electrons, that recede from the sun at high speeds. Often the velocity of these particles reaches several hundred miles per second. The solar wind increases in intensity and speed during solar activity such as the eruption of solar *flares,* when plasma clouds influence the magnetic field of the earth.

solstices The extreme positions of the sun in its apparent annual path when its declination has reached greatest northern value (summer solstice) or greatest southern value (winter solstice).

solstitial colure The hour angle that passes through the *solstices*.

Sothic cycle A cycle of 1460 years in the Egyptian calendar named after Sothis (Sirius, the Dog Star). The Egyptian civil year had 12 months of 30 days each with 5 intercalary days added. The Sothic year of 365¼ days began with the *heliacal rising* of Sirius, the Egyptian new year.

Southern Cross Constellation in the southern hemisphere. See: *Crux*.

Southern Crown Constellation in the southern hemisphere. See: *Corona Australis*.

Southern Fish Constellation in the southern hemisphere. See: *Piscis Austrinus*.

Southern Triangle Constellation in the southern hemisphere. See: *Triangulum Australe*.

south point The southern point of intersection of the meridian and the horizon.

space flight The summation of various activities, scientific, technical, medical, etc., dealing with the construction and launching of suitable vehicles into space. See: *artificial satellites*.

space probe Apparatus used to study the conditions in outer space.

space station An artificial satellite of suitable construction located beyond the atmosphere of the earth that can serve as a platform for future interplanetary space voyages.

space telescope A telescope constructed for use in an artificial satellite. By means of remote control, photographs of celestial objects as well as other data will be transmitted to stations on the earth. Smaller cameras have already been used for such purposes; the Russian Lunik III and Zond III photographed the far side of the moon, the American Tiros and Nimbus satellites telemeter pictures of cloud cover over the earth, Mariner IV obtained close-range photographs of Mars, and the American Ranger VII telemetered pictures of the surface of the moon. The construction of larger and more complicated space telescopes is under way. In the United States, an OAO (orbiting astronomical observatory) will be launched with a reflecting telescope of moderate size in addition to the other instrumentation.

spectral analysis An investigation of the spectra of light sources in order to discover the physical and chemical properties of these light sources. An analysis of stellar spectra not only reveals the chemical elements contained in stellar atmospheres (in some instances, quantity) but also the temperature, velocity, rotation, magnetic field, absolute magnitude, etc., of the stars.

spectral classes (spectral types) The different groups in which the stars are classified according to spectral characteristics. The earliest spectral classification was attempted by A. Secchi (1818–1878) of Italy who grouped the stars into four classes according to color: white (I), yellow (II), orange (III), and red (IV). Later, at Harvard Observatory, stars were grouped into 16 types from A to Q (Pickering, 1885), where spectra were classified according to characteristic lines and bands such as the hydrogen Balmer series, H and K lines of ionized calcium, etc. From this evolved the *Harvard classification,* the most important spectral classification forming the series O, B, A, F, G, K, M, which is also a scale from high to low temperature. About 99% of all stars can be arranged in this spectral series.

spectral lines Dark (absorption) or bright (emission) lines in the spectrum.

spectral-luminosity diagram The *Hertzsprung-Russell diagram.*

spectroheliogram Photographs of the sun taken with the spectroheliograph. Usually, the red line of hydrogen (Hα) or the K line of calcium located in the violet end of the spectrum is used.

spectroheliograph An instrument used to photograph the sun in the light of a single spectral line. See: *solar instruments.*

spectrometer An instrument used in the precise measurement of the positions of spectral lines.

spectrophotometric gradient The slope of the spectral energy curve from the beginning of the *Balmer jump* toward the longer wave lengths. This value is closely correlated with the color of the stars (temperature).

spectrophotometry The science of measuring the intensity of light in the spectrum, spectral lines and their contours.

spectroscope (spectrograph) Apparatus for the analysis of light. These instruments contain a narrow slit through which the light enters. The slit is placed at the focus of a positive lens called the *collimator lens* to form a beam of parallel rays. The beam of light falls on a triangular prism which separates the light into its primary colors. This spectrum can be observed with an eyepiece (in the spectroscope) or reproduced on a photographic plate (in the spectrograph). Often, a series of prisms is used to increase the amount of dispersion. Another type of spectrograph, a *diffraction grating,* uses a series of fine grooves, a grating, rather than a prism to disperse the light. Mounted on telescopes, spectrographs are used to photograph stellar spectra. A comparison spectrum of a known element is produced on the spectral plate. (Fig. S4.)

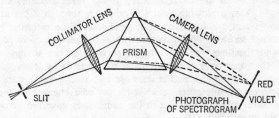

S4. Schematic diagram of a spectrograph.

spectroscopic binary A binary system that cannot be resolved in a telescope but can be identified by means of the Doppler shift of the spectral lines. As the stars revolve, they alternately approach and recede in the line of sight. This motion is apparent in their spectra as a periodic oscillation and doubling of the spectral lines. See: *binary stars.* (Fig. S5.)

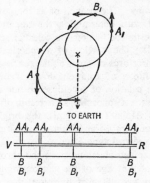

S5. Spectroscopic binary star.

spectroscopic parallax   The measurement of stellar distance by the absolute magnitude derived from the *luminosity criteria* of the spectrum and the apparent magnitude of the star.

spectrum   The band of color that is produced when white light is passed through a prism. Since violet light is bent more than red light, the various colors emerge from the prism as a rainbow of colors in the following order: red, orange, yellow, green, blue, indigo, violet. The spectra of glowing solids, liquids, and gases under high pressure are *continuous*, i.e., continuous bands of color. The spectra of glowing gases of low pressures are *bright line spectra*, a series of separate lines or bands which are characteristic for the various elements. If light from a glowing light source passes through a gas at a lower temperature than the original source, the spectrum becomes an *absorption spectrum* with dark lines that correspond with the lines of the emission spectrum of the cooler gas. Stellar spectra are continuous spectra crossed by many dark absorption lines; emission lines are also seen in some stars.

spectrum variable stars   Stars with periodic changes in their spectra; intensity changes in the continuous spectrum or certain spectral lines.

spherical aberration   An image error of a lens with a spherical surface where the rays passing through the center will be refracted to a different focus than the rays passing through the edge of the lens. The error can be partially or entirely corrected in optical instruments by employing aspherical surfaces. See: *aberration* and *Schmidt telescope*.

spherical angle   The angle between two great circles of a sphere.

spherical astronomy   The branch of astronomy that is primarily concerned with determining the apparent position and motion of celestial bodies on the celestial sphere.

spherical triangle   The portion of a spherical surface that is bounded by three arcs of great circles, each $< 180°$.

spheroid   An ellipse of rotation. From "ellipsoid." A solid formed by the rotation of an ellipse on one of its axes. Most celestial bodies are spheroids as a result of rotation.

Spica   The star Alpha (α) Virginis, the brightest star in the constellation of *Virgo*, the Virgin, of apparent visual magnitude 1.2 and spectral type B2.

spicules   Small spiked ejections from the chromosphere which are observed at the edge of the sun on monochromatic photographs. They are of short duration of 3 to 5 minutes at speeds of 20 to 30 km/sec. Chromospheric spicules are probably as abundant as granulations.

spiral arms, origin of The origin of the spiral arms in the Milky Way and other galaxies is a very complex problem that has not been resolved. There is agreement among astronomers that the arms are not permanent formations but of rather short duration. The spiral arms are apparently the result of instability occurring at a critical rotational speed when the outer portions of the galaxy's nucleus break away. After a relatively short period of time, the arms become deformed and disintegrate. New dust and gaseous matter are forced out from the nucleus to form new spiral arms.

spiral galaxy (spiral nebula) A stellar system with a spiral structure. On opposite sides of a nucleus of stars, two or more spiral arms swirl outward and around the center. Most galaxies have a spiral structure. The arms contain young stars, dark and bright nebulosity. The Milky Way system is a spiral galaxy. See: *galaxies.*

spiral nebula A *spiral galaxy.*

spirit level A device used to control the correct adjustment of an instrument in the horizontal plane. A slightly curved glass tube with both ends closed is partially filled with alcohol (or ether), leaving a small bubble of air. Since the bubble always moves to the highest point on the tube where its position can be read on a scale, the horizontal axis of an instrument may be adjusted in the horizontal plane.

spring The season of the year between the vernal equinox (March 21) and the summer solstice (June 22).

spring tide The ocean tide occurring during new or full moon when the sun and moon are in the same or opposite direction with respect to the earth. The attraction of both celestial bodies is additive, with high water rising higher and low water falling lower than normal.

Sputnik (Russian, satellite) Artificial satellites launched by the Soviet Union. The first, Sputnik I, was launched October 4, 1957, and had a period of 96 minutes and a weight of 184 lbs. It disintegrated after 93 days. Sputnik II was launched November 3, 1957, had a period of 104 minutes and a weight of 1120 lbs. After 153 days, it disintegrated. Sputnik III was launched May 15, 1958, and had a period of 106 minutes and a weight of 2134 lbs. Its lifetime was estimated to be about two years. The Soviet Union has launched many Sputniks as well as other spacecraft (*Lunik, Venik, Cosmos,* and *Vostok*).

In addition to these, the United States has launched several
types of artificial satellites (*Explorer, Discoverer, Tiros, Mercury*, etc.) so that over 100 have orbited the earth. Since
their purpose is the scientific investigation of the conditions
in space near the earth, Sputniks and other satellites are
equipped with various instruments capable of sending data
back to earth. See: *artificial satellites* and *Lunik*.

Square Constellation in the southern hemisphere. See: *Norma*.

SS Cygni stars See: *Cygnus*.

S series A branch of the *Harvard classification* of stars associated with spectral type K. See: *S stars*.

S stars Stars of spectral type S in the *Harvard classification*
of stellar spectra. These are red stars with spectra similar to
M and N stars except that prominent lines of zirconium oxide
(ZrO) are present.

standard meridian The meridian that determines zone time for
any place. In the United States and Canada, the standard
meridians are between 5 and 10 hours west of Greenwich,
75°, 90°, 105°, 120°, 135°, and 150° west longitude.

standard sequence A number of selected stars in a region of
the sky with magnitudes and colors determined with greatest
precision. Colors and magnitudes of other stars are determined by comparing them with the stars in the standard sequence. The most common standard sequence is the *polar
sequence*.

standard time The local civil time of the standard meridian.
The earth is divided into meridians, 15° or one hour apart
reckoned from Greenwich, making a total of 24 time zones.
The local civil time of the meridian is kept for all places in a
zone 7° 30′ east and west of the meridian. Large countries
such as the United States and Canada have several time
zones.

star associations Dispersed groups of stars of common origin.
See: *associations*.

star catalogue A listing of stellar co-ordinates and other data.
The oldest known star catalogue, the Almagest, was compiled
by Ptolemy about A.D. 150, and contained data for 1022 stars.
Modern catalogues' position data are divided into two general
groups. One type of survey catalogue does not possess the
greatest possible accuracy but lists the stars brighter than a
given limiting magnitude. An example is the *Bonner Durchmusterung* of F. W. A. Argelander (1862) containing the
co-ordinates and visual magnitudes of 324,000 stars from the

north celestial pole to −2° declination. The other type, precision catalogues, includes *Boss' General Catalogue* listing the precise positions and proper motions of 33,342 stars. In addition, there are several special catalogues for variable stars, binary stars, stellar spectra, nebulae, and star clusters, etc.

star chains A series of stars that appear near to one another in the sky, forming a chain. As yet, it is not known if these stars are physically joined and of common origin or independent of each other and by chance projected in the sky in the same line of sight.

star clouds Extensive regions in different parts of the Milky Way with unusually high stellar density. Examples are the Sagittarius and Scutum star clouds.

star clusters Assemblages of stars moving together through space. They are divided into two main groups: *galactic clusters* that are found principally in the plane of the Milky Way and consist of young stars (Population I), and *globular clusters* that are found in the halo surrounding the nucleus of the Milky Way and consist of old stars (Population II). (A more scattered group is regarded as an *association*.) Star clusters have been discovered in other galaxies.

star color A measure of a star's color is the *color index*, the difference between a star's photographic and visual (photovisual) magnitudes. The scale is adjusted so that white stars (spectral type A) have a color index of 0, the blue-white stars (B) have a negative color index, yellow stars (such as the sun) about +1, and the deep red stars about +2 magnitudes. See: *color* and *stars*.

star density The number of stars per unit of volume of space, i.e., per cubic parsec.

star drift A group of stars whose members move in parallel orbits in space. A number of stars in Ursa Major (Big Dipper), Sirius, and several other stars form such a group. The distances to the stars are determined from their radial velocities and proper motions.

star gauges A method used by William Herschel to investigate the structure of the Milky Way. Herschel counted the number of stars which were visible in a given area in a certain part of the sky. He divided the sky into several thousand fields selected to give the average distribution of stars with respect to the Milky Way. By assuming that the stars are uniformly distributed in space and that his instrument could penetrate to the limits of the stellar system, Herschel concluded that the diameter of the Milky Way was five times greater than its thickness. Since the stars are not uniformly distributed in space, this method can be considered to be the first attempt to gain an understanding of our stellar system.

star streams Two main star streams moving in opposite directions as the result of the rotation of the Milky Way. In 1904, the Dutch astronomer J. C. Kapteyn discovered that the stars' peculiar motion (their proper motions corrected for the sun's motion) were not at random, but had two preferential directions; one stream moving in the direction of the constellation of Orion, and the other in the constellation of Ara. The relative speed between the streams amounts to about 25 miles/sec. The phenomenon has been studied by Eddington, Schwarzschild, and others.

Stark effect The separation into several components or broadening of spectral lines when an element is influenced by an electrical field. Since the atmospheres of dwarf stars are denser than the atmospheres of giants, the Stark effect is more pronounced in dwarf stars. Since hydrogen lines are sensitive to the Stark effect, the intensity of these lines may be used as luminosity criteria for early type stars such as spectral type A.

stars Celestial bodies like the sun that are globes of incandescent gases. Through photometry, spectral analysis, and astrometry, their distances, physical characteristics (such as temperature, dimensions, mass, density, etc.), motions in space, rotation, etc., have been determined. By means of statistical analysis, their distribution in space is derived. By applying known physical laws, it is possible to gain an understanding of their interior composition, radiation, development, and evolution. There is a great physical variation among stars. Some stars radiate energy at a rate hundreds of thousands of times (or in rare cases a million times) greater than the sun. Surface temperatures also vary by a wide margin. There are *cool* stars that radiate with a deep red color at temperatures between 1600° and 2000° C. (sometimes temperatures of 1000° C. are found and such stars emit infrared radiation only), and *hot* stars with surface temperatures as high as 100,000° C. Variations in the diameters of stars are enormous. There are *white dwarfs* with dimensions smaller than the earth (with a mean density 100,000 times greater than water), and *supergiants* whose diameters can be 3000 times the diameter of the sun (with a mean density equal to 10^{-9} times the density of the sun). Variation in mass is more restricted,

with the smallest about 0.1 solar masses, and the largest, in
rare instances, can reach 100 solar masses. Generally, the
space velocity of stars amounts to a few score miles per second. The stars are sparsely distributed in the sun's vicinity. If
the stars were reduced in size to pinheads, their distances
apart would be about 20 or 30 miles.

static universe A closed universe of finite volume.

stationary point The point in the apparent path of a planet at
which its motion changes from direct to retrograde or reverse
and it appears motionless in the sky.

stationary satellite An artificial satellite placed in a circular
orbit at a distance of 22,300 miles above the earth with a
period of precisely one day. Launched toward the east (in
the direction of the earth's rotation) in the plane of the
equator, the satellite will hover over the same point on the
earth. The *Syncom* communications satellite is designed to
orbit the earth as a stationary satellite.

Stefan-Boltzmann law Stefan's law states that the total radiation emitted by a black body per cm^2/sec is directly proportional to the fourth power of its absolute temperature. In
astronomy, the law can be used to find a star's diameter from
its absolute magnitude.

stellar age See: *age.*

stellar astronomy The branch of astronomy that deals with the
study of the distribution and motions of the stars, the galaxies, and the general structure and size of the universe.

stellar atmosphere The layers of a star situated above the surface (photosphere). The line spectrum of a star originates in
its atmosphere. By analyzing these absorption lines it is possible to study the physical conditions and chemical composition of the stars.

stellar distribution The distribution of stars in space is characterized by *star density:* the number of stars per unit of volume in space. In the investigation of the structure of the
Milky Way, it is necessary to determine the distribution of the
stars in various directions and at different distances. An account of the several statistical methods that have been developed to determine stellar distributions is beyond the scope
of this work.

stellar evolution The slow developmental process of a star that
cannot be detected by observation. Indications of stellar evolution are found in the study of star clusters and the distribution of their stars on the **Hertzsprung-Russell diagram.* It

is believed that stars are formed from interstellar gas clouds. As the protostar contracts, the pressure and temperature in the interior increase and it becomes a red star which moves from Step 1 to Step 2 in the H-R diagram shown in Fig. S6.

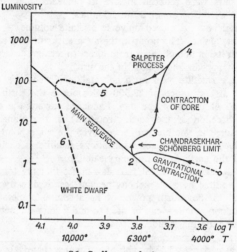

S6. Stellar evolution.

When temperatures reach a value of 12 million to 14 million degrees, nuclear reaction begins in the core (*proton-proton reaction* and, later, *carbon-nitrogen cycle*). An equilibrium is reached and the star remains for a length of time on the main sequence of the H-R diagram. (The larger the initial mass of the star, the higher up the H-R diagram it will be found.) When all available hydrogen in the core has been changed to helium, an isothermal equilibrium occurs in the core while the energy formation continues in a shell surrounding the core. This process continues until the core is about 12% of the total mass of the star (*Chandrasekhar-Schönberg limit*). At this point, the core begins to contract and the energy released causes the star to expand into a giant star; Steps 2, 3, 4 in Fig. S6. This expansion continues until the temperature in the inner portions of the star has reached a value of 2 × 10^8 degrees, when another nuclear reaction process begins (*Salpeter process*) in which helium forms into heavier elements. The star begins to contract, diminishing in magnitude between Steps 4 and 5. At Step 5, the star begins to pulsate (RR Lyrae stars), and evolution proceeds to the white dwarf stage, eventually exploding as a nova. This schematic outline of stellar evolution is subject to continuous modification.

stellar masses See: *mass* and *mass-luminosity relation*.

stellar parallax Measurement of stellar distance. See: *parallax*.

stellar photometry The measurement of the intensity of radiation from celestial bodies. In stellar photometry, radiation falls on a light-sensitive surface that reacts to the radiation or activates apparatus which measures the amount of energy received. Photometry has been divided into various branches according to the method of measurement: *visual photometry* (the retina of the eye is sensitive to wave lengths between 4000 and 7000 Å); *photographic photometry* (photographic emulsions 2000 to 11,000 Å); *photoelectric photometry* (photoelectric cells 3000 to 13,000 Å); *thermoelectric photometry* (thermocouple, all wave lengths); and **radio photometry* (radio telescopes about 1 centimeter to 15 meters). In **visual photometry,* special apparatus, *photometers,* are attached to the eyepiece of the telescope where a comparison star, either real or artificial, is varied in brightness to equal the brightness of the star to be measured. Today, **visual photometry* is mainly used to measure the brightness of binary stars with small separation, which is impossible by other methods. In photographic photometry, the intensity of the image produced by the star on a photographic plate is measured. This method is suitable when the magnitudes of many stars in the same part of the sky are desired. Magnitudes are determined by the relationship between the images produced on the plate and the intensity of the light from the star. Exceptionally accurate magnitude measurements are possible in **photoelectric photometry.* The property of alkaline metals to emit a beam of electrons when illuminated is employed to convert the light from a star to photoelectric current. The current is proportional to the intensity of the light illuminating the photoelectric cell. The light from the stars is very weak and must be amplified a million times. This is made possible by means of dynodes, called *photo-multipliers.* Very sensitive thermocouples in evacuated tubes are used in thermoelectric photometry to measure thermal radiation.

stellar population See: *population types*.

stellar radiation See: *energy production* in the interior of the stars.

stellar spectra See: *spectrum* and *spectral analysis.*

stellar statistics That branch of astronomy which deals with the distribution, motion in space, and origin of the stars through statistical methods.

stellar statistics, fundamental theorem of The integral equation which expresses the relationship between the star count function (observed number of stars in a given magnitude interval), density function (how the number of stars per unit of volume varies with distance), and luminosity function (the distribution of stars in terms of luminosity).

stellar system See: *Milky Way system.*

Stephan's quintet A group of five galaxies in Pegasus. Radial velocities show that the group is unstable.

stereocomparator An instrument by means of which two photographs of the same region can be viewed at the same time. An optical arrangement permits both plates to be seen in the field of view. By adjusting the plates so that the images coincide, any differences between the photographs, such as a displacement or absence of an image from one plate, will appear as a stereoscopic effect. By using a *blink microscope,* the plates can be viewed alternately, allowing any differences to be clearly seen as a change in position or the blinking of an image. Stereocomparators are used to scan large areas for variable stars, stars with large proper motions, and minor planets.

Stern A part of the constellation of Argo in the southern hemisphere. See: *Puppis.*

Stjärneborg One of the observatories established by Tycho Brahe on the island of Hven in Öresund.

stony meteorite A type of meteorite composed of silicates and magnesium oxides.

storm burst Powerful increases in the intensity of radio frequency radiation on the sun.

Straight Wall A lunar formation on the edge of Mare Nubium. The straight wall is about 90 miles long, several hundred yards high, and appears very conspicuous when lighted by the sun at last quarter phase. It is not a wall, but a geological fault in the lunar surface.

stratosphere The layer of atmosphere above the troposphere, located between 10 to 50 miles above the surface of the earth.

striding level A level used to adjust an instrument in the horizontal position, i.e., the axis of a transit instrument.

Strömberg, Gustaf (1882–1962) Swedish-American astronomer active at Mt. Wilson Observatory in California (1916–37). His most important investigations included stellar motion. See: *Strömberg's asymmetrical star streams.*

Strömberg's asymmetrical star streams A phenomenon of stellar motions discovered by G. Strömberg in 1924. By a comprehensive study of stellar motion, he found that stars with high radial velocity have motions in two streams in opposite directions from each other perpendicular to the direction of the center of the Milky Way. The phenomenon is a result of galactic rotation.

subdwarfs Dwarf stars one and a half to two magnitudes fainter than normal dwarfs that form a series in the H-R diagram parallel to the main sequence. They are chiefly Population II stars.

subgiants Giant stars, with a lower absolute magnitude than the normal giants, that lie between the giants and the main sequence stars on the H-R diagram.

summer Astronomical summer in the northern hemisphere is the time of year that begins at the summer solstice (about June 22) and ends at the autumnal equinox (about September 23).

summer solstice The point on the ecliptic where the sun is situated on about June 22 when it has attained its extreme northern declination and is seen overhead on the Tropic of Cancer.

summer triangle The triangle formed by the three bright stars, Vega in Lyra (α Lyrae), Deneb in Cygnus (α Cygni), and Altair in Aquila (α Aquilae), which is particularly striking in the summer night sky.

sun The central body of the solar system. A typical star, the sun is a dwarf star of spectral type G2 in the *Harvard classification* at a mean distance of 93 million miles from the earth. Its diameter is 864,000 miles, or 108 times the diameter of the earth; its volume is 1.3 million times that of the earth; its mass is 333,000 times the mass of the earth; and its density is equal to 0.26 times that of the earth. The sun's apparent visual magnitude is —26.9 and its absolute magnitude (bolometric) is +4.7. Its effective temperature is 5700° K. The period of rotation at the equator amounts to about 25 days. The visible surface of the sun, called the *photosphere,* consists of a network of bright markings on a darker background (*granulations*). *Sunspots* are also seen. The portion of the sun's atmosphere nearest the photosphere, called the *chromosphere,* is a layer of ionized gases extending to several thousand miles. Temperatures range from 4000° C. in the lower limits to 40,000° C. in the upper limits. *Prominences* appear in the chromosphere tens of thousands of miles above the photosphere. The outer portion of the sun's atmosphere, the *corona,* consists of an extensive, very tenuous envelope of gases at high temperature. Like the earth, the sun has a magnetic field, with a field strength of 1 to 2 gauss. The energy radiated by the sun is the result of nuclear processes in the interior. Temperatures in the center are at about 14 million degrees Centigrade and pressures are equal to 2.2×10^{11} atmospheres through the *proton-proton reaction* where helium is formed by the fusion of hydrogen nuclei.

Sunday letter   The dominical letter. The first seven days of the year have been designated by the first seven letters of the alphabet, A to G, repeating for the entire year. Each Sunday of the year has the same letter, called the Sunday letter. The following year adopts the preceding letter of the alphabet so that if the Sunday letter of a given year is G, the letter for the next year will be F. During leap years, two Sunday letters are assigned to account for the extra day. In 1964, the Sunday letters were E and D.

sundial   An instrument for indicating apparent solar time by the position of the shadow cast by a pin. There are several types of sundials. The simplest consists of a pin mounted parallel to the axis of the earth (along the plane of the meridian at an inclination equal to the latitude of the position). The shadow falls on a ring perpendicular to the pin. On another type of sundial the shadow falls on a wall which is perpendicular to the plane of the meridian. See: *gnomon.*

sun's motion   With respect to the nearby stars, the sun is moving at a velocity of 12 miles/sec in the direction of a point in the constellation of Hercules (*apex of the sun's way*). Meanwhile, the sun partakes in the rotation of the Galaxy at a velocity of about 170 miles/sec toward a point in galactic longitude 55° in Cygnus.

sunspot cycle   A periodic fluctuation of the number of sunspots. The formation of sunspots is the most conspicuous indication of the periodicity of all solar activity. The variability of the number of spots has been studied for more than 200 years. As a result, a cyclic variation averaging 11 years has been discovered, although the fluctuations are not uniform and the number of spots during a maximum is not constant. Long- and short-period variations in the sunspot cycle remain unconfirmed. The sunspot maximum in 1957 was the nineteenth observed since 1760. The last minimum occurred in 1964. (Fig. S7.)

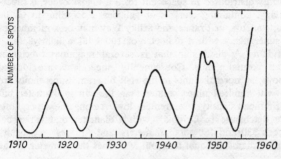

S7. Sunspot cycle.

sunspot number A measure of the intensity of sunspots, proposed by the Swiss astronomer R. Wolf. The term sunspot number expresses the number of sunspot groups and isolated spots visible on the sun at the same time.

sunspots Dark markings on the photosphere of the sun between 5° and 35° north and south of the sun's equator. The smallest, called *pores,* have a diameter of a few hundred miles and last for only a few days, while the larger spots with diameters several times the size of the earth are visible for several months. A well-developed spot consists of a dark nucleus, the *umbra,* surrounded by a lighter region called the *penumbra.* The temperature of a spot is about 1000° C. lower than the surrounding photosphere. Sunspots often appear in groups; first, a large single spot elongates and develops into two spots, one behind the other in the direction of the sun's rotation. The spots reveal strong magnetic fields (as high as 4000 gauss) and form a bipolar group with opposite polarity. Spectroheliograms of the sunspots show a whirling motion of the gases in an up-and-down circulation. At the present time, there is no satisfactory explanation for sunspots. One theory suggests that sunspots are the result of magnetohydrodynamic waves from the interior of the sun which have spread to the photosphere. The sunspot cycle is periodic, with approximately 11 years between maxima or minima. Maximum years are characterized by a large number of spots and intense solar activity. During minimum years, days and weeks can go by without the appearance of a sunspot.

supergalaxy Galaxies are often found in clusters. Some investigators have discovered that these clusters are not uniformly distributed in space but form a higher order, a supergalaxy, containing clusters of galaxies. According to G. de Vaucouleurs, of France, the Milky Way may be a member of a supergalaxy with a diameter of 100 million light-years.

supergiant A giant star that is several magnitudes brighter than normal giants. Consequently, supergiants are located above the normal giants in the H-R diagram. Supergiants are several hundred times greater than the sun in diameter but their mean density is extremely low. Among the supergiants are Betelgeuse (α Orionis), with a diameter that varies between 330 and 460 solar diameters, and Antares (α Scorpii) with a diameter equal to about 300 times the diameter of the sun.

superior conjunction The conjunction of one of the inferior planets (Mercury and Venus), when the planet is beyond the sun and its motion is direct. The planet is invisible due to its proximity to the sun.

superior culmination The meridian transit of a star between the celestial pole and the south point of the horizon. The opposite, *inferior culmination,* occurs when the star crosses the meridian between the celestial pole and the north point of the horizon.

superior planets The term applied to planets located beyond the orbit of the earth.

supernovae Extremely luminous novae (exploding or erupting stars) with absolute magnitudes which may reach -17 at maximum. They are classified into two types: Type I, with mean absolute magnitude 14.3 at maximum and Type II, with an average mean absolute magnitude amounting to -12 at maximum. See: *exploding stars.*

super-Schmidt A type of *Schmidt telescope* with a wide angle field and an f-number down to f/1.0. Sometimes used to photograph artificial satellites.

surface brightness Apparent surface brightness is the brightness per square second of arc of the star's surface measured in accordance with *Pogson's scale.* True surface brightness is the amount of energy emitted per cm^2 of the surface. Surface brightness (derived from the *Stefan-Boltzmann law*) and total luminosity will give the area of the radiating surface and from this, the diameter of the star can be theoretically calculated.

surface photometer A photometer which uses the extra focal method of measuring the brightness of stars. The brightness of the star image is compared to the brightness of an artificial star.

surface temperature of stars The temperature of the radiating layers of the stars where the continuous spectrum is produced; essentially, the photosphere and the lower layers of the atmosphere.

surge A type of prominence that occurs during an eruption of a *solar *flare.*

Swan Constellation in the northern hemisphere. See: *Cygnus.*

Swordfish Constellation in the southern hemisphere. See: *Dorado.*

synchronous rotation The rotation of a celestial body when it always turns the same side toward the body around which it revolves. The moon rotates around the earth, completing one rotation for every revolution. The planet Mercury always keeps the same side toward the sun.

synchrotron radiation Electromagnetic radiation emitted by high-velocity electrons moving in magnetic fields, first discovered in atomic accelerators of the synchrotron type. Part of the radiation from the **Crab Nebula* is believed to be radiation of this type.

synodic month The period of time required by the moon to complete all its phases, or the interval between two successive full moons. The length of the synodic month is 29.5306 days.

Syrtis Major One of the most conspicuous dark markings ("seas") on the planet Mars, first observed by C. Huygens in 1659.

systematic errors Errors that are produced by factors which repeat each time the same observations are made under similar conditions. Systematic errors are discovered by varying the conditions or methods of observation.

syzygy The term applied to three bodies in a straight line. The moon at new moon and full moon phase as well as the planets in opposition and conjunction with the sun are in syzygy.

T

Table Mountain Constellation in the southern hemisphere. See: *Mensa*.

tangential velocity The velocity of a star at 90° to the line of sight. (*Radial velocity* is the motion of the star along the line of sight.)

Tarantula Nebula An exceedingly large gaseous nebula situated in the Large Magellanic Cloud.

T associations A type of *stellar association* containing late type dwarf stars which are found embedded in dark nebulosity or nearby bright nebulae. These stars are irregular variables with hydrogen emission lines in their spectra. The prototype star for T association stars is T Tauri.

Taurus (Bull) A large constellation of the Zodiac in the northern hemisphere at approximately 4h 20m right ascension (α = 4h 20m), 16° north declination (δ = +16°). Alpha (α) Tauri, Aldebaran, is among the twenty brightest stars in the sky. Taurus contains several star clusters including the Pleiades and Hyades. The famous *Crab Nebula*, Messier 1, is situated to the west of Zeta (ζ) Tauri. RV Tauri is the prototype of RV Tauri semi-regular variable stars. These are giant stars of late spectral type with irregular changes in luminosity. RV Tauri stars often contain emission lines in their spectra.

Tautenburg telescope The largest Schmidt telescope in the world. The diameter of the correcting plate is 53 inches, the diameter of the spherical mirror 79 inches, and the focal length 157 inches. It belongs to the Karl Schwarzschild Observatory at Tautenburg, near Jena, East Germany. It was put into operation in 1960.

tektites The name applied collectively to small glassy objects of cosmic origin found in various parts of the world and named after the place of discovery. (In Australia they are called *australites;* in Czechoslovakia, *moldavites.*) Their shapes vary from completely irregular to symmetrical. They contain a large amount of silicon, oxides of aluminum, iron, calcium, and other elements. Colors vary from black to dark green. As yet, their true origin is unknown.

telemetering   In space science, transmitting observational data from satellites to the earth by radio.

Telescope   Constellation in the southern hemisphere. See: *Telescopium*.

telescope   Astronomical instrument for gathering radiation from celestial bodies. There are two main types of optical telescopes, *refractors* and *reflectors*. *Radio telescopes* of various types are used to investigate radio frequency radiation.

telescopic   A celestial body invisible to the unaided eye but visible with a telescope.

Telescopium   (Telescope) An inconspicuous constellation situated in the southern hemisphere at 19h right ascension ($\alpha = 19$h), $50°$ south declination ($\delta = -50°$).

telluric lines   Lines and bands in spectra that originate from oxygen, water vapor, and carbon dioxide in the atmosphere of the earth.

Tellus   The Latin name for the earth.

Telstar   The first active *communication satellite,* launched by the United States on July 10, 1962. Successful television programs have been exchanged between the United States and Europe. The first transmission took place on July 23, 1962.

Tempel's comet   The comet 1866 I whose orbit coincides with the Leonids and is associated with this meteor swarm.

temporary hours   A division of time first used by the ancient Egyptians. Day and night were divided into 12 hours each. Since the length of the day and night varied during the course of the year, the length of the hour in the daytime was shorter in winter than in summer when the conditions are reversed. The system continued into the 14th century when mechanical clocks with equal time divisions came into use.

temporary stars   The so-called "new stars" (novae) or exploding (eruptive) stars. See: *variable stars.*

terminator   The line on the surface of the moon which separates the bright and dark hemispheres. Since the moon's surface is uneven, the terminator is more or less irregular. Generally, the lines between the bright and the dark portions of planets and other satellites are also called terminators.

terrestrial latitude   The angular distance between a given position on the earth's surface and the equator.

terrestrial planets   The planets Mercury, Venus, Earth, Mars, and presumably Pluto. They are comparatively small bodies that are characterized by high mean density about the same as the earth, solid surfaces, tenuous atmospheres, slow axial rotation, and few if any satellites.

Tethys One of Saturn's moons, discovered by Cassini in 1684. Its period of revolution is 1.89 days and its mean distance from the planet is 183,000 miles.

Thales of Miletus (640–560 B.C.). Greek philosopher. Thales understood the earth to be spherical and was supposed to have predicted an eclipse of the sun.

theodolite An instrument for measuring angles that is used in determining the position of stars in the horizon co-ordinate system (azimuth and altitude). The theodolite is a type of *altazimuth,* or *transit instrument.* The telescope is movable in altitude on a horizontal axis. Positions are read with precision on graduated circles, *vertical circle* for altitude and *azimuth circle* for azimuth. A *spirit level* is used to assure proper alignment. The instrument is primarily used in geodesy and geography for determination of position.

theoretical astronomy That branch of astronomy which is concerned with the determination of orbits through the observation of the apparent motions of celestial bodies. Based upon celestial mechanics, theoretical astronomy was at one time restricted to motions in the solar system.

theoretical astrophysics That branch of astronomy which deals with astrophysical problems of a theoretical nature, such as the interior composition of the stars.

thermocouple An apparatus used to measure the surface temperatures of celestial bodies. A thermocouple consists of two wires of dissimilar metals welded at the ends. When one end is heated, a current will flow that can be measured with a sensitive galvanometer. Sensitivity may be increased many times by placing the thermocouple in a vacuum. Therefore, vacuum thermocouples have been applied to measure temperatures in astronomy.

three-body problem A classical problem in celestial mechanics that attempts to derive the motions of three bodies that mutually attract each other. Generally, the problem is insoluble, with the exception of special cases. Thus, J. L. Lagrange (1736–1813) found that if three bodies form an equilateral triangle, with a body at each vertex, they must always maintain the same relative positions (*Trojan *asteroids*). Another special case is the restricted problem of three bodies where the third body has infinitely small mass. In general, the orbits are not closed but, nevertheless, periodic solutions have been obtained in many instances. Such investigations have been made by H. Poincaré (1854–1912) and E. Strömgren (1870–1947), and others.

tides The rise and fall of the water in the oceans due primarily to the attraction of the moon. There are two high tides (flood tide) each day, with low tide (ebb tide) in between. The sun also exerts a tidal effect although only half as much as the moon. When the moon is new or full (in the same or opposite direction as the sun), the effects are additive and the tide becomes more pronounced (*spring tide*). When the moon is at first or last quarter, the attractions of the sun and the moon oppose one another and the phenomenon is at its lowest range (*neap tide*). (Fig. T1.)

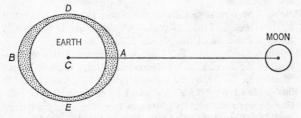

T1. The tides. D *and* E, *ebb tide;* A *and* B, *flood tide.*

time The interval between two given events. To measure time, a unit of time with constant value is required. Since antiquity, the unit of time has been one complete rotation of the earth on its axis, or a *sidereal day*. *Sidereal time* is star time, with a sidereal day defined as the time required for two successive meridian transits of the vernal equinox. Sidereal time is the hour angle of the vernal equinox. The *mean solar day* is the interval between two successive meridian transits of the *mean sun*. *Mean solar time* is equal to the hour angle of the mean sun (add 12 hours if using a 24-hour clock) (civil time). *Apparent solar time* is equal to the hour angle of the apparent sun.

time, equation of See: *equation of time.*

time, measurement of See: *chronology.*

time reckoning Various methods for securing accurate time measurements through astronomical observations. The most common as well as most accurate method employs a meridian circle or a transit instrument to compare the culmination of a star with respect to sidereal time. If the sidereal clock is accurate, the sidereal time will coincide with the right ascension of the star which is already known.

time retardation According to Einstein's theory of relativity, the slowing down of the clock rate in a system moving at a high velocity with respect to another. In the clock paradox, or "twin paradox," after a journey in the universe at great speed, the space traveler will return to earth biologically younger than his twin who remained on earth.

Tiros A type of artificial satellite. See: *weather satellites.*

Titan The planet Saturn's largest satellite, discovered by Huygens in 1655. Its period of revolution is 15.95 days and its mean distance from Saturn is 760,000 miles. Titan has a diameter of 3000 miles and an atmosphere containing methane and ammonia.

Titania The largest satellite of the planet Uranus. Discovered by Herschel in 1787, its period of revolution is 8.71 days; mean distance from the planet, 272,000 miles.

titanium oxide bands (TiO bands) Absorption bands that appear in the spectra of low temperature stars such as K and M stars in the *Harvard classification.*

Titius'-Bode's law *Bode's law.* An empirical law for the relation between the planets' distances from the sun, discovered by J. D. Titius (1766) and later discussed by J. E. Bode.

Titius' law An empirical law that expresses a planet's distance from the sun. This law is generally called *Bode's law* or *Titius'-Bode's law.*

Titov, Gherman (1935–) Soviet cosmonaut (astronaut) who completed 17 orbits of the earth in the space ship Vostok II, August 6 to 7, 1961, and landed safely in a predetermined target area.

topocentric horizon co-ordinate system A co-ordinate system with the origin located at the observer's position.

total eclipse of the sun A total eclipse of the sun occurs over the portion of the surface of the earth within the umbra of the moon's shadow. During totality, the sun is entirely hidden from view by the moon. See: *solar eclipse.* (See Fig. S3.)

total magnitude The intensity of the light received from a star cluster, nebula, or galaxy. Total magnitude is used to determine the distance to globular clusters and galaxies when their stars cannot be resolved.

Toucan Constellation in the southern hemisphere. See: *Tucana.*

tower telescope A telescope for solar observation consisting of a dome mounted on the top of a tower. Within the dome, a mirror system called a *coelostat reflects the sun's light vertically down the tower to a laboratory where the solar image can be studied or the spectrum analyzed by means of a diffraction spectrograph.

transistor An amplifier based upon the application of the properties of semi-conductors (germanium, silicon). Transistors have received wide use in modern electronics, replacing electron tubes as amplifiers and rectifiers.

transit The passage of a celestial body across the meridian. Used also to describe the passage of the planets Mercury and Venus across the disc of the sun and Jupiter's satellites and their shadows across the face of the planet.

transit instrument A *meridian passage instrument;* an instrument mounted on an east–west axis so that the telescope reticle is always in the plane of the meridian. In contrast to the *meridian circle,* the transit instrument does not have accurately graduated circles. The transit instrument is used to time a star's transit, or passage, across the meridian.

transmission coefficient The amount that light is dimmed during vertical passage through the atmosphere (the star is in the zenith), which varies with the wave length of light.

transmission grating A grating consisting of a glass plate ruled with a large number of parallel grooves.

transplutonic planets Hypothetical planets that would be found beyond the remotest known major planet, Pluto.

transverse velocity The component of a star's motion that is perpendicular to the line of sight and is expressed in linear measure (km/sec). Transverse velocity can be determined from the star's proper motion if distance is known.

Trapezium in Orion Four stars in the center of the *Orion Nebula* that form a trapezoid. The stars are physically associated with the nebula and belong to the Orion association.

Triangle A constellation in the northern hemisphere. See: *Triangulum.*

triangulation A geodetic method for measuring the linear distance between two remote points, *A* and *B.* Between these points, a number of intervening stations *C, D, E, F,* . . . etc., are selected so that each is visible from two nearby stations. The length of a base line is measured with great accuracy. With the use of an angle-measuring device such as a theodolite, the angles in the triangle are determined. When the length of the base line and the size of the angles are known,

each triangle is solved trigonometrically. The distance between *A* and *B* is found when the lines and angles in the
chain of triangles are known. The method was invented by
Snell of the Netherlands in the beginning of the 17th century.
(Fig. T2.)

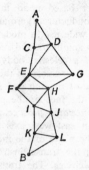

T2. Triangulation.

Triangulum   (Triangle) A constellation located in the northern
hemisphere at 2h right ascension (α = 2h), 32° north declination (δ = +32°). The famous spiral galaxy, Messier
33, is situated in Triangulum.

Triangulum Australe   (Southern Triangle) Constellation in the
southern hemisphere at 16h right ascension (α = 16h), 65°
south declination (δ = −65°).

Trifid Nebula   An emission nebula, Messier 20, located in the
constellation of Sagittarius in the southern hemisphere. The
nebula emits radio frequency radiation.

trigonometric parallax   The distance to a star determined by
means of trigonometry. As a result of the earth's motion
around the sun, the nearest stars will show a slight change in
position when compared with the more distant stars. This
parallactic displacement can be measured on photographs of
the star taken six months apart. The amount of parallax is
found from the angular displacement, which is the angle
made by the radius of the earth's orbit seen from the star.
Since the distance between the earth and the sun is known,
the distance to the star can be found from its parallax. See:
parallax. The trigonometric parallaxes of several thousand
stars have been measured.

triple-alpha process   A nuclear process discovered by E. E.

Salpeter (also called *Salpeter process*) whereby three alpha particles (helium nuclei) form a carbon nucleus, releasing energy. Heavier elements form out of successive bombardments by helium nuclei. Temperatures exceed 100 million degrees Kelvin during the process.

triple objective An objective consisting of three lenses to obtain a good image of a large field. The objective is often used in *astrographs*.

triple star A system of three stars physically connected with one another. Very often, the main component of a visual double is a spectroscopic binary and therefore the system is in reality a triple star.

triquetrum An ancient instrument used to measure the altitude of a celestial body. See: *Ptolemy's rules*.

Triton One of the two satellites of the planet Neptune, discovered by Lassell in 1846. Period of revolution is 5.88 days; mean distance from the planet, 220,000 miles.

Trojan group A group of minor planets which are influenced by the gravitational attraction of the sun and Jupiter and form an equilateral triangle with these celestial bodies. (Two points exist: one before, the other after, Jupiter.) They represent a special case of the three-body problem of J. L. Lagrange. See: *Lagrangian point*. At present, 15 such asteroids are known, the first discovered was Achilles (1906). Their names are derived from the heroes of the Trojan War.

Trojans A group of asteroids that revolve in orbits at about the same distance from the sun as the planet Jupiter. See: *Trojan group*.

tropical year The year of the seasons; the time required by the sun to complete one revolution with respect to the vernal equinox. Because of the precession of the vernal equinox along the ecliptic in the opposite direction of the sun's annual motion, the tropical year is about 20 minutes shorter than the sidereal year and amounts to 365.2422 mean solar days.

Tropics Two parallel circles on the celestial sphere and the earth at 23½° from the equator (the obliquity of the ecliptic). The *Tropic of Cancer* is north of the equator and the *Tropic of Capricorn* is south. Between the two tropics lies the Torrid Zone.

tropopause The boundary between the troposphere and the stratosphere.

troposphere The lower layer of the earth's atmosphere which extends to an altitude of 5 miles at the poles and 10 miles at

the equator. Most meteorological phenomena such as changes
between high and low pressure, clouds, winds, and rain take
place in the troposphere.

true equinoxes   The points where the equator and the ecliptic
actually intersect. The points where these great circles would
intersect in the absence of nutation are called the *mean equinoxes.*

true position   The co-ordinates of a star for a given date with
respect to the true equator and the true equinoxes for the
instant of time in question.

true sidereal time   The *sidereal time* with respect to the true
equinoxes.

Trumpler, Robert   (1886–1956) Swiss-American astronomer
whose principal work was carried out at Lick Observatory in
California. His most significant contributions were made in
investigations of open star clusters. In 1930, he proved the
existence of interstellar absorption.

Trumpler's classification of open star clusters   A method of
classifying open clusters according to three characteristics:
1. Stellar concentration toward the center of the cluster (I,
strong concentration; IV, weak concentration). 2. Classification of stars according to magnitude (1, all stars about the
same magnitude; 3, only a few bright stars and a large number of faint stars). 3. Number of stars (p, poor, less than 50
members; m, moderately rich, 50 to 100 members; and r,
rich, more than 100 members). Accordingly, the Pleiades are
classified II3r.

Trumpler's stars   Very massive stars discovered by R. J. Trumpler in open star clusters. As yet, their true natures are not
known.

Tucana   (Toucan) An extensive constellation in the southern
hemisphere at approximately 0h right ascension ($\alpha = 0h$),
65° south declination ($\delta = -65°$). Within the constellation
lies the *Small Magellanic Cloud* and the globular cluster *47
Tucanae.*

Tunguska   A river in northern Siberia where, on June 30,
1908, a gigantic fall of meteors devastated a vast forest area.

turbulence   Whirlpool motion of fluids.

turbulence theory   The theory of the origin of the solar system proposed by the German physicist C. F. von Weizsäcker.
See: *cosmogony.*

twilight   The time from sunset until the sun is 6° beneath the
horizon and it becomes impossible to read clearly (*civil twi-*

light). *Astronomical twilight* is the time interval from sunset until the sun is 18° below the horizon, when faint stars appear. The phenomenon is caused by the reflection of diffused sunlight in the atmosphere. Nautical twilight occurs when the sun is 12° below the horizon.

Twins   Constellation in the northern hemisphere. See: *Gemini*.

two-body problem   The problem of deriving the motions of two bodies that mutually attract one another in accordance with Newton's law of gravitation. The problem is entirely solved. See: *orbit determination* and *Kepler's laws*.

Tycho   One of the large ring mountains on the moon located in the southeast portion of the lunar surface. Its diameter is 56 miles. Tycho has a system of bright rays that are conspicuous at full moon.

Tycho Brahe's star   Located in Cassiopeia, one of the brightest novae that has erupted. Observed for the first time by Tycho Brahe on November 11, 1572, it was brighter than Venus at maximum magnitude and could even be seen in full daylight. It was visible to the unaided eye for one and a half years. The star was a *supernova*.

Tychonic system   A planetary system proposed by Tycho Brahe in which the sun and the moon circled around a stationary earth while the other planets orbited the sun.

U

UBV system   The magnitude and color system proposed by H. L. Johnson and W. W. Morgan and used in photographic photometry where stellar magnitude is determined in ultraviolet (U), blue (B) and yellow (V) color range.

U Geminorum stars   A class of nova type stars with irregular variation. These stars have a constant magnitude of long duration interrupted by a sudden rise in magnitude which may be an increase of 100 times in brightness. The phenomenon lasts from a few days to several weeks.

Ulug-Beg   (1394–1449) A Tartar nobleman. He founded an observatory at Samarkand and compiled a star catalogue.

umbra   1. The darkest portion of a sunspot. 2. The name of the dark central region of a shadow where no light from a source of illumination penetrates.

Umbriel A satellite of the planet Uranus, discovered by Lassell in 1851. Mean distance to the planet is 166,000 miles; period of revolution, 4.14 days.

Unicorn Constellation across the celestial equator. See: *Monoceros*.

universal time Mean solar time or the local civil time for a position on the Greenwich meridian.

universe All space, matter, and energy. Through the years, attempts have been made to interpret the structure and to construct various models of the universe. In the past 50 years, the progress made in the study of galaxies and their motions to a distance of several thousand million light-years has made a better understanding of the universe possible. Several theoretical models have been proposed based on Einstein's relativity theory as well as other points of departure. The most interesting phenomenon is the expansion of the universe observed in the motion of the galaxies. Spectroscopic investigations show the spectral lines of the galaxies displaced toward the red (*red shift*) indicating that the galaxies are receding. The speed of recession increases with distance at a constant amount for each one million light-years (*Hubble's constant*). This increase in velocity has not been determined with certainty but is believed to be 20 to 30 km/sec per one million light-years. The expansion is a characteristic property of the universe and a study of the red shift can date the beginning of the expansion and, from this, the age of the universe. At the present time, the universe is believed to be about 20,000 million years old. In its initial stage, the universe must have been extremely dense with all matter and energy concentrated in a "primordial atom." This atom exploded, transforming energy to matter which formed into stars and galaxies moving outward in all directions and observed as the expanding universe. According to other views, the universe is pulsating, alternately expanding and contracting, so that all matter contained will alternately be matter and energy. Matter can therefore be interpreted as a latent state of energy. Other investigators believe that the universe is in a steady state. If this be true, new matter is continuously created to replace the old which is receding into space. This process occurs too slowly to be detected.

unseen component An invisible companion of a star whose disturbing influence on the primary component is detected as variations in proper motion. Periodic changes in trigonometric parallax have been explained as the gravitational influence of an unseen component. Such stars as μ Draconis, ξ Boötis, and 61 Cygni have invisible companions. The mass of these components is very small, amounting to about 10 times the mass of Jupiter.

Urania   The goddess of astronomy in Greek mythology.

Uranianborg   A combination castle and observatory established on the isle of Hven in Öresund by Tycho Brahe (1576). For its time, the observatory was equipped with superior instruments.

uranometry   (celestial measurement) An earlier name applied to maps or charts and catalogues of the fixed stars. For example, the *Uranometria* of J. Bayer (1603) and the *Uranometria Argentina* compiled by Gould (1879).

Uranus   The seventh major planet measured from the sun was discovered by W. Herschel in 1781. The planet's distance from the sun amounts to 19.2 astronomical units, or 1783 million miles, and its period of revolution is 84 years. The planet's mass is 14.6 earth masses, its diameter 29,300 miles, and period of rotation 10.7 hours. The axis of rotation lies almost in the plane of the orbit and therefore the equator stands at right angles to the orbital plane. Uranus is a giant planet and evidently has the same internal composition as the other giants. The atmosphere probably consists largely of hydrogen and methane. The planet has five satellites; the largest, Titania, has a diameter approaching 2000 miles.

Ursa Major   (Greater Bear) An extensive constellation in the northern hemisphere at approximately 10h 40m right ascension (α = 10h 40m), 56° north declination (δ = +56°). The seven brightest stars form the well-known *Big Dipper*.

Ursa Major Cluster   A moving star cluster to which the five brightest stars in the Big Dipper belong. Several other stars across the sky, including Sirius, belong to the Ursa Major Cluster.

Ursa Minor   (Lesser Bear) Constellation situated in the northern hemisphere at 15h right ascension (α = 15h), 79° north declination (δ = +79°). The brightest star, Alpha (α) Ursae Minoris, is *Polaris,* the Pole Star near the north celestial pole.

UV   Abbreviation for ultraviolet radiation at wave lengths between about 100 and 4000 Å.

V

vacuum thermocouple   A very sensitive thermocouple mounted in a vacuum tube, used to measure temperatures of the planets.

Van Allen belts   Radiation belts situated around the earth, discovered by James A. Van Allen (United States) from information gathered by Explorer I, the first American satellite (launched January 31, 1958). The discovery has been confirmed by other satellites and lunar probes. Basically, the Van Allen belts consist of two concentric belts above the earth's equator. The more energetic inner belt has a maximum intensity at about 3000 km altitude, while the less energetic outer belt is situated at about 16,000 km above the surface of the earth. The belts consist of protons and electrons at extremely high energy levels. They are particles that have been captured by the earth's magnetic field. Their energy and number fluctuate with solar activity. It is probable that similar radiation belts are possessed by other planets. These radiation belts constitute a serious hazard to man's journey into space.

variable nebulae   Two galactic nebulae in Corona Australis and in Monoceros with variations in their brightness. It has been established that the nearby stars producing the luminescence of the nebulae are variable stars.

variable stars (variables)   Stars that vary in brightness. These stars are classified into two main classes, *intrinsic variables*, with changes in brightness due to changes in internal condi-

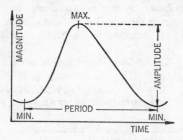

V1. Light curve of a variable star.

tions; and *eclipsing variables,* with light variations caused by one star eclipsing the other. See: *binary stars.* Essentially, the investigation of variable stars consists of the study of light variations by means of a *light curve* that illustrates the relationship of the change in magnitude with respect to time. (Fig. V1.) The physical variables are divided into several subgroups depending upon the length of the period and the nature of the changes in luminosity. There are variables with completely irregular light variations while other stars vary in brightness with clocklike regularity. The most important types of variable stars are outlined below:

Pulsating Stars

Name or Prototype	Period in days	Population
RR Lyrae	< 1	II
Classical cepheids	1–50	I
W Virginis	10–30	II
RV Tauri	30–100	II
Mira stars (Me stars)	100–1000	I
Short-period Me stars	< 250	II

Exploding or Eruptive Stars

Supernovae
Normal novae
Recurrent novae
Flare stars

variation A perturbation of the moon discovered by Tycho Brahe. The period is one-half synodic month (14¾ days) and its value is 39.′5. Variation is caused by the sun's gravitational influence upon the orbital motion of the moon.

variation of constants A method developed by Lagrange in 1772 for solving more difficult problems in celestial mechanics by varying the constants in a simpler analogous problem.

variation of latitude Small variation in latitude caused by changes in the location of the poles on the earth. The phenomenon was pointed out by Nyrén, of Sweden, in 1873, but had been predicted theoretically by Euler as early as the 18th century. Variations are now systematically studied at observatories around the world through international cooperation. Observations show that the terrestrial pole moves in an irregular curve around an average position of about 60 feet diameter. The movement of the poles has two motions:

an annual motion connected with atmospheric changes, snow accumulation, and another with a period of about 14 months which was predicted by Euler. Other phenomena related to variation make interesting study. (Fig. V2.)

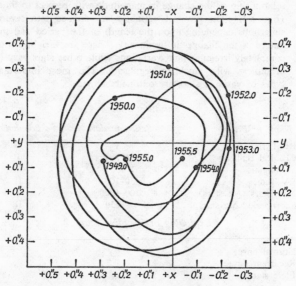

V2. Variations of latitude.

Vassenius, Birger (1687–1771) Astronomer and lecturer in mathematics at Göteborg. He was the first to depict *prominences during the total eclipse of the sun, which he observed in 1733.

Vega The star Alpha (α) Lyrae, of apparent visual magnitude 0.1 and spectral type A0.

Vela (Sails) A part of the constellation *Argo* (Ship) in the southern hemisphere at 10h right ascension (α = 10h), 50° south declination (δ = −50°).

velocity of escape See: *escape velocity.*

Venik (Venus probe) Soviet space probe launched on March 12, 1961, calculated to make a close approach to the planet Venus. Radio contact was lost after a few weeks.

Venus The second major planet measured outward from the sun at a mean distance of 67.2 million miles and a period of

revolution of 225 days. The diameter of Venus is 7700 miles
and its mass is 0.82 (earth's = 1). Since the orbit of Venus
is closer to the sun than the orbit of the earth is, the planet is
invisible at inferior conjunction when it is nearest to the
earth. At greatest elongation, its angular distance is 47° east
or west of the sun. If the planet is west of the sun, it rises
before the sun and shines as the "morning star." When situated east of the sun, Venus sets after the sun and shines as
the "evening star." As the planet revolves, more or less of its
lighted surface is seen from the earth. Therefore, Venus
shows phases similar to those of the moon and Mercury.
(Fig. V3.) Bright and dark patches which have been ob-

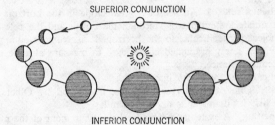

SUPERIOR CONJUNCTION

INFERIOR CONJUNCTION

*V3. Planet Venus. Its phases and relative size as seen from
earth.*

served with difficulty are presumed to be shadings in the thick
cloud layer that hides the surface of the planet from view.
These patches are too indistinct to be used in determining
the period of rotation. According to recent radar observations,
a period of rotation of 250 days (retrograde) has been determined. The atmosphere of Venus is found to contain carbon
dioxide and faint traces of water vapor, while oxygen remains
undetected. Several viewpoints exist regarding the nature of
the clouds. It is not known whether the clouds consist of
particles of water or ice or an obscuration similar to smog
on earth. Measurements using radio astronomy techniques
reveal a surface temperature of at least 600° F. The Venus
probe, Mariner II, measured the surface temperature at
800° F. At present, the conditions of the surface are not
known with certainty.

Venus transits The time when the planet Venus is seen crossing the bright disc of the sun. Transits take place in pairs.
The last transits occurred in 1874 and 1882 and the next pair

is expected on June 8, 2004, and June 6, 2012. During a transit, the atmosphere of Venus appears as a bright ring surrounding the dark disc of the planet. This effect was observed for the first time by M. V. Lomonosov in Russia and T. Bergman in Sweden, during the transit of 1761.

vernal equinox One of the points of intersection between the ecliptic and the equator. The sun reaches the vernal equinox on about March 21, when it crosses the equator from south to north. The vernal equinox is the point from which right ascension and celestial longitude are measured. It is also known as the First Point of Aries.

vertex The point in the sky toward which a star stream appears to move.

vertical circle 1. An arc of a great circle in the horizon coordinate system passing through the zenith and the celestial object perpendicular to the horizon. 2. Instrument equipped with a finely graduated circle, used to measure altitude and zenith distance.

vertical line A *plumb line*.

Vesta One of the larger asteroids, discovered by Olbers in 1807. Its diameter is about 240 miles.

vignetting A systematic error in the measurement of the magnitudes of stars located at great distance from the optical axis of the instrument.

violet layer A layer of haze in the atmosphere of Mars that is visible in photographs taken in violet light. Generally, this layer is opaque to short-wave radiation and possibly consists of ice or crystals of carbon dioxide. Occasionally, a clearing will occur in the layer, allowing surface details to be photographed in blue light.

Virgo (Virgin) A large constellation of the Zodiac situated at the celestial equator at 13h right ascension (α = 13h), 2° south declination ($\delta = -2°$). The brightest star, Alpha (α) Virginis, Spica, has an apparent visual magnitude of 1.2 and spectral type B2. The star Gamma (γ) Virginis, Porrima, is a well-known double star with a period of 180 years.

Virgo cluster A large cluster of galaxies containing several thousand members, located in the constellation of *Virgo* at a distance of about 20 million light-years.

visual A term used in astronomy when referring to observations made with the eye.

visual binaries Double stars with apparent distance great enough to permit separation in a telescope. The apparent distance between the stars must be greater than about 0″.1 to be separated by the largest telescope. There are *optical* and *physical* double stars. An optical double consists of two stars that only appear near to each other because they lie in the same line of sight. A physical double consists of two stars united by gravitation and described orbits around a common center of gravity. At the present time, more than 60,000 visual binaries have been catalogued. For less than 10% of these stars, part of a complete revolution in orbit has been observed. Orbits have been calculated for less than 1% of these stars. The shortest known period observed is about 1.7 years (BD–8°4352) and the longest is several hundred years. (In the systems where orbits have not been determined, the periods are very long and are measured in thousands or millions of years.) Using the law of gravitation, the masses of the stars can be determined from the period of revolution and the dimensions of the orbit. Generally, the orbits of visual binaries are ellipses with large eccentricity. (Fig. V4.) The dis-

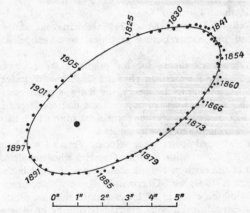

V4. The apparent orbit of a visual binary star. The large period (dot) mark represents the primary star. The component's positions at various dates are indicated by the smaller dots.

tance between the stars in a visual binary system varies between 5 and 30 astronomical units and therefore amounts to hundreds of millions of miles.

visual magnitude   The magnitudes secured through visual observations giving the star's magnitude in the color sensitivity region of the human eye (maximum sensitivity of the eye is at a wave length of 5600 Å). Today, these magnitudes are determined photographically using color-sensitive plates and appropriate yellow filters (the so-called *photovisual magnitudes*).

visual photometry Photometry based upon the ability of the eye to distinguish slight differences in the brightness of two light sources. A comparison is made between the magnitude of the star to be measured and a real or artificial star whose light can be varied in the instrument. During observations, the magnitude of the comparison star is made to appear the same as the star to be measured. In the various types of photometers, the light of the comparison star is changed by means of polarizing elements or a wedge of tinted glass. At the present time, visual photometry is used only if photographic or photoelectric methods are not possible, such as in the study of close components in a binary system.

Volans (Flying Fish) Constellation in the southern hemisphere at 7h 40m right ascension ($\alpha = $ 7h 40m), 70° south declination ($\delta = -70°$).

von Seeliger, Hugo (1849–1924) German astronomer who carried out comprehensive statistical investigations of the stars.

von Weizsäcker's theory for the origin of the solar system Proposed by the German physicist C. F. von Weizsäcker in 1945. According to the theory, the sun was surrounded by a rotating nebulous disc of dust and gas that condensed into a series of concentric whirling formations from which the planets are assumed to have originated.

Vostok Manned Soviet space vehicles. Vostok I was launched April 12, 1961, with Yuri A. Gagarin, who completed one orbit of the earth in 108 minutes. Vostok II was launched on August 6, 1961, with Gherman S. Titov, who completed 17 orbits of the earth in 25 hours and 18 minutes. Vostok III was placed in orbit with Andrian Nikolayev on August 11, 1962, for 94 hours and 35 minutes, completing 64 orbits. On August 12, 1962, Pavel Popovich became Nikolayev's "space twin" in Vostok IV, completing 48 orbits in 70 hours and 57 minutes. Vostok V was launched with Valery F. Bykovsky on June 14, 1963. On June 16, 1963, Valentina Tereshkova became the first woman in space in Vostok VI.

V2 Originally a German military rocket, improved by the United States and equipped with instruments to study the ultraviolet spectrum of the sun. The rockets have been launched several hundred miles in altitude, resulting in many valuable observations.

Vulcan The name of a hypothetical planet in an orbit formerly believed to be located between Mercury and the sun. In spite of enthusiastic investigation, no "intramercurial planet" has been found, and it now seems certain that Vulcan does not exist.

Vulpecula (Fox) A faint constellation in the northern hemisphere at 20h right ascension ($\alpha = $ 20h), 25° north declination ($\delta = +25°$).

W

walled plains The largest ring mountains or craters on the moon with diameters between 30 and 185 miles.

wandering of the poles Small variations in the latitude of a point caused by changes in the position of the poles. See: *variations of latitude.*

wandering stars The name applied to the planets since antiquity. In contrast, the true stars were called *fixed stars.*

Water Bearer Constellation in the southern hemisphere. See: *Aquarius.*

water clock An antique clock, used by the Egyptians, consisting of a water container with a small hole from which the water slowly dripped. Time was reckoned by the level of the water.

Water Snake Constellation in the southern hemisphere. See: *Hydra.*

wave length (indicated by λ) Distance between two successive oscillations of a wave motion, i.e., the distance between two maxima or two minima.

weather satellites American artificial satellites equipped with special cameras and TV devices to study cloud cover and other meteorological phenomena on the earth. They are called the *Tiros* and *Nimbus* series. The first, *Tiros 1,* was launched April 1, 1960.

wedge photometer See: *photometer, wedge.*

week A division of time containing seven days which has been used continuously for thousands of years. The week is completely independent of the month and the year. Unlike the month or the year, the week is an artificial unit of time lacking an equivalent astronomical period.

West European time The standard time zone in western Europe that coincides with Greenwich civil time.

West Ford An American project consisting of many millions of copper needles scattered in a belt around the earth to facilitate long-distance telecommunications. The project was considered unfortunate by astronomers because of possible adverse effect on radio astronomy observations. The first attempt to launch the needles in October 1961 was unsuccessful. In May 1963 the project was accomplished.

west point The western point of intersection between the horizon and celestial equator. The corresponding eastern point of intersection is called the east point.

Whale Constellation in the southern hemisphere. See: *Cetus*.

white corona The overlapping components of the solar corona including the K corona composed of free electrons and the F corona consisting of dust particles. See: *solar corona*.

white dwarfs Early type stars of low intrinsic luminosity, whose spectra are characterized by diffuse lines. About 150 white dwarfs are known, but their total number in the Milky Way system is estimated to be 5000 million. The size of these stars is on the order of the earth but their mass is equal to the sun's mass, with a mean density 100,000 times that of water (in some instances perhaps 10 million to 20 million times that of water). The core of a white dwarf star is on the order of 100 million times the density of water. In a white dwarf, matter is completely ionized and only atomic nuclei and free electrons are found. This substance is in the state of "degenerate matter," packed more closely together than the nuclei and electrons of a normal atom, making enormous densities possible. Observation of some white dwarfs such as the Companion of Sirius give conclusive evidence of the displacement of spectral lines to the red as predicted by the General Theory of Relativity. The Companion of Sirius was the first white dwarf star discovered. The role of white dwarf stars in cosmogony is unknown. They may mark the final stage of stellar evolution.

white nebulae An earlier name for spiral galaxies which appeared white to the eye when observed in the telescope. The term is not adequate since later studies of spectra and colors show that the central regions have color characteristics that agree with stars of spectral type G and K. Stars of spectral type B and A are found only in the spiral arms.

white spots A phenomenon that frequently appears on the planet Saturn as a white spot of short duration, seen foremost in the equatorial region. A very prominent white spot was visible in 1933. They are probably caused by eruptions in the lower layers of Saturn's atmosphere.

Widmanstätten figures The patterns formed on the polished surface of iron meteorites etched with an acid.

Wien's law According to this law, the wave length at which radiation from a light source is most intense is inversely proportional to its absolute temperature. The higher the temperature, the greater the intensity of radiation is shifted to the violet portion of the spectrum. Using Wien's law, it is possible to determine the temperature of incandescent bodies.

Wild's trio Three galaxies photographed at Palomar Observatory by P. Wild in 1953. Internal perturbations have caused the spiral arms to be drawn out into long filaments.

Wilson's phenomenon (Wilson Effect) The appearance of a sunspot as a depression in the photosphere when seen near the limb of the sun. Since the sun is spherical, a sunspot is foreshortened by perspective with the center of the spot apparently displaced toward the penumbral region nearest the center of the sun because the level of the sunspot is below the surface of the photosphere.

winter Astronomical winter, in the northern hemisphere of the earth, is the time of year that includes the interval between the winter solstice (December 22) and vernal equinox (March 21).

winter solstice 1. The southernmost point on the ecliptic, when the sun reaches the Tropic of Capricorn on December 22. 2. The time of the year when the sun has its greatest south declination and appears at its lowest altitude above the horizon at noon.

Wolf Constellation in the southern hemisphere. See: *Lupus*.

Wolf diagram A graph named after W. Max Wolf which is used to determine the distance to and the absorption characteristics of dark nebulae. Star counts and brightness measurements are made within obscured regions and compared with an unobscured region nearby. The number of stars per square degree represents the ordinate, and apparent magni-

tude, the abscissa of the diagram. (Fig. W1.) The two curves
illustrate how the number of stars increases as magnitude
decreases and the effect of obscuration on the star count.
The distance to the nebula, as well as its absorption characteristics, is found by comparing the two curves. The method
has been modified in some respects and has become very important in the investigation of dark nebulae.

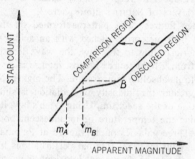

W1. Wolf diagram.

Wolf-Palisa charts   Photographic charts of the sky in the region of the Zodiac by W. Max Wolf and his co-worker Palisa
at Heidelberg.

Wolf-Rayet stars   Stars with spectra characterized by broad absorption bands. Discovered by Wolf and Rayet at the Paris
Observatory in 1867. See: *W stars.*

world line   The curve described by an object in the space-time
continuum of Einstein's relativity theory.

world models   Theories for the origin and development of the
universe. Most theories in modern cosmology are based upon
Einstein's theory of relativity, giving a mathematical expression of how the size of the universe varies with respect to
time. The *red shift* of the galaxies plays a vital role when
theories are tested with observations. See: *universe.*

world system   Various concepts for the origin of the solar system. The most important are the *geocentric system* of Ptolemy
with the earth in the center, and the *heliocentric system* of
Copernicus. Modern theories are based upon observation and
known natural laws.

W stars   A group of stars of spectral type W in the *Harvard
classification* with spectra characterized by broad emission
bands of hydrogen and neutral and ionized helium. Among

later types, carbon and oxygen appear in different states of ionization. Absolute magnitude is also very high, about —3.4, and temperatures amount to 80,000° C. These stars are called *Wolf-Rayet stars* after Wolf and Rayet who discovered the first star of this type at the Paris Observatory in 1867. Emission bands indicate that the stars are surrounded by a rapidly expanding gas shell.

W Virginis A cepheid variable in the constellation of *Virgo*. See: *W Virginis stars*.

W Virginis stars A type of cepheid variable stars with periods ranging between 15 and 30 days. The light curve of W Virginis stars is characterized by a maximum that is wider than the light curves of classical cepheids with the same period. These stars are members of Population II. The prototype star is *W Virginis,* whose period is 17.2 days.

X

X radiation Electromagnetic radiation between about 8 and 100 Å. X rays from the sun have been measured with counters mounted in high altitude rockets and satellites. During solar eruptions, stronger and shorter wave length X rays are emitted. By means of balloon observations, X rays from the stellar system have also been discovered. A few sources of strong X ray radiation are supposed to emanate from *neutron stars*.

Y

Yagi antenna A type of antenna used in radio astronomy, consisting of a dipole element, a parallel rod called a "reflector" situated behind the dipole, and a series of rods placed in front of the dipole at given distances called "directors." The reflector and directors are connected in such a way that radiation is more effectively concentrated on the dipole. Often, an antenna system will consist of a series of Yagi antennas.

year Generally speaking, the time required for the earth to complete one revolution. In astronomy, a distinction is made between various kinds of years, depending upon the refer-

ence point used to measure the period of revolution. **1.** TROPI-
CAL YEAR. The *solar year*. The time required by the sun to
complete one revolution in its apparent orbit with respect to
the equinoxes (the points of intersection between the ecliptic
and the equator). The length of the tropical year is 365.2422
mean solar days. **2.** SIDEREAL YEAR. The time required by the
sun to complete one revolution with respect to the same star.
The length of the sidereal year amounts to 365.2564 mean
solar days. **3.** ANOMALISTIC YEAR. The time required by the
earth to complete one revolution around the sun between
two successive passages of the perihelion. Because the perihelion point moves eastward, the anomalistic year is about
4m 43.5s longer than a sidereal year. The length of the anomalistic year is 365.2596 mean solar days. In addition, the
calendar year, based upon the **Gregorian calendar,* contains
365.2425 mean solar days. A *cosmic year* is the time required for one complete rotation of the Milky Way at the
sun's distance, or about 225 million years. A **lunar year* contains 12 synodic months, amounting to about 354 days.

year of the seasons   The same as *tropical year*. See: *year*.

yellow clouds   Yellow clouds occasionally observed on Mars.
They are probably dust clouds blown from the deserts on the
planet's surface.

Yerkes Observatory   American observatory near Chicago located at Lake Geneva, Williams Bay, Wisconsin. The observatory was constructed from 1892–97 and was financed by
Charles T. Yerkes, who donated the observatory to the University of Chicago. The observatory has the world's largest
refractor with a diameter of 40 inches and a focal length of
62 feet. Together with the University of Texas, Yerkes Observatory maintains a branch observatory in Texas. See:
McDonald Observatory.

Yerkes refractor   The largest refracting telescope in the world.
See: *Yerkes Observatory.*

ylem   The name suggested by G. Gamow for hypothetical matter in the primordial atom, consisting of protons, neutrons,
and electrons. Accordingly, the basic elements were formed
from ylem in a few moments during the development of the
universe when temperatures were as high as several thousand
million degrees.

Z

Zeeman effect The splitting of spectral lines in a magnetic field into one or more components. When the magnetic field is weak, the effect is a widening of the spectral lines. The study of this phenomenon in the spectra of the sun and the stars makes possible the determination of the strength of their magnetic fields. The effect was discovered by the Dutch physicist P. Zeeman in 1896.

zenith (Arab. *semt-ar-ras,* direction of the head.) *Astronomical zenith* is the point on the celestial sphere that is located directly above the head at 90° distance from the horizon and amounts to the extension of a plumb line to the celestial sphere. (The opposite of the zenith is the *nadir.*) *Geocentric zenith* is the point on the celestial sphere marking the extension of a line connecting the point of observation with the center of the earth. Since the earth is a spheroid rather than a sphere, these two points do not coincide.

zenith attraction A displacement of the radiant of a meteor swarm by the gravitational attraction of the earth. Approaching the earth, the meteors accelerate, producing a curvature in their orbits. The radiant will appear to be displaced toward the observer's zenith by an amount approaching 17° as maximum.

zenith circle A circle on a star chart joining all stars observed in the zenith for a given position.

zenith distance Angular distance between the zenith and a celestial body, measured along the vertical circle. Zenith distance is the complement of altitude. *Topocentric zenith distance* is the zenith distance of the body as seen from the position of observation. *Geocentric zenith distance,* measured from the center of the earth, is determined from topocentric zenith distance and the earth's radius, if the distance to the celestial body is known.

zenith refraction In determining **refraction* (the bending of light in the atmosphere), it is assumed that surfaces with the same air density are horizontal. If the layers of air slope toward the horizon, anomalies of refraction appear which cause stars in the zenith to be subjected to minor displacements called zenith refraction.

zenith stars The stars that culminate in the zenith.

zenith telescope A telescope mounted on a vertical axis, equipped with a declination micrometer to measure zenith distances. To determine the latitude of a position with great accuracy, two stars, one north, the other south of the zenith are observed to transit the meridian. Latitude will be equal to one half the sum of the declinations plus one half the difference in the zenith distances.

Zeta (ʒ) The sixth letter in the *Greek alphabet*. Zeta Aurigae (variables); see: *Auriga*.

Zodiac A series of constellations along the ecliptic named after living creatures, with the exception of Libra. In the course of a year, the sun proceeds through the constellations as follows: *Aries,* the Ram; *Taurus,* the Bull; *Gemini,* the Twins; *Cancer,* the Crab; *Leo,* the Lion; *Virgo,* the Virgin; *Libra,* the Scales; *Scorpius,* the Scorpion; *Sagittarius,* the Archer; *Capricornus,* the Sea Goat; *Aquarius,* the Water Bearer; and *Pisces,* the Fish. (For the symbols of the Zodiac, see: *astronomical signs and symbols.*) The vernal equinox, the point when the ecliptic intersects the equator, is presently in Pisces but in ancient times the vernal equinox was in Aries. As a result of *precession,* the vernal equinox slowly moves westward through the Zodiac. The Babylonians divided the ecliptic into 12 "signs," 30° in length, that coincided with the constellations of the same name. The sun passed through a different sign each month. Owing to precession, these signs no longer coincide with the constellations bearing the same name. The signs of the Zodiac have played an important role in *astrology.*

zodiacal light A cone-shaped faint glow seen along the ecliptic with its base on the horizon. In the tropics, the zodiacal light appears throughout the entire year. In the middle latitudes, it is visible in the west at sunset during spring and in the east before dawn in autumn when the inclination of the ecliptic to the horizon is at a maximum. Apparently, the zodiacal light is the result of sunlight reflected by meteoric dust concentrated in the plane of the ecliptic. Photographic studies reveal a zodiacal band completely around the ecliptic. Opposite the sun is a secondary brightness called the *Gegenschein,* or counterglow. The zodiacal light may be considered as the continuation of the sun's *F corona.*

Zollner's photometer A visual photometer that at one time was widely used for the measurement of the apparent magnitude of stars. It consists of a tube with an artificial star whose light can be regulated by means of Nicol prisms. The photometer is attached to the ocular of a refracting telescope so that the artificial star and the star to be measured are seen together. The magnitude of the artificial star is regulated so that both stars appear to have the same magnitude. The magnitude of the real star can be determined from the setting of the Nicol prism.

zone A division of a spherical surface bounded by two parallel circles. The most densely populated zones on the earth are the temperate zones included between the parallels $\pm66°5$ and $\pm23°5$.

zone observations Determinations of position by zones, i.e., a series of observations of stars located between two given parallels of declination. For large, international observational programs, the sky is divided into zones which are suitably located for investigation from the participating observatories. The photographic sky atlas, *Carte du Ciel,* was developed in this manner.

zone of avoidance A region of uneven width (between 10° and 40°) in the immediate proximity of the plane of the Milky Way that is almost devoid of galaxies. In a detailed study of the distribution of galaxies, Edwin Hubble found a decrease in the number of galaxies in the vicinity of the Milky Way. The widespread belt of dark matter in the plane of the Milky Way obscures the view of more distant galaxies. See: *interstellar absorption.*

ÅKE WALLENQUIST is a professor of astronomy at the Kvistaberg Observatory, a part of Uppsala University located in Bro outside of Stockholm, Sweden. Dr. Wallenquist is the author of many technical papers as well as of many popular books in Swedish on astronomy.

SUNE ENGELBREKTSON, Chairman of the Department of Education of The American Museum of Natural History, has had extensive experience in both teaching and administration at all levels of education. Since 1957, he has been a guest lecturer in the sky presentations of The American Museum-Hayden Planetarium and has also taught Planetarium courses in astronomy and space science. Dr. Engelbrektson received his B.A., M.A., and Ed.D. from New York University. He presently lives in Pleasantville, New York.

ANCHOR BOOKS

ANCHOR BOOKS

SCIENCE STUDY SERIES

Science Study Series (continued)

ANCHOR BOOKS

CHEMISTRY IN ACTION SERIES

CHEMICALS FROM FERMENTATION—Peter A. Hahn, AMC3
CHEMICAL ENGINEERING—David H. Killeffer, AMC1
SILICA AND ME—Guy Alexander, AMC2
WATER IS EVERYBODY'S BUSINESS: The Chemistry of Water Purification—A. S. Behrman, AMC4

0 0 2 1 5 5 1

DICTIONARY OF ASTRONO
MICAL TERMS

WALLENQUIST